Ch CR ry r A2

Graham Hill ■
Andrew Hunt ■

DYNAMIC LEARNING
Innovate • Motivate • Personalise

HODDER
EDUCATION
AN HACHETTE UK COMPANY

Hachette UK's policy is to use papers that are natural, renewable and recyclable products and made fron [sustainable] forests. The logging and manufacturing processes are expected to conform to the environmental regulations of the c[ountry of origin].

Orders: please contact Bookpoint Ltd, 130 Milton Park, Abingdon, Oxon OX14 4SB. Telephone: (44) ( ) Lines are open 9.00 – 5.00, Monday to Saturday, with a 24-hour message answering service. Visit our we[bsite]

© Graham Hill, Andrew Hunt 2009
First published in 2009 by
Hodder Education,
An Hachette UK Company
338 Euston Road
London NW1 3BH

Impression number 5 4 3 2 1
Year   2013 2012 2011 2010 2009

Cover photo © Steve Gschmeissner/Science Photo Library
Illustrations by Ken Vail Graphic Design, Cambridge and Barking Dog Art
Typeset in Goudy 10.5pt by Ken Vail Graphic Design, Cambridge
Indexing by Indexing Specialists (UK) Ltd
Printed in Italy

A catalogue record for this title is available from the British Library

ISBN: 978 0340 959299

The Publishers would like to thank the following for permission to reproduce copyright material:

Photo credits: p.1 Photodisc; **p.2** *b* Rex Features, *t* AJ Photo/Science Photo Library; **p.7** Andrew Lambert/Science Photo Library; **p.8** Mireille Vautier/Alamy; **p.12** Photodisc; **p.13** Martyn f Chillmaid/Science Photo Library; **p.17** Advertising Archives; **p.19** Steve Gshmeissner/Science Photo Library; **p.21** Shelia Terry/Science Photo Library; **p.25** Andrew Lambert/Science Photo Library; **p.28** *t* Andrew Syred/Science Photo Library, *b* Anthony Cooper/Science Photo Library; **p.29** Susan Wilkinson; **p.32** BSIP Chassenet/Science Photo Library; **p.34** Chris Sattleburger/Science Photo Library; **p.37** *t* BSIP Chassenet/Science Photo Library, *b* Cordelia Molloy/Science Photo Library; **p.38** Corbis; **p.40** *l* Saturn Stills/Science Photo Library, *r* Roger Scruton; **p.45** Roger Scruton; **p.46** Colin Underhill/Alamy; **p.56** Science Photo Library; **p.58** Roger Scruton; **p.61** Pascal Goetscheluck/Science Photo Library; **p.62** *l* Jeremy Burgess/Science Photo Library, *r* Kenneth Eward/Science Photo Library; **p.63** *t* Roger Scruton, *b* Images Etc Ltd/Alamy; **p.65** James Holmes/Science Photo Library; **p.66** Getty Images; **p.68** Sally & Richard Greenhill/Alamy; **p.69** Advertising Archives; **p.70** Corbis; **p.71** Eye of Science/Science Photo Library; **p.73** Peter Ryan/Science Photo Library; **p.74** Dr P Marazzi/Science Photo Library; **p.75** Shelia Terry/Science Photo Library; **p.77** James Bell/Science Photo Library; **p.80** Peter Menzel/Science Photo Library; **p.83** Colin Cuthbert/Science Photo Library; **p.87** PAPhotos; **p.88** Leonard Lessin/Science Photo Library; **p.90** Geoff Tompkinson/Science Photo Library; **p.91** Tim Evans/Science Photo Library; **p.93** *t* Geoff Tompkinson/Science Photo Library, *b* Sinclair Stammers/Science Photo Library; **p.96** *t* Jerry Mason/Science Photo Library, *b* Corbis; **p.98** James Holmes/Science Photo Library; **p.99** Michael Donne/Science Photo Library; **p.101** Jurgen Scriba/Science Photo Library; **p.105** Gareth Price; **p.108** Mauro Fermariello/Science Photo Library; **p.111** (both) Philippe Psala/Science Photo Library; **p.112** Gareth Price; **p.117** Corbis; **p.122** Maximilian Stock/Science Photo Library; **p.125** Martyn f Chillmaid/Science Photo Library; **p.135** Clive Freeman/Science Photo Library; **p.138** *l* Steve Gschmeissner/Science Photo Library, *r* Tek Images/Science Photo Library; **p.142** Andrew Lambert/Science Photo Library; **p.144** *t* Charles D Winter/Science Photo Library, *b* Andrew Lambert/Science Photo Library; **p.145** Carols Goldin/Science Photo Library; **p.147** *l* Patrick Landman, *r* European Space Agency Multimedia Gallery; **p.149** Charles D Winter/Science Photo Library; **p.151** Bob Gibbons/Science Photo Library; **p.152** Corbis; **p.157** *l* Junior Bildarchiv/Alamy, *r* BSIP Chassenet/Science Photo Library; **p.159** Jim Dowdalls/Science Photo Library; **p.160** Mauro Fermariello/Science Photo Library; **p.161** *c* Maximilian Stock/Science Photo Library, *r* Andrew Lambert/Science Photo Library; **p.166** *tl* Bjanka Kadic/Science Photo Library, *cl, cr, b* Andrew Lambert/Science Photo Library; **p.168** Martin Fowler/Alamy; **p.171** Andrew Lambert/Science Photo Library; **p.181** Corbis; **p.186** *tl, tr* Oxford Scientific Films/Photolibrary; *bl* Corbis, *br* Tony Craddock/Science Photo Library; **p.187** Carlos Bach/Science Photo Library; **p.190** Charles D. Winter/Science Photo Library; **p.193** *t* Sam Ogden/Science Photo Library, *b* Maximilian Stock/Science Photo Library; **p.194** Robert Gugliemo/Science Photo Library; **p.197** David Wentraub/Science Photo Library; **p.200** NASA/Science Photo Library; **p.202** (both) Andrew Lambert/Science Photo Library; **p.208** *t* Roger Scruton; *b* Andrew Lambert/Science Photo Library; **p.212** *t* Roger Scruton, *b* Mike Devlin/Science Photo Library; **p.213** Colin Palmer/Alamy; **p. 215** Martin Bond/Science Photo Library; **p.216** Courtesy of Honda UK; **p.217** Courtesy of Honda UK; **p.220** Alistair Laming/Alamy; **p.221** Andrew Lambert/Science Photo Library; **p.226** Andrew Lambert/Science Photo Library; **p.228** Biosym Technologies/Science Photo Library; **p.230** Philippa Unwins/Science Photo Library; **p.231** Andrew Lambert/Science Photo Library; **p.235** Tate Images; **p.239** *t* Andrew Lambert, *all* Martyn f Chillmaid; **p.242** Roger Scruton; **p.271** Corbis
b = bottom, *c* = centre, *l* = left, *r* = right, *t* = top

Acknowledgements: Every effort has been made to trace all copyright holders, but if any have been inadvertently overlooked the Publishers will be pleased to make the necessary arrangements at the first opportunity.

Although every effort has been made to ensure that website addresses are correct at time of going to press, Hodder Education cannot be held responsible for the content of any website mentioned in this book or associated resources. It is sometimes possible to find a relocated web page by typing in the address of the home page for a website in the URL window of your browser.

OCR Chemistry

for A2

Graham Hill
Andrew Hunt

A Note for Teachers

OCR Chemistry for A2 Network disc

The OCR Chemistry for A2 Network disc which accompanies the Student's Book and Dynamic Learning Student website provides a complete bank of resources for teachers and technicians following the OCR specification. Powered by Dynamic Learning, the Network disc contains the same interactive version of the Student's Book that is available on the Dynamic Learning Student's website, plus every resource that teachers might wish to use in activities, discussions, practical work and assessment.

These additional resources on the Network disc include:

- a synoptic Topic overview for each of the sixteen topics showing how the text and resources cover and follow the OCR specification, including coverage of 'How Science Works'. These synopses also indicate how the resources on the Network disc can be used to create a teaching programme and lesson plans
- Introductory PowerPoints for each topic
- Practical worksheets for students covering the entire course
- Teacher's and technician's notes for all practicals showing the intentions of each practical, a suggested approach to it, health and safety considerations, the materials and apparatus required by each group and answers to the questions on the worksheets
- additional Weblinks
- additional Activities involving data analysis, application and evaluation
- 3D Rotatable models of molecules of interest
- answers to all Review questions in the Student's Book, as well as answers to all Extension questions available to students from the Dynamic Learning Student website and to questions in the additional Activities on the Network disc
- Interactive objective tests for each topic with answers.

All these resources are launched from interactive pages of the Student's Book on the Network disc. Teachers can also search for resources by resource type or key words to allow greater flexibility in using the resource material.

A Lesson Builder allows teachers to build lessons by dragging and dropping resources they want to use into a lesson group that can be saved and launched later from a single screen.

The tools provided also enable teachers to import their own resources and weblinks into the lesson group and to populate a VLE at the click of a button.

Risk assessment

As a service to users, a risk assessment for this text and associated resources has been carried out by CLEAPSS and is available on request to the Publishers. However, the Publishers accept no legal responsibility on any issue arising from this risk assessment; whilst every effort has been made to check the instructions for practical work in this book and associated resources, it is still the duty and legal obligation of schools to carry out their own risk assessment.

Contents

Unit 4 Rings, polymers and analysis   1

Unit 5 Equilibria, energetics and elements   121

Introduction

Welcome to *OCR Chemistry for A2*. This book covers everything in the OCR specification with 9 topics for Unit 4 and 7 topics for Unit 5. Test yourself questions throughout the book will help you to think about what you are studying while the Activities give you the chance to apply what you have learned in a range of modern contexts. At the end of each topic you will find exam-style Review questions to help you check your progress.

Student support for this book can be found on the **Dynamic Learning Student** website, which contains an interactive copy of the book. Students can access a range of free digital resources by visiting **www.dynamic-learning-student.co.uk** and using the code printed on the inside front cover of this book to gain access to relevant resources. These free digital resources include:

- Data tables, for use when answering questions
- Tutorials, which work through selected problems and concepts using a voiceover and animated diagrams
- Practical guidance to support experimental and investigative skills
- Weblinks that provide access to relevant social, environmental and economic contexts and help with the more demanding concepts and practical techniques.

All diagrams and photographs can be launched and enlarged directly from the pages. There are also Learning outcomes available at the beginning of every topic, and answer files to all Test yourself and Activity questions. Extension questions, covering some ideas in greater depth, are available at the end of each topic. The Student Online icon, shown on the right, indicates where a resource such as a Data sheet, Tutorial, Practical guidance or Extension questions is provided on the Dynamic Learning Student website. All other resources are linked to interactive areas on the page or associated with particular pages in the resources menu. In addition, all these resources can be saved to your local hard drive.

With the powerful Search tool, key words can be found in an instant, leading you to the relevant page or alternatively to resources associated with each key word.

Acknowledgements

We would like to acknowledge the suggestions from Ian Davis, Neil Dixon and Tim Joliffe – teachers who commented on our initial plans. The team at Hodder Education, led by Katie Mackenzie-Stuart, has made an extremely valuable contribution to the development of the book and the Network disc and website resources. In particular, we would like to thank Anne Trevillion, the project manager, Anne Wanjie, Deborah Sanderson, Anne Russell and Tony Clappison for their skilful work on both the print and electronic resources.

Graham Hill and Andrew Hunt
February 2009

Unit 4

Rings, polymers and analysis

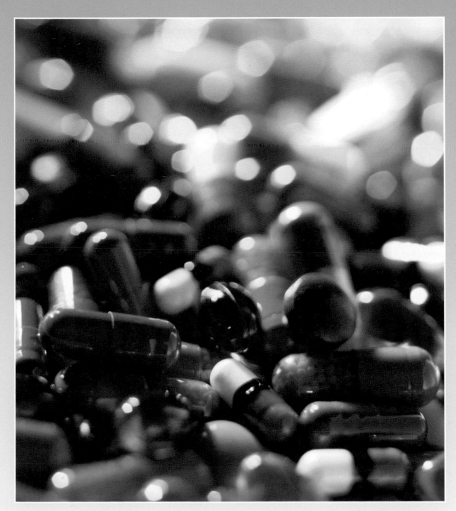

1 Arenes – aromatic hydrocarbons

Figure 1.1 ▲
The antiseptics used in some throat sprays are similar in structure to TCP and Dettol.

> Aspirin, paracetamol and ibuprofen are three tried and tested painkillers. Dettol and TCP are two important and effective antiseptics. Terylene and polystyrene are two versatile polymers produced in millions of tonnes every year.
>
> At the heart of all these widely different products is a remarkably stable ring of six carbon atoms – the benzene ring, a constituent of all arenes.

1.1 Arenes

Arenes are hydrocarbons, such as benzene, methylbenzene and naphthalene. They are ring compounds in which there are delocalised electrons. The simplest arene is benzene. Traditionally, chemists have called the arenes 'aromatic' ever since the German chemist Friedrich Kekulé was struck by the fragrant smell of oils such as benzene. In their modern name 'arene', the '**ar**-' comes from **ar**omatic and the ending '**-ene**' points to the fact that they are unsaturated hydrocarbons like the alkenes.

Definitions

Arenes are hydrocarbons with a ring or rings of carbon atoms in which there are delocalised electrons.

Delocalised electrons are bonding electrons which are not fixed between two atoms in a bond, but shared between three or more atoms. (See also Section 6.6 in *OCR Chemistry for AS*.)

Figure 1.2 ▶
Benzene is an important and useful chemical. It was first isolated in 1825 by the fractional distillation of whale oil, which was commonly used for lighting homes. Later it was obtained by the fractional distillation of coal tar. Today, it is obtained by the catalytic reforming of fractions from crude oil.

1.2 The structure of benzene

Friedrich Kekulé played a crucial part in our understanding of the structure of benzene thanks to a dream. The dream helped Kekulé to propose a possible structure for benzene, which he knew to have an empirical formula of CH and a molecular formula of C_6H_6. Kekulé had been working on the problem of the structure of benzene for some time. Then one day in 1865, while dozing in front of the fire, he dreamed of a snake biting its own tail. This inspired him to think of a ring structure for benzene (Figure 1.3).

Figure 1.3 ▶
Kekulé's snake with his structural and skeletal formulae for benzene. Kekulé's formula would have the systematic name cyclohexa-1,3,5-triene.

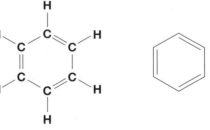

Kekulé's structure explained many of the properties of benzene. It was accepted for many years, but still left some problems.

The absence of isomers of 1,2-dichlorobenzene

Kekulé's structure suggests that there should be two isomers of 1,2-dichlorobenzene – one in which the chlorine atoms are linked by a single carbon–carbon bond; the other in which the chlorine atoms are linked by a double carbon–carbon bond (Figure 1.4).

Figure 1.4 ◀
Possible isomers of 1,2-dichlorobenzene.

In practice, it has never been possible to separate two isomers of 1,2-dichlorobenzene, or any other 1,2-disubstituted compound of benzene. To get round this problem, Kekulé suggested that benzene molecules might somehow alternate rapidly between the two possible structures, but this failed to satisfy his critics.

The bond lengths in benzene

The Kekulé structure shows a molecule with alternate single and double bonds. This implies that three of the bonds are similar in length to the carbon–carbon single bond in alkanes, while the other three are similar in length to the carbon–carbon double bond in alkenes. X-ray diffraction studies show that the carbon atoms in a benzene molecule are actually at the corners of a regular hexagon. All the bonds are the same length, shorter than single bonds but longer than double bonds (Figure 1.5).

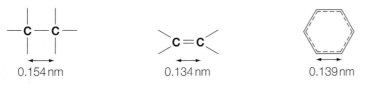

Figure 1.5 ◀
Carbon–carbon bond lengths in ethane, ethene and benzene.

The resistance to reaction of benzene

An inexperienced chemist looking at the Kekulé structure might expect benzene to behave chemically like a very reactive alkene and to take part in addition reactions with bromine, hydrogen bromide and similar reagents. Benzene does not do this. The compound is much less reactive than alkenes and its characteristic reactions are substitutions, not additions.

The stability of benzene

A study of enthalpy (energy content) changes show that benzene is more stable than expected for a compound with the Kekulé formula. This conclusion is based on a comparison of the enthalpy changes of hydrogenation of benzene and cyclohexene.

Cyclohexene is a cyclic hydrocarbon with one carbon–carbon double bond. Like other alkenes, it adds hydrogen in the presence of a nickel catalyst at 140 °C to form cyclohexane. The enthalpy change of the reaction, $\Delta H^{\ominus}$, is $-120 \, \text{kJ} \, \text{mol}^{-1}$ (Figure 1.6).

cyclohexene   cyclohexane

Figure 1.6 ◀
Cyclohexene is a cyclic hydrocarbon with one carbon–carbon double bond.

So, if benzene has three carbon–carbon double bonds as in Kekulé's structure, we might reasonably predict that $\Delta H^\ominus$ for the hydrogenation of benzene should be $-360\,\text{kJ}\,\text{mol}^{-1}$. But when the hydrogenation is carried out, the measured enthalpy change is only $-208\,\text{kJ}\,\text{mol}^{-1}$.

The measured enthalpy change is much less exothermic than the estimated value. This suggests that the addition of hydrogen to benzene does not involve three normal double bonds, and that benzene is actually much more stable than expected (Figure 1.7).

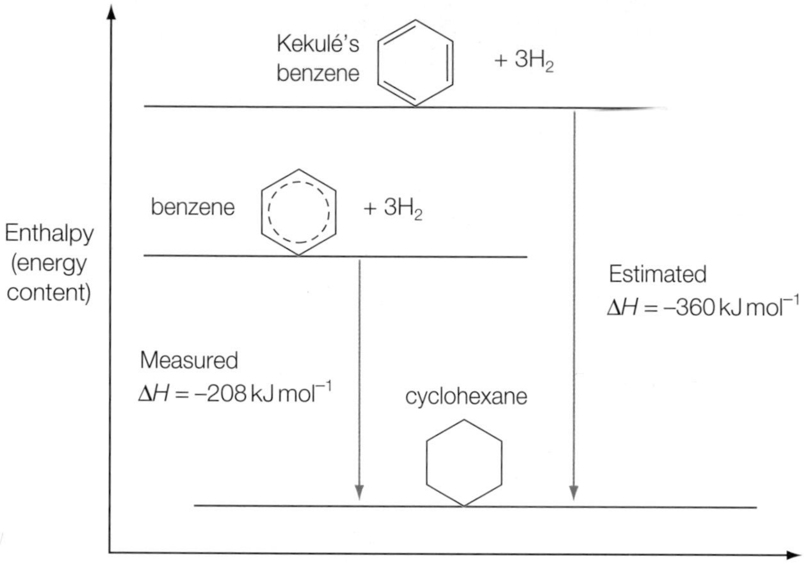

Figure 1.7 ▶
Comparing the measured enthalpy change of hydrogenation of benzene with the estimated enthalpy change of hydrogenation for Kekulé's structure.

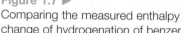

Test yourself

1 Assume that the empirical formula of benzene is CH. What further information is needed to show that its molecular formula is C_6H_6? What methods do chemists use to obtain this information?

2 Draw one possible structure for C_6H_6 which does not include a ring. Why does this structure not fit with Kekulé's structure for benzene?

3 An arene consists of 91.3% carbon.
   a) What is the empirical formula of this arene?
   b) What is the molecular formula of the arene if its molar mass is $92\,\text{g}\,\text{mol}^{-1}$?
   c) Draw the structure of the arene.

4 a) Look carefully at Figure 1.7. How much more stable is the real benzene than Kekulé's structure for benzene?
   b) Predict the enthalpy change for the complete hydrogenation of cyclohexa-1,3-diene.

1.3 Delocalisation in benzene

The accumulation of the evidence discussed in Section 1.2 led to increased activity in the search for a more accurate model for the structure of benzene. The 'quick fix' was to treat the carbon–carbon bonds in benzene as halfway between single and double bonds, and draw them with a full line and a dashed line side-by-side as in the right-hand diagram in Figure 1.5. This model explains the absence of isomers of 1,2-dichlorobenzene, the equal carbon–carbon bond lengths in benzene and also its resistance to reaction. In recent years, the bonding between carbon atoms in benzene has been simplified to a circle inside a hexagon as in Figure 1.8.

Although the structure in Figure 1.8 allows an improved understanding of the properties of benzene, a better insight comes from considering its electronic and orbital structure.

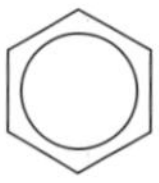

Figure 1.8 ▲
The usual way of representing benzene today.

Figure 1.9 shows benzene with normal covalent sigma bonds (σ bonds) between its carbon and hydrogen atoms. Each carbon atom uses three of its electrons to form three σ bonds with its three neighbours. This leaves each carbon atom with one electron in an atomic p-orbital.

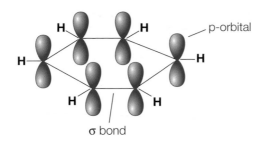

Figure 1.9 ◄
Sigma bonds in benzene, with one electron per carbon atom remaining in a p-orbital.

These six p-orbital electrons do not pair up to from three carbon–carbon double bonds (consisting of a σ bond plus a π bond) as in the Kekulé structure. Instead, they are shared evenly between all six carbon atoms giving rise to circular clouds of negative charge above and below the ring of carbon atoms (Figure 1.10). This is an example of a delocalised π electron system which results in any molecule where the conventional structure shows alternating double and single bonds. Within the π electron systems, the electrons are free to move anywhere.

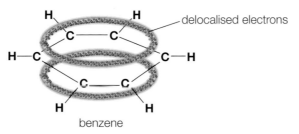

Figure 1.10 ◄
Representation of the delocalised π bonding in benzene. The circle in a benzene ring diagram represents six delocalised electrons.

Molecules with delocalised electrons, in which the charge is spread over a larger region than usual, are more stable than might otherwise be expected. In benzene, this accounts for the compound being 152 kJ mol⁻¹ more stable than expected for the Kekulé structure. This way of showing the structure explains the shape and stability of benzene.

The development of ideas concerning the structure of benzene illustrates the way in which theories develop and get modified as new knowledge becomes available.

1.4 Naming arenes

The name 'benzene' comes from *gum benzoin*, a natural product containing benzene derivatives. These derivatives of benzene are named either as substituted products of benzene or as compounds containing the phenyl group, C_6H_5-.

The names and structures of some derivatives of benzene are shown in Table 1.1.

Systematic name	Substituent group	Structure
chlorobenzene	chloro, −Cl	C_6H_5-Cl
nitrobenzene	nitro, −NO$_2$	$C_6H_5-NO_2$
methylbenzene	methyl, −CH$_3$	$C_6H_5-CH_3$
phenol	hydroxy, −OH	C_6H_5-OH
phenylamine	amine, −NH$_2$	$C_6H_5-NH_2$

Table 1.1 ◄
The names and structures of some derivatives of benzene.

When more than one hydrogen atom is substituted, numbers are used to indicate the positions of substituents on the benzene ring (Figure 1.11). The ring is usually numbered clockwise, and the numbers used are the lowest ones possible. In some cases the ring is numbered anticlockwise to get the lowest possible numbers.

In phenyl compounds, such as phenol and phenylamine, the –OH and –NH$_2$ groups are assumed to occupy the '1' position.

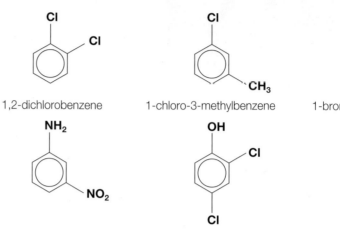

1,2-dichlorobenzene　　　1-chloro-3-methylbenzene 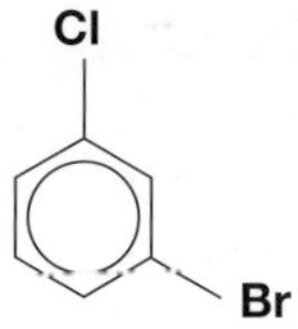　　　1-bromo-3-chlorobenzene

3-nitrophenylamine　　　2,4-dichlorophenol

Figure 1.11 ▲
Naming disubstituted products of benzene and phenol.

Test yourself

5　How does the model of benzene molecules with delocalised π electrons account for the following?
　a)　The benzene ring is a regular hexagon.
　b)　There are no isomers of 1,2-dichlorobenzene.
　c)　Benzene is less reactive than cycloalkenes.
6　When chemists thought that benzene had alternate single and double bonds, it was sometimes named cyclohexa-1,3,5-triene. Why is this now an unsatisfactory systematic name for benzene?
7　Why is the top right compound in Figure 1.11 named 1-bromo-3-chlorobenzene and not 1-chloro-3-bromobenzene?

1.5 The properties and reactions of arenes

DL
www
Data

Arenes are non-polar compounds with weak intermolecular forces between their molecules. The boiling points of arenes depend on the size of the molecules. The bigger the molecules, the higher the boiling point. Benzene and methylbenzene are liquids at room temperature, while naphthalene is a solid (Figure 1.12).

Figure 1.12 ▲
Three arenes – benzene, methylbenzene and naphthalene

Arenes, like other hydrocarbons, do not mix with water, but they do mix freely with non-polar solvents such as cyclohexane.

Test yourself

8 Explain the existence of weak attractive forces between benzene molecules, which are uncharged and non-polar.
9 Explain why benzene does not mix with water.
10 Name a solvent, other than cyclohexane, with which you would expect benzene to mix freely.

The chemical reactions of arenes

Arenes burn in air. Unlike straight-chain alkanes and alkenes of similar molar mass, they burn with a very smoky flame because of the high ratio of carbon to hydrogen in their molecules (Figure 1.13).

Benzene and other arenes are similar to alkenes in having a prominent and superficial electron-dense region. In arenes this is a delocalised ring of π electrons, while in alkenes it is a single π bond.

Because of this similarity, both arenes and alkenes react with electrophiles in many of their reactions. However, the similarity ends there because the overall reactions of arenes involve substitution, unlike those of alkenes which involve addition.

It is quite easy to see why addition reactions are difficult for arenes. If, for example, benzene reacted with bromine in an addition reaction, the ring of delocalised π electrons would be broken (Figure 1.14). Given the stability associated with the delocalised π system, this would require much more energy than that needed to break the one double bond in ethene.

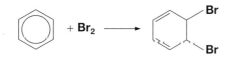

So, arenes tend to retain their delocalised π electrons and undergo substitution rather than addition reactions.

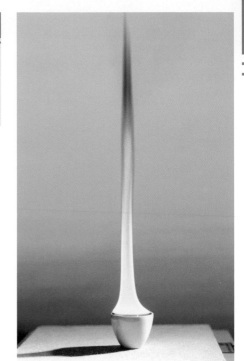

Figure 1.13 ▲
A sample of methylbenzene burning in air showing the yellow flame and very smoky fumes.

Figure 1.14 ◄
Benzene does not combine with bromine in an addition reaction because its ring of delocalised π electrons would be broken.

1.6 The substitution reactions of arenes

Nitration

When benzene is warmed to about 55 °C with concentrated nitric acid in the presence of concentrated sulfuric acid, the major product is yellow, oily nitrobenzene (Figure 1.15).

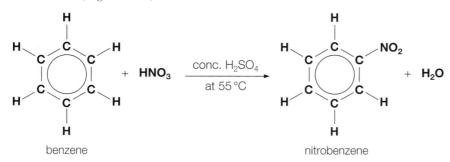

benzene   nitrobenzene

Figure 1.15 ◄
The reaction of benzene with concentrated nitric acid.

A substitution reaction occurs in which hydrogen is replaced by a nitro group, $-NO_2$.

If the reaction mixture is heated above 55 °C, further nitration occurs forming dinitrobenzene.

Nitration of benzene and other arenes is important because it produces a range of useful products including dyes and powerful explosives such as TNT (trinitrotoluene, now called 1-methyl-2,4,6-trinitrobenzene).

Figure 1.16 ►
Nitrated organic compounds, like TNT (trinitrotoluene) and nitroglycerine, are useful explosives in mining, tunnelling and road-building.

Halogenation

Benzene will not react with chlorine or bromine in the dark. The halogen molecules are non-polar and have no centre of positive charge to initiate an attack of the delocalised electron system. However, if benzene is warmed with bromine plus a catalyst of iron or iron(III) bromide, a reaction occurs forming bromobenzene (Figure 1.17).

Figure 1.17 ►
The reaction of benzene with bromine.

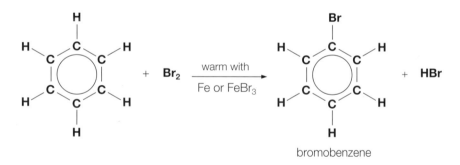
bromobenzene

A similar reaction occurs when benzene is warmed with chlorine in the presence of iron, iron(III) chloride or aluminium chloride.

Test yourself

11 Boiling benzene reacts with chlorine gas in the presence of iron(III) chloride or aluminium chloride.
   a) Sketch the apparatus which could be used to carry out this reaction on a small scale (though not in a teaching laboratory where benzene is banned).
   b) Write an equation for the reaction.
12 Three possible isomers of dinitrobenzene can be produced. One of these isomers is called 1,2-dinitrobenzene.
   a) Draw and name the structures of the other two dinitrobenzenes.
   b) Why is there no isomer called 1,6-dinitrobenzene?
13 a) Draw the structure of TNT. (*Hint:* Look closely at its systematic name of 1-methyl-2,4,6-trinitrobenzene.)
   b) Why is TNT mixed with a compound containing a high proportion of oxygen, such as potassium nitrate, when it is used as an explosive?

1.7 The mechanism of electrophilic substitution

Electrophilic substitutions are the characteristic reactions of arenes, such as benzene, in which the delocalised π electrons are attacked by strong electrophiles.

Nitration

The mixture of concentrated nitric and sulfuric acids which reacts with benzene is called a nitrating mixture. At 55 °C, concentrated nitric acid on its own reacts very slowly with benzene, and concentrated sulfuric acid by itself has practically no effect. However, in a mixture of the two, sulfuric acid reacts with nitric acid to produce nitronium ions, NO_2^+, which are very reactive electrophiles:

$$HNO_3 + H_2SO_4 \rightarrow NO_2^+ + HSO_4^- + H_2O$$

The nitronium ions are formed by removal of OH^- ions from nitric acid by sulfuric acid. In this reaction, HNO_3 is acting as a base and H_2SO_4 is acting as an acid.

The NO_2^+ ion is a reactive electrophile which is strongly attracted to the delocalised electrons in benzene. As it approaches the benzene ring, the NO_2^+ ion forms a covalent bond to one of the carbon atoms using two electrons from the π system (Figure 1.18).

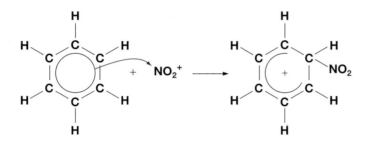

Figure 1.18 ◄
Electrophilic nitronium ions attack the delocalised electrons in benzene to form an intermediate cation.

The formation of a covalent bond in an intermediate cation disrupts the delocalised ring. A large input of energy is needed to do this and the reaction has a fairly high activation energy.

The unstable intermediate cation quickly breaks down producing nitrobenzene. This involves the return of two electrons from a C–H bond to the π electron system. The stability of the delocalised ring is restored and energy is released (Figure 1.19).

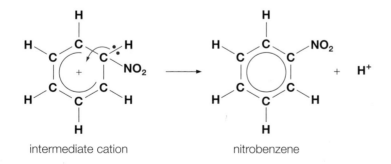

intermediate cation   nitrobenzene

Figure 1.19 ◄
The intermediate cation breaks down to form nitrobenzene.

Halogenation

When benzene is warmed with bromine in the presence of iron filings, the bromine first reacts with the iron to form iron(III) bromide:

$$2Fe(s) + 3Br_2(l) \rightarrow 2FeBr_3(s)$$

The iron(III) bromide then acts as a catalyst for the reaction of bromine with benzene by polarising further bromine molecules as $Br^{\delta+}$–$Br^{\delta-}$ (Figure 1.20).

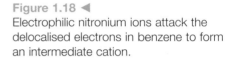

Figure 1.20 ◄
Fe^{3+} ions in iron(III) bromide polarise bromine molecules as $Br^{\delta+}$–$Br^{\delta-}$.

Definition

Chemists sometimes use the term **halogen carrier** to describe substances – such as iron(III) bromide, aluminium chloride and iron – which catalyse the reaction of benzene with chlorine or bromine.

DL
www
Tutorial

The remaining steps in the bromination of benzene are similar to nitration. The $\delta+$ bromine atoms in the polarised Br_2 molecules act as electrophiles in a similar way to NO_2^+ ions.

An intermediate cation is first produced when the $Br^{\delta+}$ atom forms a covalent bond with two electrons from the delocalised π system leaving a Br^- ion. This intermediate then breaks down to form bromobenzene as two electrons are returned from the C–H bond to the π system and the stable, delocalised ring is restored (Figure 1.21). At the same time, an H^+ ion is released from the intermediate cation. This H^+ ion immediately combines with the Br^- ion released in stage 1 to form hydrogen bromide.

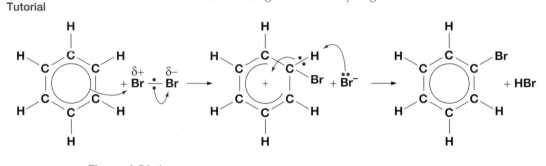

Figure 1.21 ▲
The mechanism for the bromination of benzene.

Activity

Studying the reaction of benzene with chlorine

Figure 1.22 shows the apparatus which might once have been used to prepare chlorobenzene by heating benzene with chlorine gas in the presence of iron filings. This preparation is now banned in teaching laboratories in schools and colleges.

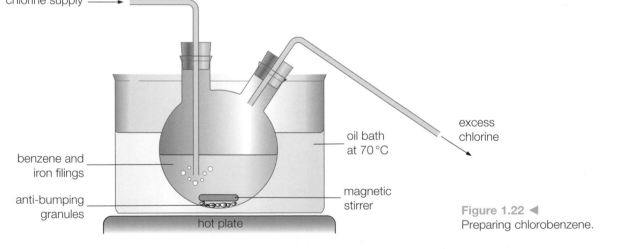

Figure 1.22 ◄
Preparing chlorobenzene.

1 Why is this reaction banned in teaching laboratories in schools?

2 a) Why should the reaction be carried out in a fume cupboard?

   b) Why is a hot plate used?

   c) Why is the oil bath at 70 °C?

3 During the reaction, iron reacts with chlorine to form iron(III) chloride, which then acts as an electron pair acceptor, polarising the Cl_2 molecules as $Cl^{\delta+}-Cl^{\delta-}$. Write equations to show:

   a) the formation of iron(III) chloride

   b) the polarisation of Cl_2 as $Cl^{\delta+}-Cl^{\delta-}$ by iron(III) chloride.

4 Write a mechanism, in two steps, for the reaction of polarised $Cl^{\delta+}-Cl^{\delta-}$ molecules with benzene to form an intermediate cation plus Cl^- in the first step, and then chlorobenzene plus HCl in the second step.

5 The reaction shown in Figure 1.22 is just as effective if aluminium chloride or iron(III) chloride is used in place of iron. These three substances (Fe, $FeBr_3$ and $AlCl_3$) are often described as 'catalysts' and 'halogen carriers'.

   a) Why are these substances described as halogen carriers for the reaction?

   b) Why is it correct to describe aluminium chloride and iron(III) chloride as catalysts?

   c) Why is it incorrect to describe iron as a catalyst for the reaction?

6 Aluminium chloride acts as a catalyst for the chlorination of benzene by polarising Cl_2 molecules in the same way as iron(III) chloride.

   a) Do you think aluminium chloride will be more effective or less effective than iron(III) chloride?

   b) Explain your answer to part **a)**.

7 Aluminium chloride can also be used with halogenoalkanes, such as chloromethane, CH_3Cl, to add alkyl groups to benzene and other arenes. The aluminium chloride increases the polarity of the $C^{\delta+}-Cl^{\delta-}$ bond of chloromethane and promotes the action of the methyl group, $^{\delta+}CH_3-$, as an electrophile.

Write a possible mechanism for the electrophilic action of $CH_3^{\delta+}Cl^{\delta-}$ on benzene to form an intermediate cation, which then breaks up to form methylbenzene and hydrogen chloride.

1.8 Comparing the reactions of arenes and alkenes

The electrophilic substitution of benzene occurs in three distinct steps whatever the final product.

Step 1: The formation of a reactive electrophile, such as NO_2^+, $Br^{\delta+}-Br^{\delta-}$, $Cl^{\delta+}-Cl^{\delta-}$ or $^{\delta+}CH_3-Cl^{\delta-}$.

Step 2: The attack of the delocalised π system by the reactive electrophile forming an unstable, intermediate cation.

Step 3: The decomposition of this intermediate cation producing a substituted-benzene (nitrobenzene, bromobenzene, methylbenzene).

Notice that the first two steps of this mechanism (Figure 1.23) are similar to the first two steps in the electrophilic addition of electrophiles – such as chlorine, bromine and hydrogen bromide – to alkenes.

Step 1 Formation of an electrophile, $\overset{\delta+}{Br}$ — $\overset{\delta-}{Br}$

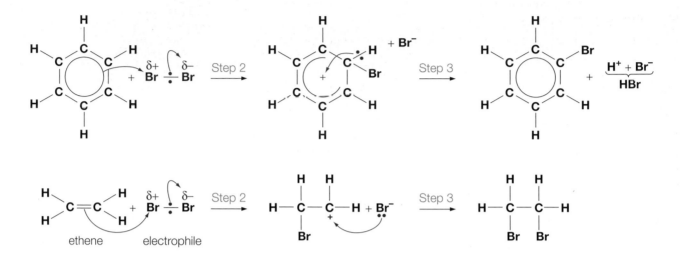

Figure 1.23 ▲
Comparing the mechanisms of the reactions of bromine with benzene and with ethene.

The third step of the mechanism is, however, very different. With benzene, the intermediate cation loses its charge by capturing two electrons from a C–H bond and releasing an H^+ ion. The delocalised, stable aromatic system is restored and a *substitution* reaction occurs.

With alkenes, there is no delocalised system or its associated stability. So, in this case the intermediate cation combines with an anion, such as Br^- or Cl^- and an *addition* reaction occurs.

These reactions of arenes and alkenes with electrophiles also differ in another important way – their relative reactivities.

Benzene and arenes are resistant to bromination, chlorination and nitration because of the stability of their delocalised π electrons. They must be heated, and catalysed as well in the case of halogenation, before a reaction occurs.

Alkenes, however, will react with halogens and hydrogen halides rapidly at room temperature because of the localised electron density of the C=C bond. Electrons in the π bond of ethene and other alkenes are readily available to any attacking electrophile.

Test yourself

14 a) Describe briefly how you would prepare bromobenzene from benzene.
   b) Why does benzene not react with bromine unless a halogen carrier is present?

15 Iodine will not react with hot benzene even in the presence of iron, but good yields of iodobenzene can be produced by reacting benzene with iodine(I) chloride.
   a) Why do you think iodine will not react with hot benzene even in the presence of iron?
   b) How is iodine(I) chloride polarised?
   c) Using your answer to part b), explain why iodine(I) chloride reacts with benzene to give good yields of iodobenzene.

1.9 Phenols

Phenols are examples of compounds with a functional group directly attached to a benzene ring. In phenols, the functional group is –OH. Experiments show that the –OH group affects the behaviour of the benzene ring, while the benzene ring also modifies the properties of the –OH group. As a result of this, phenols have some distinctive and useful properties.

Figure 1.24 ▲
Crystals of phenol.

Structures and names

In general, phenols are compounds with one or more –OH groups directly attached to a benzene ring. The simplest and most important is phenol itself.

The –OH group gives rise to hydrogen bonding in phenol and, therefore, much stronger intermolecular forces than in benzene. As a result of this, phenol is a solid at room temperature (Figure 1.24). The –OH group also allows phenol to interact with and dissolve slightly in water.

Derivatives of phenol are named in a similar way to those of benzene – by numbering the carbon atoms in the benzene ring, starting from the –OH group. The numbering runs clockwise or anticlockwise to give the lowest possible numbers for the substituted groups (Figure 1.25).

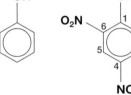

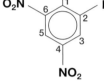

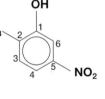

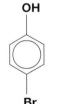

phenol   2,4,6-trinitrophenol   2-methyl-5-nitrophenol   4-bromophenol
                                              (not 6-methyl-3-nitrophenol)

Figure 1.25 ◄
The structure of phenol and other phenols.

Test yourself

16 Explain in terms of intermolecular forces why:
  a) phenol is a solid while benzene is a liquid at room temperature
  b) phenol, unlike benzene, is slightly soluble in water
  c) phenol does not mix with water as freely as ethanol.
17 What would you expect to observe on heating phenol until it burns?

1.10 Reactions of the –OH group in phenol

Reaction with sodium

Phenol reacts with sodium in a similar way to ethanol. Bubbles of hydrogen form when a small cube of sodium is added to molten phenol or to a solution of phenol in an inert solvent. The main product of the reaction is sodium phenoxide.

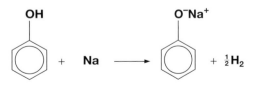

sodium
phenoxide

Figure 1.26 ◄
The reaction of phenol with sodium.

Reaction with alkalis

The benzene ring makes the –OH group more acidic in phenol than it is in alcohols. However, phenol is not as acidic as carboxylic acids (Section 3.2). It does not ionise significantly in water and it does not react with carbonates to produce carbon dioxide. But phenol, unlike alcohols, is acidic enough to form soluble salts with aqueous alkalis. So, phenol reacts readily with a solution of sodium hydroxide to form a solution of sodium phenoxide (Figure 1.27).

Figure 1.27 ▶
Phenol reacting with alkali.

The phenoxide ion is more stable than might be expected because the negative charge on the oxygen atom can be spread by delocalisation over the whole molecule (Figure 1.28). This cannot happen in alcohols.

Figure 1.28 ▶
The phenoxide ion showing the delocalisation of the negative charge.

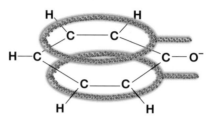

1.11 Reactions of the benzene ring in phenol

Comparing the reactivity of benzene and phenol

The –OH group in phenol activates the benzene ring and makes the ring more reactive than in benzene itself. A lone pair of electrons on the –OH group interacts with the delocalised electrons in the benzene ring releasing electrons into the ring and making electrophilic attack easier. As a result, electrophilic substitution takes place under much milder conditions with phenol than with benzene.

Reaction with bromine

An aqueous solution of phenol reacts readily with bromine water to produce an immediate white precipitate of 2,4,6-tribromophenol as the orange/yellow bromine colour fades. The reaction with bromine water is rapid at room temperature. There is no need to heat the mixture or to use a catalyst (Figure 1.29).

Figure 1.29 ▶
The reaction of phenol with bromine water.

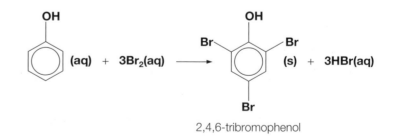

2,4,6-tribromophenol

A test for phenols

Phenols give a purple colour when mixed with a neutral solution of iron(III) chloride. The colour is due to a complex ion formed between the Fe^{3+} ions and phenols.

Test yourself

18 Identify one way in which the reaction of the —OH group is similar in phenol and ethanol, and one way in which it differs.

19 a) What would you expect to observe if you added enough dilute hydrochloric acid to a solution of phenol in sodium hydroxide to make the mixture acidic?
   b) Explain the reaction that occurs.

20 Dilute nitric acid reacts rapidly with phenol at room temperature to form 2-nitrophenol and 4-nitrophenol.
   a) Draw the structures of the two products.
   b) How do these conditions for nitrating phenol compare with the conditions for nitrating benzene?

Activity

Manufacturing phenol

Phenol is manufactured from benzene, propene and oxygen in two stages. The procedure is called the cumene process (Figure 1.30).

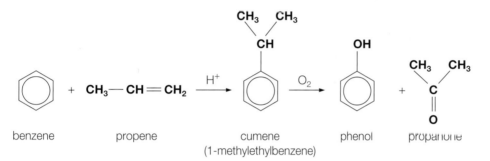

| benzene | propene | cumene (1-methylethylbenzene) | phenol | propanone |

- The first stage of the process involves the acid-catalysed electrophilic substitution of benzene with propene to form cumene.

- The second stage involves the air oxidation of cumene.

This produces equimolar amounts of phenol and propanone, a valuable co-product. About 100 000 tonnes of phenol are manufactured each year in the UK using the cumene process.

Figure 1.30 ▲
The manufacture of phenol by the cumene process.

1 Benzene and propene are obtained from crude oil for use in the cumene process. What processes, starting with crude oil, are used to produce:

   a) benzene   b) propene?

2 In the first stage of the cumene process, H⁺ ions react with propene to produce electrophiles.

   a) Write the formulae of two possible electrophiles produced when H⁺ ions react with propene.

   b) Explain why one of these electrophiles is more stable than the other. (*Hint:* alkyl groups are slightly electron-donating.)

   c) Name and draw the structure of a second possible product of this first stage, besides cumene.

3 a) Write an equation for the reaction of the stable electrophile, identified in **2b)**, with benzene to produce cumene.

b) Why is this reaction described as 'acid catalysed'?

4 Write an equation for the second stage of the process, in which cumene is oxidised to phenol and propanone.

5 The overall yield in the cumene process is 85%. Calculate the mass of benzene required to manufacture 1 tonne of phenol, and the mass of propanone formed at the same time.

6 In the USA, some phenol is manufactured by refluxing chlorobenzene with concentrated sodium hydroxide solution at 400 °C and a pressure of 150 atmospheres (Figure 1.31).

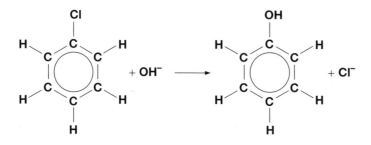

Figure 1.31 ◄
The reaction of chlorobenzene with hydroxide ions to form phenol.

a) What kind of reagent are OH⁻ ions in this reaction?

b) Why do you think the reaction requires such harsh conditions to produce phenol?

1.12 The uses and importance of phenol

The main uses of phenol are in the production of:
- antiseptics and disinfectants
- thermosetting plastics
- intermediates for the manufacture of nylon (Section 6.3).

Antiseptics and disinfectants

Phenol is a powerful disinfectant which has been used to kill germs ever since it was isolated from coal tar in the nineteenth century. For a time, phenol was famous as a chemical which made surgery safe. In the mid-nineteenth century many doctors were puzzled by the life-threatening infections in many hospitals. These were so common that most of their patients died of gangrene after serious operations. Then, in 1857, a young surgeon called Joseph Lister, working in Glasgow, read Louis Pasteur's papers about the germ theory of disease. Lister realised that he could use a disinfectant chemical while operating to prevent the onset of an infection. He developed a technique of spraying a solution of phenol over open wounds during operations. As a result of this, his patients had a much better chance of their wounds healing without becoming infected. However, Lister eventually came to the conclusion that scrupulous attention to cleanliness was preferable to spraying with chemicals.

Unfortunately, there are also risks involved with the use of phenol. It is an unpleasant chemical which burns the skin and is therefore unsuitable as an antiseptic. Since Lister's time, chemists have discovered substituted phenols which are suitable as antiseptics. These include Dettol and TCP (Figure 1.32) in which chlorination increases the antibacterial properties of phenol and also improves its healing properties as an antiseptic.

Definitions

Disinfectants are chemicals which destroy microorganisms. Phenol is a disinfectant and so is chlorine. Unlike antiseptics, disinfectants cannot be used on skin and other living tissues.

Antiseptics are chemicals which kill microorganisms but, unlike disinfectants, they can be used safely on the skin.

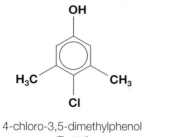

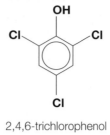

Figure 1.32 ◄
The structure of Dettol and TCP.

4-chloro-3,5-dimethylphenol
(Dettol)

2,4,6-trichlorophenol
(TCP)

Thermosetting plastics (resins)

When phenol is heated with methanal, $H_2C=O$, in the presence of an acid or an alkali as catalyst, a hard and brittle plastic is formed. Initially, the reaction links phenol molecules through their 2 and 6 positions to form a linear polymer. These linear polymers then react further with methanal molecules to form links through their 4 positions (Figure 1.33).

The final product is a molecular network in which all the benzene rings are substituted in the 2, 4 and 6 positions. This polymer is very hard because of its extensively cross-linked network The hard, dark brown material was discovered in 1905 in the USA by Leo Baekeland and named 'Bakelite'. Bakelite is an excellent thermal and electrical insulator which is still widely used for heat-resistant handles and knobs as well as electrical plugs and fittings.

Bakelite has the disadvantage that it sets hard as it forms and cannot be remelted or softened. This makes it difficult to mould. Polymers of this kind are described as thermosetting and are sometimes called resins. In contrast, polymers such as polythene and pvc, soften on heating and can be moulded into different shapes, which they retain on cooling. These polymers are described as thermoplastic.

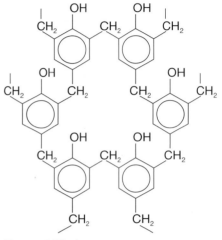

Figure 1.33 ▲
The thermosetting plastic produced from phenol and methanal.

Figure 1.34 ◄
An advert for Bakelite in the 1950s praising its properties. Bakelite was the first commercially successful plastic.

Definitions

Thermoplastic polymers soften on heating and can be moulded into a different shape which is retained on cooling.

Thermosetting polymers (or resins) set hard on formation and cannot be softened or moulded into different shapes.

17

REVIEW QUESTIONS

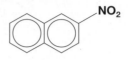

1 a) Describe the structure and bonding in benzene and explain why benzene is less reactive with electrophiles than alkenes. **(9)**

b) Describe the conditions needed for the nitration of benzene to form nitrobenzene, and outline the mechanism of the reaction using curly arrows where appropriate. **(5)**

2 a) Chlorobenzene can be produced from benzene and chlorine with a suitable catalyst.

i) Name the catalyst. **(1)**

ii) Describe briefly how chlorobenzene can be prepared. **(3)**

b) Under suitable conditions benzene can be used to make the halogenoalkane shown below.

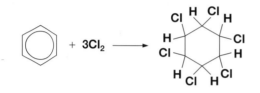

i) What type of reaction occurs? **(1)**

ii) What is the name of the halogenoalkane produced? **(2)**

c) The halogenoalkane from part b) reacts on warming with excess aqueous sodium hydroxide.

i) Draw the structure of the final product with excess sodium hydroxide solution. **(1)**

ii) What type of reaction occurs? **(2)**

3 Naphthalene is an arene containing two fused benzene rings. Its skeletal formula is

a) What is i) the molecular formula; ii) the empirical formula of naphthalene? **(2)**

b) Describe the delocalisation of electrons in naphthalene, including the shape of the delocalised system and the number of delocalised electrons. **(5)**

c) Naphthalene reacts with nitric acid in the presence of sulfuric acid to form

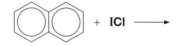

i) Describe the conditions required for the reaction. **(2)**

ii) What type of reaction occurs and what is the reactive species? **(2)**

d) Copy, complete and balance the following equation for the reaction of naphthalene with iodine(I) chloride: **(2)**

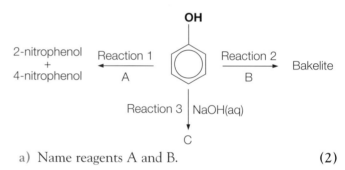

4 Three reactions of phenol are summarised in the flow diagram below.

a) Name reagents A and B. **(2)**

b) Draw the structural formula of C. **(2)**

c) Under suitable conditions, nitrophenols can be converted to dinitrophenols.

i) Suggest the reaction conditions for converting nitrophenols to dinitrophenols. **(2)**

ii) One possible dinitrophenol is 2,3-dinitrophenol. Write the names of all the other possible dinitrophenols. **(3)**

d) Draw the structure of the molecule produced when two molecules of phenol react with one molecule of reagent B. **(2)**

2 Carbonyl compounds

The two types of carbonyl compounds are the aldehydes and the ketones. The reactive carbonyl group plays an important part in the chemistry of living things, in laboratory chemistry and in industry. As expected for a double bond, the characteristic reactions are addition reactions. The C=O bond is polar because oxygen is highly electronegative. As a result, the mechanism of addition to carbonyl compounds is not the same as the mechanism of addition to alkenes.

2.1 Aldehydes

Names and structures

Aldehydes are carbonyl compounds in which a carbonyl group (C=O) is attached to two hydrogen atoms, or to a hydrocarbon group and a hydrogen atom. So the carbonyl group is at the end of a carbon chain. The names are based on the alkane with the same carbon skeleton, with the ending changed from –**ane** to –**anal**.

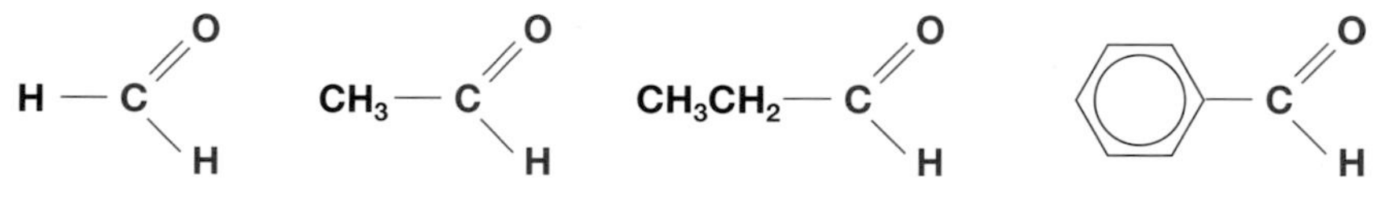

Figure 2.1 ▶
Structures and names of aldehydes. The –CHO group is the functional group which gives aldehydes their characteristic reactions.

methanal   ethanal   propanal   benzenecarbaldehyde
                                                      (benzaldehyde)

Occurrence and uses

Biologists use a solution of methanal to preserve specimens. Since the beginning of the twentieth century it has been the main ingredient of the fluids used by embalmers. Methanal is also an important industrial chemical because it is a raw material for the manufacture for a range of thermosetting plastics (see Sections 1.12 and 6.1).

> **Note**
>
> Always write the aldehyde group as –CHO. Writing –COH is unconventional and can easily lead to confusion with alcohols.

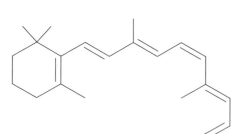

Figure 2.3 ▲
The skeletal formula of retinal, which is a naturally occurring aldehyde. Combined with a protein it forms the light sensitive part of the visual pigment in the rod cells of the retina. When light falls on a rod cell, the retinal molecule changes shape. This sets off a series of changes that lead to a signal being sent to the brain.

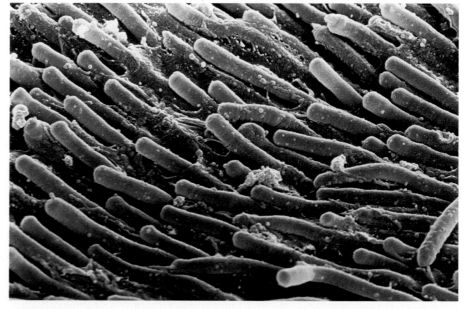

Figure 2.2 ▲
A coloured scanning electron micrograph of rod cells in the retina of an eye. The cells are magnified about 3000 times. Rod cells contain a visual pigment that can respond to dim light but cannot distinguish colours.

Physical properties

Methanal is a gas at room temperature. Ethanal boils at 21 °C so it may be a liquid or gas at room temperature depending on the conditions. Other common aldehydes are all liquids. The simpler aldehydes such as methanal and ethanal are freely soluble in water.

**www
Data**

Test yourself

1 Write the structure of 2-methylbutanal.
2 a) Show that the boiling points of aldehydes are higher than corresponding alkanes with similar relative molecular masses, but lower than corresponding alcohols.
  b) Account for the values of the boiling points of aldehydes relative to those of alkanes and alcohols in terms of intermolecular forces.
3 Why does an aldehyde such as ethanal mix freely with water, while benzenecarbaldehyde (benzaldehyde) is much less soluble?

Activity

Converting an alcohol to an aldehyde

A 3 g sample of sodium dichromate(VI) is added to 10 cm³ of dilute sulfuric acid in a pear-shaped flask. Then 1.5 cm³ of propan-1-ol are added, a few drops at a time. The flask is gently shaken to mix the contents until all the solid has dissolved. The flask is fitted with a condenser as shown in Figure 2.4. Then 2–3 cm³ of liquid is distilled into a small flask from the reaction mixture.

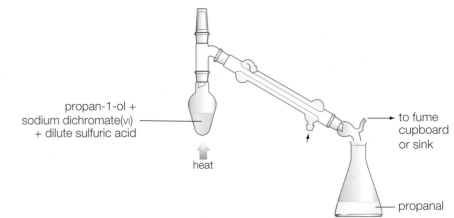

propan-1-ol +
sodium dichromate(VI)
+ dilute sulfuric acid

heat

to fume
cupboard
or sink

propanal

Figure 2.4 ▲
Apparatus used to oxidise an alcohol.

1 What type of alcohol is propan-1-ol?

2 What type of reagent is an acidic solution of sodium dichromate(VI)?

3 Write an equation for the reaction.

4 Suggest a reason for adding the propan-1-ol a few drops at a time.

5 Explain why the reaction mixture is not heated in a flask fitted with a reflux condenser before distilling off the product.

6 Describe two tests that can be used to show that the product of this reaction is an aldehyde and not a carboxylic acid (see Section 2.5).

Formation

Oxidation of primary alcohols by heating with a mixture of dilute sulfuric acid and potassium dichromate(VI) produces aldehydes under conditions which allow the aldehyde to distil off as it forms. Unlike ketones, aldehydes are easily oxidised further to carboxylic acids by longer heating with an excess of the reagent.

2.2 Ketones

Names and structures

In ketones, the carbonyl group is attached to two hydrocarbon groups. Chemists name ketones after the alkane with the same carbon skeleton by changing the ending -**ane** to -**anone**. Where necessary, a number in the name shows the position of the carbonyl group.

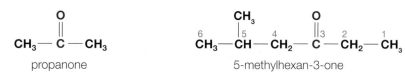

propanone   5-methylhexan-3-one

Figure 2.5 ▲
Structures and names of two ketones.

Occurrence and uses

The most widely used ketone is propanone, which is a common solvent. It has a low boiling point and evaporates quickly, making it suitable for cleaning and drying parts of precision equipment. Propanone is also the starting point for producing the monomer of the glass-like addition polymer in display signs, plastic baths and the covers of car lights (see Section 6.2). Propanone, and other ketones, form during normal metabolism, especially at night and during fasting when the levels of propanone and other ketones in the blood rise.

Physical properties

All the common ketones are liquids with boiling points similar to those of the corresponding aldehydes. The simplest ketone, propanone, mixes freely with water.

Formation

Oxidation of secondary alcohols with hot, acidified potassium dichromate(VI) produces ketones which, unlike aldehydes, are not easily oxidised further.

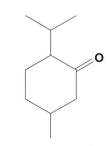

Figure 2.6 ▲
A bottle of peppermint oil and leaves of the peppermint plant. The oil is used in aromatherapy. Peppermint oil contains menthone together with a range of chemicals which include menthol, methyl ethanoate and volatile oils.

Figure 2.7 ▲
The skeletal formula of the naturally occurring ketone called menthone, which is found in the oils extracted from some plants.

Test yourself

4 Write the structure of 4,4-dimethylpentan-2-one.
5 What is the molecular formula of menthone (Figure 2.7)?
6 Show that propanone and propanal are functional group isomers.
7 Write an equation for the oxidation of butan-2-ol to butanone. (Represent the oxygen from the oxidising agent as [O].)

Activity

Chemicals in perfumes

The perfume 'Chanel No. 5' was innovative when produced for the first time in 1921. As well as natural extracts from flowers, the scent includes a high proportion of synthetic aldehydes such as dodecanal. This produces a highly original perfume.

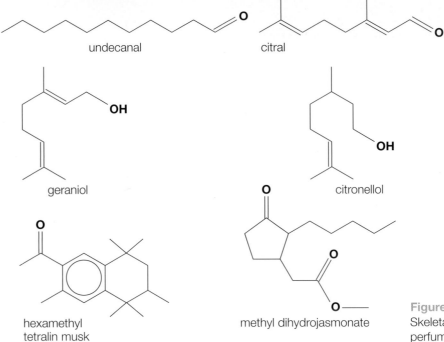

Figure 2.8 ◄
Skeletal formulae of some perfume chemicals.

The people who devise new perfumes think of the mixture as a sequence of 'notes'. You first smell the 'top notes', but the main effect depends on the 'middle notes' while the more lasting elements of the perfume are the 'end notes'. The overall balance of the three is critical. This means that the volatility of perfume chemicals is of great importance to the perfumer.

Note	Natural chemicals	Synthetic chemicals	Boiling point or melting point
top	citrus oils lavender	octanal (citrus) undecanal (green)	b.p. 168 °C b.p. 117 °C
middle	rose violet	geraniol (floral) citronellol (rosy)	b.p. 146 °C b.p. 224 °C
end	balsam musk	indane (musk) hexamethyl tetralin (musk)	m.p. 53 °C m.p. 55 °C

Table 2.1 ◄
Natural and synthetic chemicals used to make perfumes.

1 Draw the skeletal formula of octanal.

2 Suggest two advantages for the perfumer of using synthetic chemicals instead of chemicals extracted from living things.

3 Identify the carbonyl compounds among the compounds shown in Figure 2.8. In each case state whether the compound includes the functional group of an aldehyde or of a ketone.

4 Like many perfume chemicals, geraniol is a terpene. Terpene molecules are built from units derived from 2-methylbuta-1,3-diene.

a) What is the structure of 2-methylbuta-1,3-diene?

b) How many 2-methylbuta-1,3-diene units are needed to make up the hydrocarbon skeleton of geraniol?

5 Use your knowledge of intermolecular forces to explain why:

a) aldehydes are useful as top notes while alcohols are more commonly used as middle notes

b) the musks used as 'end notes' also help to 'fix', or retain, the more volatile components of a perfume

c) geraniol is more soluble in water than undecanal.

2.3 Reactions of aldehydes and ketones

Oxidation

Oxidising agents easily convert aldehydes to carboxylic acids. It is much harder to oxidise ketones – this is only possible with powerful oxidising agents which break up the carbonyl molecules. Chemical tests to distinguish aldehydes and ketones are based on the difference in the ease of oxidation (see Section 2.5).

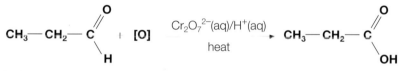

Acidified potassium dichromate(VI) is orange and contains $Cr_2O_7^{2-}$ ions. When oxidising an aldehyde to a carboxylic acid, the reagent turns green giving a solution containing green Cr^{3+} ions.

Figure 2.9 ◄
Oxidation of propanal to propanoic acid.

Reduction

Sodium tetrahydridoborate(III), $NaBH_4$, reduces aldehydes to primary alcohols, and ketones to secondary alcohols.

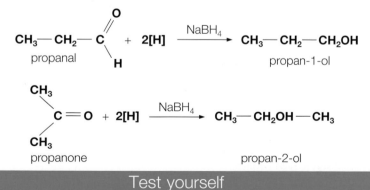

Figure 2.10 ◄
Reduction of propanal and propanone. The 2[H] comes from the reducing agent. This is a shorthand way of balancing complex equations involving reduction.

Test yourself

8 Identify the oxidation states of chromium before and after the oxidation of an aldehyde by a solution of potassium dichromate(VI).

9 a) Outline the reagents and conditions for converting butanal to butanoic acid
  b) What apparatus is used **i)** to carry out the reaction **ii)** to separate the product from the reaction mixture?

10 Name the products of reducing butanal and butanone. Which is a primary alcohol and which a secondary alcohol?

11 Show that reduction of an aldehyde or ketone with $NaBH_4$ has the effect of adding hydrogen to the double bond.

2.4 Nucleophilic addition

The carbonyl group in aldehydes and ketones is polar because oxygen is much more electronegative than carbon. The shared electrons in the double bond are drawn towards the oxygen atom. This leaves a slight positive charge on the carbon atom. As a result, the carbon atom in a carbonyl group is open to attack by nucleophiles.

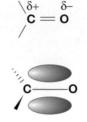

Figure 2.11 ▲
Two ways of representing the polarity of the double bond in a carbonyl group.

The reduction of a carbonyl compound with $NaBH_4$ is an example of a nucleophilic addition reaction.

An incoming nucleophile uses its lone pair of electrons to form a new bond with the carbon atom. This displaces one pair of electrons in the double bond onto the oxygen atom. So, the oxygen atom has gained one electron from carbon and now has a negative charge.

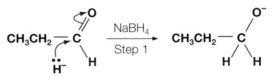

Figure 2.12 ▲
The first step of the nucleophilic addition. The hydride ion from $NaBH_4$ is the nucleophile.

To complete the reaction, the negatively charged oxygen atom acts as a base and gains a proton.

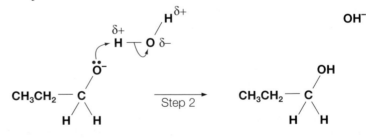

Figure 2.13 ▲
The second step of the nucleophilic addition. The negatively charged oxygen atom acts as a base and gains a proton.

Test yourself

12 Answer these questions about the nucleophilic addition of hydrogen by reaction of a carbonyl compound with $NaBH_4$.
   a) What features of the hydride ion mean that it is a nucleophile?
   b) What type of bond breaking takes place in each step?
   c) Explain why there is a negative charge on the oxygen atom at the end of step 1.
   d) Which molecule acts as an acid in step 2?

2.5 Tests for aldehydes and ketones

Recognising carbonyl compounds

Today, chemists can identify aldehydes and ketones with the help of instrumental techniques such as mass spectrometry and infrared spectroscopy (Topic 9). Traditionally, chemists characterised these compounds by combining them with a reagent that could convert them to a solid product. The solid, a so-called crystalline derivative, is a chemical which can be purified by recrystallisation and then identified by measuring its melting point.

For example, the reagent 2,4-dinitrophenylhydrazine reacts with carbonyl compounds forming 2,4-dinitrophenylhydrazone derivatives which are solid at room temperature and bright yellow or orange (Figure 2.14). The solid derivative has no practical use but it can be filtered off, recrystallised and identified by measuring its melting point. Together with the boiling point of the original aldehyde or ketone, this makes it possible to identify the carbonyl compound.

Distinguishing aldehydes and ketones

Tollens' reagent (ammoniacal silver nitrate) is a mild oxidising agent which is used to distinguish aldehydes from ketones – aldehydes are easily oxidised but ketones are not.

Tollens' reagent consists of an alkaline solution of diamminesilver(I) ions, $[Ag(NH_3)_2]^+$. It forms a complex with ammonia and this keeps the silver(I) ions in solution under alkaline conditions. The silver ions can oxidise aldehydes but not ketones. Aldehydes reduce the silver ions to metallic silver.

Figure 2.14 ▲
A bright orange 2,4-dinitrophenylhydrazone derivative.

Figure 2.15 ▲
Warming Tollens' reagent with an aldehyde produces a precipitate of silver which coats clean glass with a shiny layer so that it acts like a mirror (left). There is no reaction with a ketone (right).

Test yourself

13 a) Write an equation for the reaction of Tollens' reagent with propanal. Use the symbol [O] to represent the reagent.
   b) Use the oxidation numbers of the metal ions and atoms to show that propanal reduces Tollens' reagent.
14 Hydrolysis of A, C_4H_9Cl, with hot, aqueous sodium hydroxide produces B, $C_4H_{10}O$. Heating B with an acidic solution of potassium dichromate(VI) and distilling off the product as it forms give C, C_4H_8O. C gives a yellow precipitate with 2,4-dinitrophenylhydrazine and forms a silver mirror when warmed with Tollens' solution. Give the names and structures of these compounds.

Activity

Identifying an unknown carbonyl compound

Figure 2.16 shows stages in making, purifying and identifying a carbonyl compound.

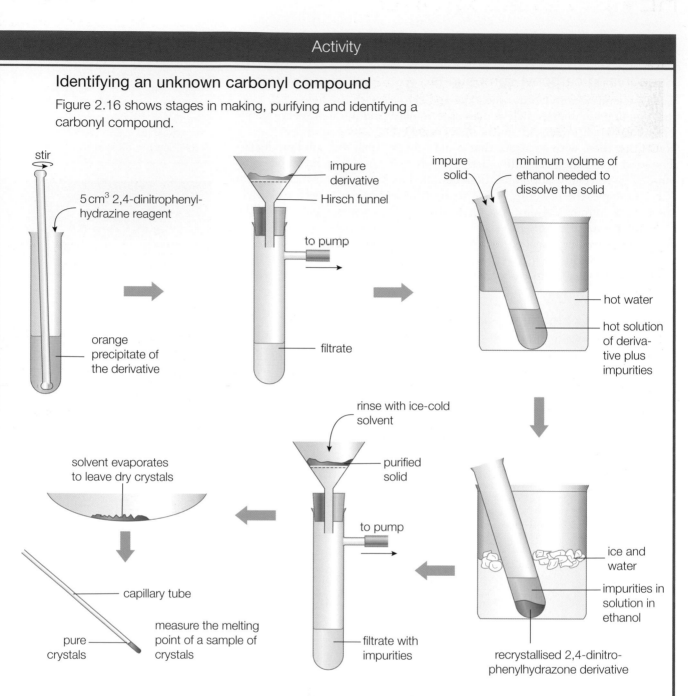

1 Why is it necessary to purify the derivative before measuring its melting point?

2 Explain how the procedure illustrated in Figure 2.16 removes impurities from the derivative.

3 In this instance, ethanol is the solvent used for recrystallising the derivative. What determines the choice of solvent?

4 When measuring the melting point, what are the signs that the derivative is pure?

5 Identify the carbonyl compound which forms a 2,4-dinitrophenylhydrazone that melts at 115 °C. It boils at 80 °C. The compound does not form a silver mirror with Tollens' reagent.

Figure 2.16 ▲
Making a pure crystalline derivative of a carbonyl compound.

Practical guidance

Data

REVIEW QUESTIONS

Extension questions

1 Copy and complete the table to show three different reactions of propanal. (6)

Reactant	Reagent	Organic product	
		Name	Displayed formula
CH₃CH₂CHO	Tollens' reagent		
CH₃CH₂CHO		propanoic acid	
CH₃CH₂CHO	NaBH₄		

2 The molar mass of a hydrocarbon W is $56\,g\,mol^{-1}$ and it contains 85.7% carbon. W reacts with hydrogen bromide to form X. Heating X under reflux with aqueous sodium hydroxide produces Y. Heating Y with an acidified solution of potassium dichromate(VI) converts it to Z. Z gives a yellow precipitate with 2,4-dinitrophenylhydrazine but it does not give a silver mirror with Tollens' reagent.

a) Identify W, X, Y and Z and give your reasoning. (8)

b) Write equations for the reactions of W, X and Y mentioned. (3)

3 Describe the mechanisms for the reactions of:

a) propene with bromine

b) propanone with NaBH₄.

Identify similarities and differences between the two mechanisms with reference to the nature of the bonds and bond breaking, the reagents involved, the formation of intermediates and the overall effects of the change. (10)

4 Cinnamaldehyde is the chemical that gives cinnamon its flavour. Vanillin is the chemical mainly responsible for the flavour of vanilla.

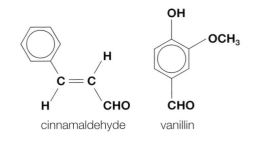

cinnamaldehyde   vanillin

a) i) Work out the molecular formula of vanillin. (1)

   ii) Name the two functional groups (other than the benzene ring) in cinnamaldehyde. (2)

   iii) Name the functional group which is also present in vanillin. (1)

   iv) Describe a test that could be used to show that both cinnamaldehyde and vanillin contain this functional group. (2)

b) Describe a test that could be used to distinguish vanillin from cinnamaldehyde. (2)

c) Give the structure of a *cis/trans* isomer of cinnamaldehyde. (1)

d) i) Draw the structure of the product after treating vanillin with NaBH₄. (1)

   ii) Draw the structure of the compound formed when this product reacts with excess aqueous sodium hydroxide solution. (1)

3 Carboxylic acids and esters

Many organic acids are instantly recognisable by their odours. Ethanoic acid, for example, gives vinegar its taste and smell. Butanoic acid is responsible for the foul smell of rancid butter, while the body odour of goats is a blend of the three unbranched organic acids with 6, 8 and 10 carbon atoms. Organic acids play a vital part in the biochemistry of life because of the great variety of their reactions. The acids are also important in laboratory and industrial chemistry and help to give rise to a range of new materials – especially synthetic fibres and plastics.

3.1 Carboxylic acids

Occurrence

Carboxylic acids are compounds with the formula R–COOH, where R represents an alkyl group, aryl group or a hydrogen atom. The carboxylic acid group –COOH is the functional group which gives the acids their characteristic properties.

Figure 3.1 ▲
The traditional names for organic acids were based on their natural origins. The original name for methanoic acid was formic acid because it was first obtained from red ants and the Latin name for 'ant' is 'formica'. This red wood ant can spray attackers with methanoic acid (magnification ×10).

Figure 3.2 ◄
Many vegetables contain ethanedioic acid, which is commonly called oxalic acid. The level of the acid in rhubarb leaves is high enough for it to be dangerous to eat the leaves. The acid kills by lowering the concentration of calcium ions in blood to a dangerously low level.

Names and structures

The carboxylic acid group can be regarded as a carbonyl group, C=O, attached to an –OH group, but is better seen as a single functional group with distinctive properties.

Chemists name carboxylic acids by changing the ending of the corresponding alk**ane** to **-oic acid**. So, ethane becomes ethanoic acid.

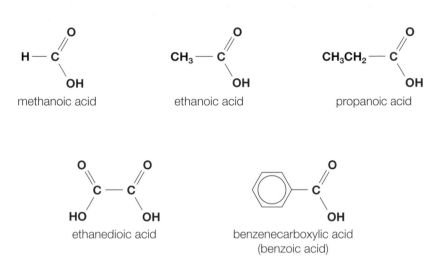

methanoic acid   ethanoic acid   propanoic acid

ethanedioic acid   benzenecarboxylic acid
(benzoic acid)

Figure 3.3 ▲
Names and structures of carboxylic acids.

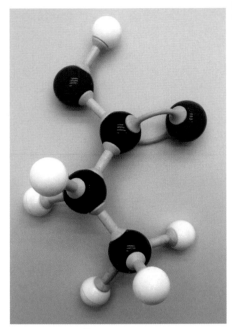

Figure 3.4 ▲
Ball-and-stick model of a carboxylic acid.

Test yourself

1 Write out the structural formulae and give the systematic names of the three carboxylic acids that were traditionally derived from the Latin word 'caper' meaning goat: caproic acid (6C), caprylic acid (8C) and capric acid (10C).
2 Give the molecular formula, skeletal formula and name of the acid shown in Figure 3.4.

Physical properties

Even the simplest acids, such as methanoic acid and ethanoic acid, are liquids at room temperature because of hydrogen bonding between the carboxylic acid groups. Carboxylic acids with more than eight carbon atoms in the chain are solids. Benzenecarboxylic acid (benzoic acid) is also a solid at room temperature. Carbon–oxygen bonds are polar.

There is also the possibility of hydrogen bonding between water molecules and the –OH groups and oxygen atoms in carboxylic acid molecules. This means that the acids are soluble in water.

Test yourself

3 Draw a diagram to show hydrogen bonding between ethanoic acid molecules and water molecules.
4 In a non-polar solvent, ethanoic acid molecules dimerise through hydrogen bonding.
  a) Suggest a reason why the acid dimerises in a non-polar solvent, but not in water.
  b) Draw a diagram to show an ethanoic acid dimer with two hydrogen bonds between the molecules.

3.2 Reactions of carboxylic acids

Reactions as acids

Carboxylic acids are weak acids (see Section 12.3). They are only slightly ionised when they dissolve in water:

$$CH_3COOH(aq) \rightleftharpoons CH_3COO^-(aq) + H^+(aq)$$

The aqueous hydrogen ions in the solutions of these compounds mean that they show the characteristic reactions of acids with metals, bases and carbonates.

Carboxylic acids are sufficiently acidic to produce carbon dioxide when added to a solution of sodium carbonate or sodium hydrogencarbonate. This reaction distinguishes carboxylic acids from weaker acids such as phenols (see Section 1.10).

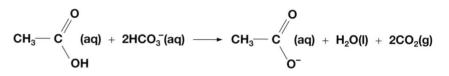

Figure 3.5 ▲
The reaction of ethanoic acid with hydrogencarbonate ions.

Test yourself

5 For each of these pairs of chemicals describe what you would observe when they react, write equations for the reactions and name the organic products:
   a) methanoic acid and magnesium
   b) ethanoic acid and potassium hydroxide
   c) propanoic acid and sodium carbonate
   d) butanoic acid with ammonia.
6 Benzenecarboxylic acid (benzoic acid) is only very slightly soluble in water but it dissolves freely in aqueous sodium hydroxide. Use le Chatelier's principle to explain why this happens – start by writing an equation for the equilibrium between solid benzenecarboxylic acid and its aqueous ions in solution.

Esterification

Carboxylic acids react with alcohols to form esters (see Section 3.3). The two organic compounds are mixed and heated under reflux in the presence of a small amount of a strong acid catalyst, such as concentrated sulfuric acid.

$$CH_3-\overset{\displaystyle O}{\overset{\|}{C}}_{OH}(l) + CH_3CH_2CH_3OH(l) \underset{heat}{\overset{H^+(aq)}{\rightleftharpoons}} CH_3-\overset{\displaystyle O}{\overset{\|}{C}}_{OCH_2CH_2CH_3}(l) + H_2O(l)$$

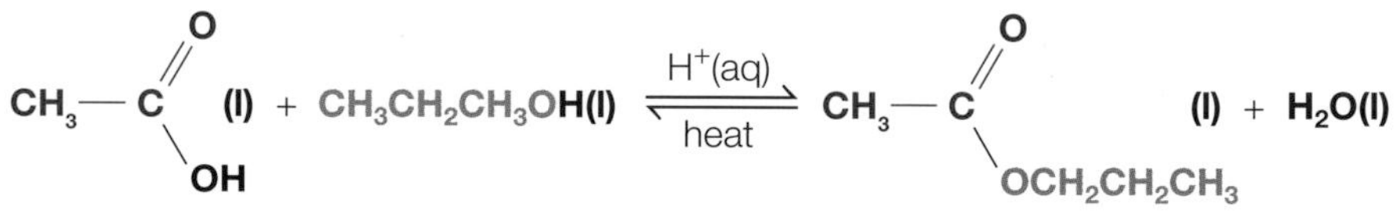

Figure 3.6 ▲
Formation of an ester from ethanoic acid and propan-1-ol.

This reaction is reversible. The conditions for reaction have to be arranged to increase the yield of the ester. One possibility is to use an excess of either the acid or the alcohol, depending on which is more available or cheaper. Using more concentrated sulfuric acid than needed for its catalytic effect can help too because the acid reacts with water. In some esterification reactions it is possible to distil off either the ester or the water as they form.

Test yourself

7 Use le Chatelier's principle to explain the methods used to increase the yield of an ester formed from an acid and an alcohol.

Activity

Preparation of an ester

This sequence of diagrams shows the procedure for preparing a small sample of an ester.

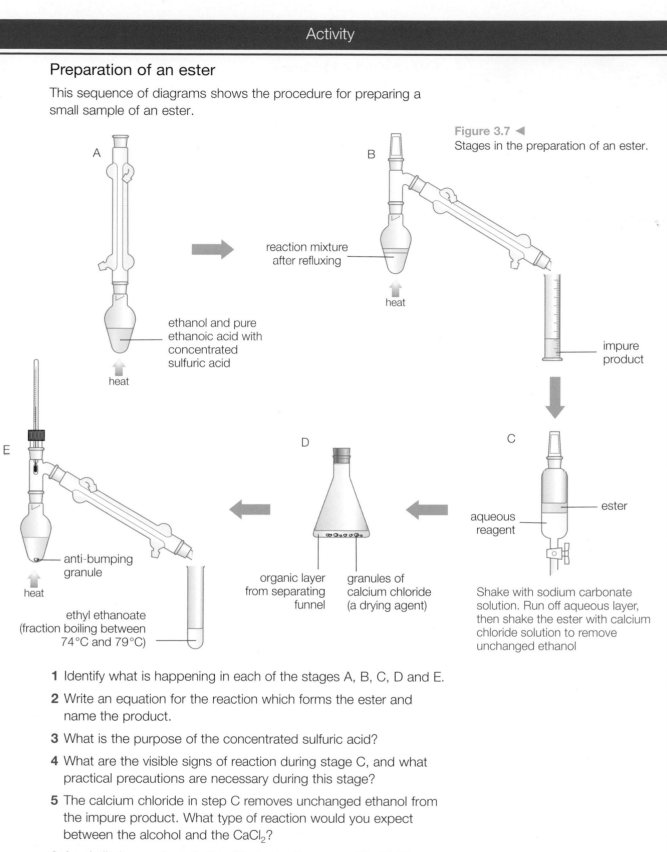

Figure 3.7 ◄
Stages in the preparation of an ester.

A

reaction mixture after refluxing

B

heat

ethanol and pure ethanoic acid with concentrated sulfuric acid

heat

impure product

E

D

C

anti-bumping granule

heat

ethyl ethanoate (fraction boiling between 74 °C and 79 °C)

organic layer from separating funnel

granules of calcium chloride (a drying agent)

aqueous reagent

ester

Shake with sodium carbonate solution. Run off aqueous layer, then shake the ester with calcium chloride solution to remove unchanged ethanol

1 Identify what is happening in each of the stages A, B, C, D and E.

2 Write an equation for the reaction which forms the ester and name the product.

3 What is the purpose of the concentrated sulfuric acid?

4 What are the visible signs of reaction during stage C, and what practical precautions are necessary during this stage?

5 The calcium chloride in step C removes unchanged ethanol from the impure product. What type of reaction would you expect between the alcohol and the $CaCl_2$?

6 A volatile by-product distils off in the boiling range 35–40 °C before the ester in stage E. Suggest a structure for this by-product, which has the molecular formula $C_4H_{10}O$.

7 Calculate the percentage yield of the ester if the actual yield is 50 g from 40 g ethanol and 52 g ethanoic acid.

DL
www
Practical guidance

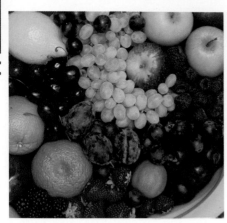

Figure 3.8 ▲
Natural fruit flavours are complex mixtures. Some simpler esters on their own have odours which resemble fruit flavours. Examples are propyl ethanoate (pear), ethyl butanoate (pineapple), octyl ethanoate (orange), 2-methylpropyl ethanoate (apple).

Definition

Essential oils are the oils which chemists extract from plants as a source of chemicals for perfumes, food flavourings and other uses. They often include esters.

3.3 Esters

Occurrence and uses

Many of the sweet-smelling compounds found in perfumes and fruit flavours are esters. Some drugs used in medicine are esters, including aspirin, paracetamol and the local anaesthetics novocaine and benzocaine. The insecticides malathion and pyrethrin are also esters. Compounds with more than one ester link include fats and oils as well as polyester fibres. Other esters are important as solvents and plasticisers.

Names and structures

The general formula for an ester is RCOOR′, where R and R′ are alkyl or aryl groups.

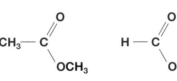

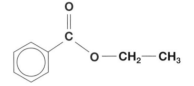

methyl ethanoate   ethyl methanoate   ethyl benzenecarboxylate (ethyl benzoate)

Figure 3.9 ▲
Names and structures of esters.

Test yourself

8 Give the name and displayed formulae of the esters formed when:
 a) butanoic acid reacts with propan-1-ol
 b) ethanoic acid reacts with methanol
 c) ethanoic acid reacts with butan-1-ol.

Physical properties

Common esters such as ethyl ethanoate are volatile liquids and only slightly soluble in water.

www Data

Test yourself

9 Explain, in terms of intermolecular forces, why the boiling point of ethyl ethanoate is similar to that of ethanol, but lower than that of ethanoic acid.

Making esters with acid anhydrides

Acid anhydrides are reactive compounds that can be used to make valuable products such as the pain-killer aspirin, which is an ester.

The functional group in an acid anhydride is formed by eliminating a molecule of water from two carboxylic acid groups. Sometimes this happens simply on heating the acid but, generally, anhydrides are made in other ways.

Figure 3.10 ▶
Structures of two acid anhydrides.

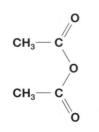

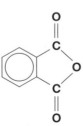

ethanoic anhydride   benzene-1,2-dicarboxylic anhydride

Acid anhydrides are acylating agents. They react with alcohols to form esters.

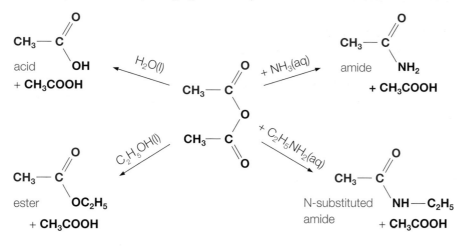

Figure 3.11 ◄
Reactions of ethanoic anhydride. The ethanoyl group (the acyl group) is shown in red.

Definitions

An **acyl group** consists of all the parts of a carboxylic acid except the −OH group. The ethanoyl group, $CH_3CO–$, is an example of an acyl group.

An **acylating agent** is a chemical which substitutes an acyl group for a hydrogen atom when it reacts with an −OH group or an −NH₂ group.

Test yourself

10 a) Show that butenedioic acid can exist as two *cis/trans* isomers.
   b) One of these isomers forms an anhydride quite easily on heating above its melting point. Which isomer would you expect it to be? Draw the structure of the anhydride formed.
11 Write a balanced equation for the reaction of ethanoic anhydride with propan-1-ol.
12 Name the type of reaction taking place when ethanoic anhydride reacts with water.

DL
www
Practical
guidance

Hydrolysis reactions

Hydrolysis is a reaction that splits an ester into an acid and an alcohol (Figure 3.12).

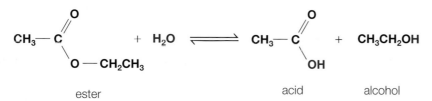

ester   acid   alcohol

Figure 3.12 ▲
Hydrolysis of an ester. These are the products when an ester is heated with an excess of dilute aqueous acid, such as hydrochloric acid. This reaction is reversible.

Acids or bases can catalyse the hydrolysis. Hydrolysis catalysed by acid is a reversible reaction. It is the reverse of the reaction used to synthesise esters from carboxylic acids (see Section 3.2).

Base catalysis is generally more efficient because it is not reversible (Figure 3.13). This is because the acid formed loses its proton by reacting with excess alkali. This turns it into a negative ion which does not react with the alcohol.

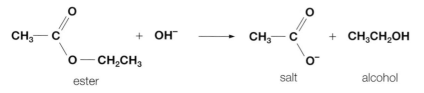

ester   salt   alcohol

Figure 3.13 ▲
The result of hydrolysing ethyl ethanoate by heating it with an aqueous alkali, such as sodium hydroxide. The salt and alcohol produced do not react with each other so this reaction is not reversible.

Test yourself

13 Identify the products of heating:
   a) propyl butanoate with dilute hydrochloric acid
   b) ethyl methanoate with aqueous sodium hydroxide.
14 The reaction of ethyl ethanoate with water is reversible under acid conditions.
   a) What conditions favour the hydrolysis of the ester?
   b) How do these conditions compare with those for the synthesis of the ester?

33

3.4 Triglycerides

Fats, oils and fatty acids

Fats and vegetable oils are esters of long-chain carboxylic acids and the alcohol propane-1,2,3-triol, better known as glycerol. There are three –OH groups in a glycerol molecule so the alcohol can form three ester links with carboxylic acids, giving rise to triglycerides (Figure 3.14).

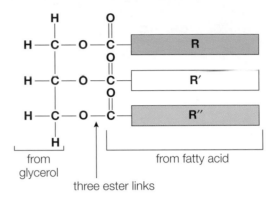

Figure 3.14 ▲
The general structure of a triglyceride. In natural fats and vegetable oils, the hydrocarbon chains may all be the same or they may be different.

Figure 3.15 ▲
A farmer inspecting sunflowers in a field. He is growing the flowers for their seeds which will be compressed to extract oil for cooking.

Definitions

A **triglyceride** is an ester of glycerol (propane-1,2,3-triol) and three carboxylic acid molecules. The carboxylic acids may or may not all be the same.

Fatty acids are the naturally occurring carboxylic acids in triglycerides. The acids have long hydrocarbon chains. **Saturated fatty acids** do not have double bonds in the hydrocarbon chain. There is at least one C=C double bond in a molecule of an **unsaturated fatty acid**.

Fats and oils belong to the family of compounds called lipids. Lipids are a broad class of biological compounds which are soluble in organic solvents such as ethanol but insoluble in water. Lipids are very varied and include fatty acids, fats, vegetable oils, phospholipids and steroids. Lipids release more energy per gram when oxidised than carbohydrates. This makes lipids important as a concentrated energy store in living organisms.

The carboxylic acids in fats are usually referred to as 'fatty' acids (Table 3.1). Saturated fatty acids do not have double bonds in the hydrocarbon chain, but there are double bonds in the molecules of unsaturated fatty acids.

Table 3.1 ▶
Examples of fatty acids.

Fatty acid	Chemical name	Formula
palmitic	hexadecanoic	$CH_3(CH_2)_{14}COOH$
stearic	octadecanoic	$CH_3(CH_2)_{16}COOH$
oleic	*cis*-octadec-9-enoic	$CH_3(CH_2)_7CH=CH(CH_2)_7COOH$
linoleic	*cis*, *cis*-octadec-9,12-dienoic	$CH_3(CH_2)_4CH=CHCH_2CH=CH(CH_2)_7COOH$

Fats are solid at around room temperature (below 20 °C). Fats contain a high proportion of saturated fatty acids. Solid triglycerides are generally found in animal fats. In lard, for example, the main fatty acids are palmitic acid (28%), stearic acid (8%) and 56% oleic acid.

The triglycerides with unsaturated fatty acids have a less regular structure than saturated fats (see Figure 3.16). The molecules do not pack together so easily to make solids so they have lower melting points and have to be cooler before they solidify. Triglycerides of this kind occur in plants and are liquids at around room temperature. In a vegetable oil such as olive oil the main fatty acids are oleic acid (80%) and linoleic acid (10%).

In the food industry, some fatty acids are labelled omega-3 or omega-6. This naming system is based on omega, Ω, the last letter of the Greek alphabet. The numbers 3 and 6 refer to the carbon atoms numbered from the end of the chain furthest from the carboxylic acid group – the last carbon atom in the chain. Counting in this way, omega-3 fatty acids have the first double bond between carbon atoms 3 and 4, while omega-6 acids have the first double bond between carbon atoms 6 and 7.

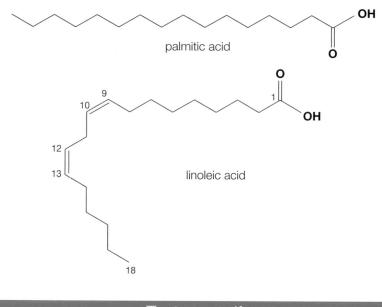

palmitic acid

linoleic acid

Figure 3.16 ◄
Skeletal formulae to compare the shape of palmitic acid and linoleic acid.

Test yourself

15 Classify each of the acids in Table 3.1 as saturated or unsaturated.
16 Draw the skeletal formula of cis, cis, cis-octadec-9,12,15-trienoic acid.
17 Is octadec-9,12,15-trienoic acid (linolenic acid) an omega-3 or an omega-6 fatty acid?

Hydrolysis

Hydrolysis of triglycerides produces soaps and glycerol. Soaps are the sodium or potassium salts of fatty acids (Figure 3.17).

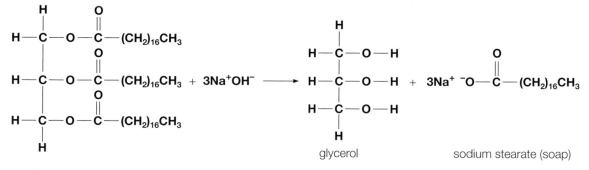

glycerol   sodium stearate (soap)

Figure 3.17 ▲
The hydrolysis of a fat or vegetable oil (triglyceride) with alkali to make soap. This process is also called saponification.

Soaps are surfactants which help to remove greasy dirt because they have an ionic head (water-loving) and a long hydrocarbon tail (water-hating). Soaps first help to separate greasy dirt from surfaces. Then they keep the dirt dispersed in water so that it rinses away.

Most toilet soaps are made from a mixture of animal fat and coconut palm oil. Soaps from animal fat are less soluble and longer lasting. Soaps from palm oils are more soluble, so they lather quickly but wash away more quickly. Bars of soap also often contain dyes and perfumes, together with an antioxidant to stop the soap and air combining to make irritant chemicals.

Test yourself

18 Why is hydrolysis with alkali preferred to acid hydrolysis when making soaps from fats and oils?

Hydrogenation

Margarine was invented as a cheap substitute for butter. The production of margarine originally depended on adding hydrogen to the double bonds in vegetable oils to turn them into saturated fats. This process turns a liquid oil into a solid fat, so it is sometimes called 'hardening'.

The catalyst for hydrogenating a vegetable oil is finely divided nickel which is suspended in the oil during hydrogenation and then recovered by filtration. It is not necessary to hydrogenate all the double bonds in an oil for it to be sufficiently hardened for use in foods.

Margarine, and other non-dairy spreads, are blends of vegetable oils. Some of them contain partly-hardened fats to make the product a spreadable solid. Fats made by hardening vegetable oils are also used to manufacture products such as cakes and biscuits.

Naturally occurring fatty acids exist as the *cis*-isomers. In the presence of the nickel catalyst for hydrogenation, some of the *cis*-isomers become *trans*. This means that there is a proportion of *trans*-fats in products made using partially hardened oils. There is growing concern that *trans*-fats may be bad for health.

The formation of *trans*-fats contributes to the hardening process because a molecule of a *trans*-fat is straight, rather than kinked. This means that its shape is very much like the straight chain of a fully saturated fat.

Definitions

Polyunsaturated fats contain fatty acids with two or more double bonds in the chain.

Some fats or oils provide fatty acids which are essential in the human diet. Two **essential fatty acids** are linoleic and linolenic acids.

Cholesterol plays an important part in metabolism. It makes up part of cell membranes and is converted in the body to steroid hormones, such as the sex hormones testosterone and progesterone. High levels of cholesterol in the blood may lead to deposits building up in arteries, resulting in heart disease.

Test yourself

19 Name the fatty acid formed by completely hydrogenating linoleic acid (see Table 3.1).
20 a) Draw skeletal formulae for *cis*-octadec-9-enoic acid (oleic acid) and *trans*-octadec-9-enoic acid (elaidic acid).
   b) What has to happen during hydrogenation for the *cis*-isomer to turn into the *trans*-isomer?
   c) Suggest a reason why a triglyceride with three elaidic acid molecules has a higher melting point than a triglyceride with oleic acid molecules.

Rearranging esters in food

Food scientists have now found ways of turning vegetable oils into solid spreads without hydrogenation. Instead they use a process which allows triglycerides to swap fatty acid molecules. The result of this process of 'inter-esterification' is a product with a higher melting point. This happens because the process happens in a way that allows the molecules to pack together more neatly to make a denser material.

Inter-esterification does not produce *trans*-fats but it does produce triglycerides that are not found naturally. Catalysts for inter-esterification include sodium methoxide and the enzyme lipase.

Test yourself

21 Draw a simple diagram to represent the process of inter-esterification.
22 Sodium methoxide is used as a catalyst for inter-esterification. Suggest reasons why:
   a) this can be hazardous
   b) the catalyst is destroyed if there is water present in the vegetable oil.

Activity

Health risks and fats

The Food Standards Agency advises the public about diet and health. The agency explains on its website that it is important to have some fat in our diet because fat helps the body to absorb some vitamins, it's a good source of energy and a source of the essential fatty acids that the body cannot make itself. However, the agency also warns that having a lot of fat makes it easy to have more energy than we need, which means we might be more likely to put on weight.

We are told that we should be cutting down on food that is high in saturated fats or *trans*-fats, or replacing these foods with ones that are high in unsaturated fats instead. We should also be having more omega-3 fatty acids, which are found in oily fish.

Figure 3.18 ▲
Milk, full-fat yogurt, cheeses and eggs are rich in saturated fats. Having too much saturated fat can increase the amount of cholesterol in the blood, which increases the chance of developing heart disease.

Figure 3.19 ◄
Foods containing hydrogenated vegetable oil. Hydrogenated vegetable oil is used because it both cheap and extends the shelf-life of foods. *Trans*-fats in these foods can have a similar effect on blood cholesterol as saturated fats – they raise the type of cholesterol in the blood that increases the risk of heart disease.

Unsaturated fats can be a healthy choice. These types of fats can actually reduce cholesterol levels and provide us with the essential fatty acids that the body needs. They include the unsaturated fats found in oily fish, which may help prevent heart disease. Oily fish is also the best source of omega-3 fatty acids.

A person who has never studied advanced chemistry has looked at the Food Standards Agency website but wants to know more about fats in the diet. Give answers to these questions using words and diagrams suitable for a non-specialist.

1 What is the difference between a fat and a fatty acid?

2 Why are some fatty acids essential in the diet, while others are not?

3 What is the difference between a saturated fat and an unsaturated fat?

4 Why are *trans*-fats unnatural and how do they get into the food we eat?

5 Why do some spreads include *trans*-fats while others do not?

6 What are omega-3 fatty acids, and what makes them special?

Figure 3.20 ▲
Mackerel and sardines, walnuts and flax seeds are rich in omega-3 fatty acids. These fatty acids have been shown to help protect against heart disease.

Esters for biodiesel

Biodiesel is a renewable fuel made from triglycerides in vegetable oils or animal fats. The triglyceride is heated with methanol or ethanol in the presence of a base to act as catalyst. If the base catalyst is sodium hydroxide, it can be dissolved in the alcohol before being added to the triglyceride. When the reaction is complete, the fatty acids are converted to methyl or ethyl esters and glycerol separates as a by-product. Chemists call this 'trans-esterification'.

Figure 3.21 ▶
Trans-esterification of fatty acids in a triglyceride with methanol. R_1, R_2 and R_3 represent the hydrocarbon chains of the fatty acids.

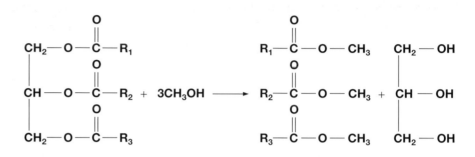

The use of biodiesel is increasing because of the urgent need to reduce carbon dioxide emissions to the atmosphere. The carbon dioxide released when biodiesel burns is equivalent to the carbon dioxide taken in by photosynthesis during growth. However, across the whole life cycle of these fuels they are not carbon neutral because of the energy resources used during the production of the fuel, including the manufacture of fertilisers, plant cultivation, harvesting, extraction of oil and processing of the oil into fuel.

Some studies have investigated the carbon dioxide emissions resulting from preparing rainforests, peatlands and grasslands to grow palms or soya beans for biodiesel. Clearing the land can release between 17 and 420 times more carbon than the annual savings from replacing fossil fuels.

Figure 3.22 ▲
A tube of biofuel made from soy oil extracted from soybeans at a biodiesel plant in Argentina.

Test yourself

23 Suggest a reason why the product of the reaction of a vegetable oil with methanol produces a better fuel than the original oil itself.
24 Suggest a reason why the alcohol and the triglyceride must be very dry to ensure a good yield of biodiesel.
25 a) Explain why the production and use of biodiesel could, in theory, be carbon neutral.
   b) Why, in practice, is the production of biodiesel not carbon neutral?

REVIEW QUESTIONS

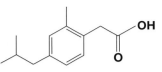

1 a) Describe two examples of test-tube reactions that you could use to show the similarities and differences between ethanoic acid and hydrochloric acid. **(6)**

   b) Explain, with the help of equations, the observations you have described in part **a)**. **(6)**

2 This question is about the reaction scheme involving 2-hydroxybenzenecarboxylic acid shown below.

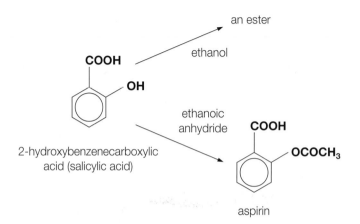

   a) Give the formula of the product when 2-hydroxybenzenecarboxylic acid reacts with excess dilute sodium hydroxide. **(2)**

   b) i) Write the structure of the ester formed by its reaction with ethanol. **(1)**

     ii) What are the conditions for making the ester from 2-hydroxybenzoic acid? **(2)**

   c) i) Write the displayed formula of ethanoic anhydride. **(1)**

     ii) Which functional group is present in aspirin as a result of the reaction of 2-hydroxybenzenecarboxylic acid with ethanoic anhydride? **(1)**

   d) i) Give the structural formula of the product when aspirin reacts with cold, dilute sodium hydroxide solution. **(1)**

     ii) Suggest an advantage of using the product in part **d i)** as a drug instead of the form of aspirin shown at the start of this question. **(1)**

3 Ibuprofen is a painkiller with this skeletal formula:

   a) What it the molecular formula of ibuprofen? **(1)**

   b) Suggest whether or not ibuprofen is soluble or insoluble in water. Explain your answer in terms of intermolecular forces. **(3)**

   c) Draw the displayed formula of the organic products when ibuprofen reacts with:

     i) dilute sodium hydroxide solution **(1)**

     ii) ethanol and a little sulfuric acid on warming. **(1)**

4 Octadecanoic acid and *cis*-octadec-9-enoic acid are fatty acids present in the triglycerides that make up fats and vegetable oils.

   a) Suggest an explanation for the fact that octadecanoic acid is a solid while *cis*-octadec-9-enoic acid is a liquid at room temperature. **(3)**

   b) Describe a chemical test that could be used to distinguish between the two fatty acids. **(3)**

   c) Explain what is meant by a triglyceride. **(2)**

   d) Reaction with hydrogen in the presence of a nickel catalyst is used to harden vegetable oils for the food industry. During partial hydrogenation, some of the fatty acids change from the *cis* to the *trans* form.

     i) What happens to *cis*-octadec-9-enoic acid when it reacts with hydrogen? **(1)**

     ii) What is the difference between *cis*-octadec-9-enoic acid and *trans*-octadec-9-enoic acid? **(2)**

     iii) Why should people be concerned by the use of partial hydrogenation to prepare ingredients for foodstuffs? **(2)**

4 Amines

Amines can be very smelly. Ethylamine, for example, has a fishy smell. However, the importance of the amine functional group is not its smell, but the role it plays in biochemistry and medicine. The amine group is present in amino acids, the monomers for proteins (Topic 5). As a result of this, the amine group plays an important part in metabolism and it appears in the structures of many medical drugs. In the chemical industry, aromatic amines have commercial value because they are the basis of the manufacture of a wide range of colourful dyes.

Figure 4.1 ▲
The active constituent of asthma inhalers is salbutamol, which contains the amine group.

Figure 4.2 ▶
The smell of fish is partly due to ethylamine.

4.1 Structures and names

Amines are nitrogen compounds in which one or more of the hydrogen atoms in ammonia, NH_3, is replaced by an alkyl or an aryl group. The number of these groups determines whether the compound is a primary amine, a secondary amine or a tertiary amine. If one H atom in ammonia is replaced by an alkyl or aryl group, the compound is a primary amine; if two H atoms are replaced, the compound is a secondary amine; and if all three H atoms in ammonia are replaced, the compound is a tertiary amine.

Chemists have two systems for naming amines.

Simple amines

Simple amines are treated as a combination of the alkyl or aryl group followed by the ending –**amine**. So, $CH_3CH_2NH_2$ is ethylamine, $C_6H_5NH_2$ is phenylamine and $CH_3CH_2NHCH_3$ is ethylmethylamine. The prefixes di- and tri- are used when there are two or three of the same alkyl or aryl group (Figure 4.3).

> **Note**
>
> Notice that the terms primary, secondary and tertiary do not have the same meaning with amines as they do with alcohols.

Figure 4.3 ▶
The structures and names of primary, secondary and tertiary amines containing the methyl group.

methylamine
(a primary amine)

dimethylamine
(a secondary amine)

trimethylamine
(a tertiary amine)

More complex amines

The prefix 'amino-' is used in compounds that have a second functional group which appears at the end of the name. This is the case with amino acids that

contain the 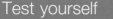 group.

So, the systematic name for NH_2CH_2COOH is aminoethanoic acid. The prefix 'diamino-' is used for compounds containing two amino groups.

Test yourself

1 Draw the structures of:
   a) diethylamine
   b) ethylmethylpropylamine
   c) 1,6-diaminohexane
   d) 1,2-diaminopentane, which contributes to the smell of rotting flesh and has the common name cadaverine
   e) 1-phenyl-2-aminopropane, an amphetamine which is an addictive stimulant.
2 Salbutamol is the active ingredient in asthma inhalers.

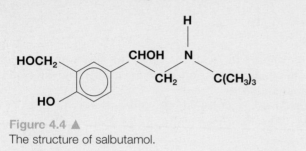

Figure 4.4 ▲
The structure of salbutamol.

   a) Is its amine group primary, secondary or tertiary?
   b) What other functional groups does salbutamol contain?

4.2 The properties and reactions of amines

The physical and chemical properties of the simplest amines are similar to those of ammonia. So, methylamine and ethylamine are gases at room temperature and they smell like ammonia, though with a fishy character.

Alkyl amines with short hydrocarbon chains are freely soluble in water, like ammonia. Phenylamine, with its large non-polar benzene ring, is only slightly soluble in water.

Test yourself

3 Methylamine, like ammonia, will mix with and dissolve in water whatever proportions are mixed together. Why is this?
4 Ethane (b.p. −89 °C) and methylamine (b.p. −6 °C) have very similar molar masses, but very different boiling points. Why is this?
5 Look at the boiling points of methylamine, dimethylamine and trimethylamine on the data sheets on the Dynamic Learning Student website. Why do you think the boiling point of trimethylamine, $(CH_3)_3N$, is lower than that of dimethylamine?

www
Data

Amines as bases

Primary amines, like ammonia, can act as bases. The lone pair of electrons on the nitrogen atom of ammonia and amine molecules is a proton (H^+ ion) acceptor.

Figure 4.5 ◀
Comparing the structures and basic character of methylamine and ammonia.

41

Reaction with water

Methylamine and other simple amines dissolve freely in water because they react with it. The amines act as bases removing H^+ ions (protons) from water molecules to form an equilibrium mixture containing ions.

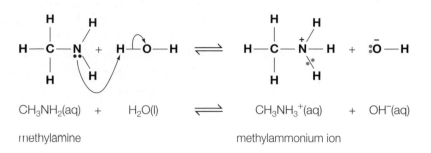

$$CH_3NH_2(aq) + H_2O(l) \rightleftharpoons CH_3NH_3^+(aq) + OH^-(aq)$$

methylamine   methylammonium ion

Figure 4.6 ▲
The reaction of methylamine with water.

The reactions of simple amines, like methylamine, with water are very similar to that of ammonia with water:

$$NH_3(aq) + H_2O(l) \rightleftharpoons NH_4^+(aq) + OH^-(aq)$$

Reaction with acids

Amines react even more readily with acids than they do with water. The lone pair on the nitrogen atom rapidly accepts an H^+ ion (proton) from an acid to form a substituted ammonium salt.

When ethylamine vapour reacts with hydrogen chloride gas, the product is ethylammonium chloride. This forms as a white smoke which settles as a white solid (Figure 4.7).

$$CH_3CH_2NH_2(g) + HCl(g) \rightarrow CH_3CH_2NH_3^+Cl^-(s)$$
ethylamine   ethylammonium chloride

This reaction is very similar to that of ammonia with hydrogen chloride to form ammonium chloride.

$$NH_3(g) + HCl \rightarrow NH_4^+Cl^-(s)$$

Phenylamine, $C_6H_5NH_2$, is only slightly soluble in water, but it dissolves in concentrated hydrochloric acid very easily. This is because it reacts with H^+ ions in the acid to form phenylammonium ions, which are soluble in the aqueous mixture.

$$C_6H_5NH_2(l) + H^+(aq) \rightarrow C_6H_5NH_3^+(aq)$$

If a strong base, such as sodium hydroxide, is added to the aqueous phenylammonium ions, H^+ ions are removed from the phenylammonium ions and yellow, oily phenylamine reforms.

$$C_6H_5NH_3^+(aq) + OH^-(aq) \rightarrow C_6H_5NH_2(l) + H_2O(l)$$
phenylamine

glass rod dipped in conc. HCl

white smoke

concentrated solution of ethylamine

Figure 4.7 ▲
The vapours from ethylamine solution and concentrated hydrochloric acid react to form a white smoke.

Amines as nucleophiles

Amines are strong nucleophiles as well as strong bases, just like ammonia. As nucleophiles, their lone pair of electrons is attracted to any positive ion or positive centre in a molecule.

So, amines will react with the δ+ carbon atoms in the C–Hal bond of halogenoalkanes (Figure 4.8).

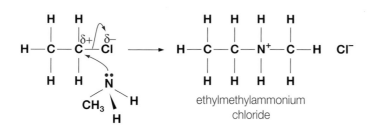

Figure 4.8 ▲
The reaction of methylamine with chloroethane

4.3 The preparation of amines

Two key reactions are used in the preparation of amines – one for aliphatic amines, the other for aromatic (aryl) amines.

Preparing aliphatic amines

An aliphatic amine can be prepared by heating the corresponding halogenoalkane in a sealed flask with excess ammonia in ethanol. Ammonia acts as a nucleophile during the reaction. The initial product is a salt of the amine. The free amine can be liberated from its salt by adding dilute sodium hydroxide solution (Figure 4.9).

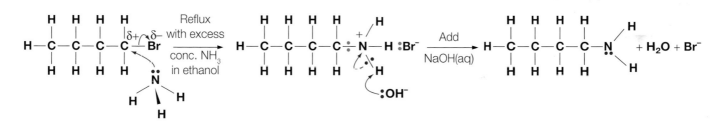

Figure 4.9 ▲
The preparation of butylamine from 1-bromobutane and excess concentrated ammonia in ethanol.

Preparing aromatic amines

The usual laboratory method for introducing an amine group into an aromatic compound is a two-step process – first nitration to make a nitro compound, and then reduction (Figure 4.10).

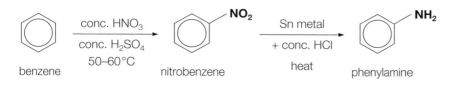

Figure 4.10 ▲
The two-step preparation of phenylamine from benzene.

8 Describe the mechanism, using appropriate curly arrows, for the nucleophilic substitution of 1-chloropropane with ammonia.

9 When preparing primary alkylamines from halogenoalkanes:
   a) excess ammonia is used. Why is this? (*Hint:* How would the alkylamine which forms react with any excess halogenoalkane?)
   b) a solution of ammonia in ethanol is used rather than ammonia in water. Why is this? (*Hint:* ammonia reacts with water to produce an alkaline solution containing OH⁻ ions.)

Figure 4.11 ▶
Reducing nitrobenzene to phenylamine by refluxing with tin and hot, concentrated hydrochloric acid.

Figure 4.12 ▶
Preparing benzenediazonium chloride from phenylamine.

The reduction of the nitroarene is achieved by boiling under reflux with tin and concentrated hydrochloric acid (Figure 4.11). The aromatic amine dissolves in excess concentrated HCl forming a salt. The free amine can be liberated from the solution by adding sodium hydroxide solution and is then separated from the mixture by steam distillation.

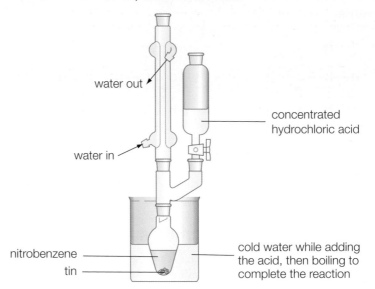

4.4 Diazonium salts

Alkyl and aryl amines react with nitrous acid, HNO_2, below 10 °C to produce diazonium salts containing the diazo group, $N{\equiv}N^+{-}$. The diazonium salts of aryl amines are important intermediates in the manufacture of azo dyes.

Diazonium salts are unstable. However, the diazonium salts of aryl amines are stabilised by delocalisation and they are useful reagents if kept cool. Benzenediazonium chloride is prepared by adding a cold solution of sodium nitrite, $NaNO_2$, to a solution of phenylamine in concentrated hydrochloric acid at 5 °C.

Initially, the sodium nitrite reacts with the hydrochloric acid to form nitrous acid. This then reacts with the phenylamine and more conc. HCl to produce benzenediazonium chloride.

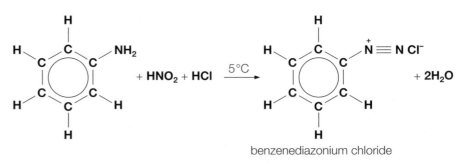

benzenediazonium chloride

The diazonium salts of alkyl amines are much more unstable and decompose immediately to form the corresponding alcohol and nitrogen gas, even at 5 °C.

$$CH_3CH_2{-}NH_2 + HNO_2 + HCl \xrightarrow{5\,°C} CH_3CH_2{-}N^+{\equiv}NCl^- + 2H_2O$$

then $CH_3CH_2{-}N^+{\equiv}NCl^- + H_2O \rightarrow CH_3CH_2OH + N_2 + HCl$

Nitrous acid itself is also unstable. It is a weak acid which looks very pale blue in aqueous solution. At room temperature, nitrous acid starts to decompose forming water, nitrogen monoxide and nitrogen dioxide:

$$2HNO_2(aq) \rightarrow H_2O(l) + NO(g) + NO_2(g)$$

The nitrogen dioxide is very soluble in water, but the nitrogen monoxide escapes into the air and turns brown as it reacts with oxygen to form nitrogen dioxide:

$$2NO(g) + O_2(g) \rightarrow 2NO_2(g)$$

As the nitrous acid is unstable, it is usually prepared as and when needed by adding hydrochloric acid to sodium nitrite. The nitrous acid is said to be generated *in situ*.

4.5 Azo dyes

The positive charge on the $N \equiv N^+-$ group means that diazonium ions are strong electrophiles. So, we would expect them to attack aryl compounds with delocalised π electrons, particularly those that have an electron-donating group, such as $-OH$ in phenols (Figure 4.13) and $-NH_2$ in aromatic amines.

4-hydroxyazobenzene

Reactions like this between diazonium ions and phenols or aromatic amines are called coupling reactions. If a cold solution of benzenediazonium chloride is added to a cold solution of phenol in sodium hydroxide, an orange precipitate forms. The precipitate is 4-hydroxyazobenzene, which is an azo dye.

Figure 4.13 ▲
The reaction between benzenediazonium ions and phenol.

The commercial importance of diazonium salts is based on their coupling reactions with phenols and aromatic amines to form azo dyes. Most of these dyes are red, orange or yellow. As we have already seen, benzenediazonium chloride reacts with phenol to give an orange dye. With phenylamine it produces a yellow dye 4-aminoazobenzene (Figure 4.14).

4-aminoazobenzene

Unlike diazonium compounds, azo compounds are very stable and unreactive.

The bright colours of azo compounds result from the extended delocalised electron systems that spread across the whole molecule through the azo group, $-N=N-$. These delocalised azo systems absorb light in the blue region of the spectrum which results in the yellow, orange and red dyes.

Figure 4.14 ▲
The reaction of benzenediazonium chloride with phenylamine to form the yellow dye 4-aminoazobenzene.

Amines

Figure 4.15 ▲
This shirt is dyed with azo dyes.

When azo dyes were first discovered in the late nineteenth century, they heralded a new regime for the dyeing of different fabrics. Vegetable dyes, which had been used in the past, faded easily. Azo dyes fade much more slowly as a result of atmospheric oxidation and are not removed by water, soap or other cleaning agents because they attach themselves more strongly to fabrics.

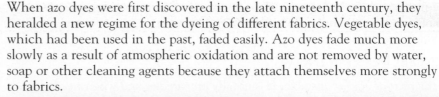

Test yourself

14 a) Write an equation for the coupling reaction between benzenediazonium chloride and naphthalen-2-ol (Figure 4.16) to form an azo dye.
b) Why is the reaction usually carried out with the naphthalen-2-ol dissolved in sodium hydroxide solution?

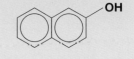

Figure 4.16 ▲

15 a) Draw the structures of the diazonium compound and the amine which could be used to make the red form of the acid–base indicator, methyl orange, in Figure 4.17.

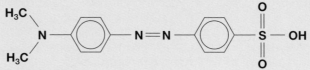

Figure 4.17 ▲
The red form of methyl orange.

b) Draw the structure of the amine used to make the diazonium compound in part a).
c) Draw the structure of the yellow form of methyl orange which is produced in an alkaline solution such as NaOH(aq).

Figure 4.18 ▲
Azo dyes are used to colour foods such as sweets and fruit drinks.

Azo dyes are also used in some foods (Figure 4.18) in spite of their toxicity. Fortunately, azo dyes are so strongly coloured that the quantities used amount to only milligrams per kilogram of food. Even so, some azo dyes have been banned from use in food (see the Activity on page 96). The toxicity arises not from the azo dyes themselves, but when they are metabolised and broken down in the body. Their breakdown produces aromatic amines, some of which are carcinogenic.

Some azo dyes were once thought to increase, or possibly cause, hyperactivity in children. Since the late 1970s, there have been several studies into the effects of azo dyes on hyperactivity, but most have proved inconclusive.

However, there is more substantial evidence to suggest that certain azo dyes, especially tartrazine (Figure 4.19), increase the allergic reactions to some drugs and cause increased breathing problems in people with asthma.

Figure 4.19 ▶
Tartrazine.

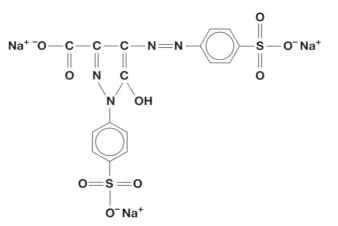

Activity

Synthesising the azo dye, dispersol fast yellow

Azo dyes account for about 60–70% of all the dyes used in food and textile manufacture. In theory, they can provide a complete spectrum of colours, but red, orange and yellow dyes are more common than blues and greens.

One important azo dye used with textiles is dispersol fast yellow. This can be synthesised from phenylamine using the five-step process shown in Figure 4.20.

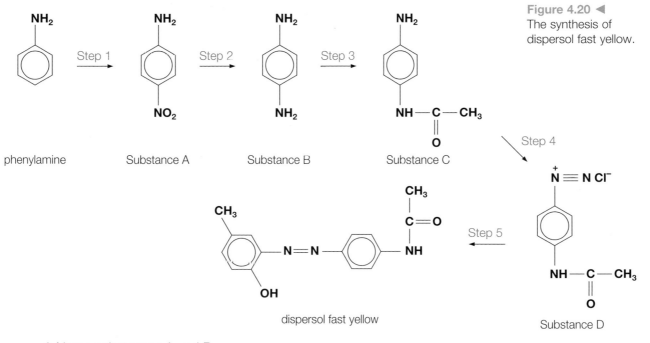

Figure 4.20 ◀
The synthesis of dispersol fast yellow.

1 Name substances A and B.

2 In aromatic amines, the $-NH_2$ group contributes the lone pair of electrons on the nitrogen atom into the delocalised electron system of the benzene ring, in a similar manner to the $-OH$ group in phenols. With this in mind, predict the reagent and conditions required for step 1.

3 Name the reagents and conditions required for step 2.

4 The reagent used to carry out step 3 is ethanoyl chloride, $CH_3-C(=O)-Cl$.

  a) What is the other product of step 3 besides substance C?

  b) Is ethanoyl chloride acting as an electrophile or a nucleophile in step 3?

  c) Why is step 3 likely to be inefficient?

5 State the names of the reagents, in addition to substance C, and the reaction conditions required for step 4.

6 **a)** Give the name and structural formula of the reagent used with substance D in step 5.

  b) Why do you think that coupling in step 5 is to one of the carbon atoms next to that to which the $-OH$ group is attached?

7 Suggest two essential properties which a commercial dye must have in addition to being coloured.

REVIEW QUESTIONS

1 Diazonium compounds are important intermediates in the manufacture of synthetic azo dyes.

a) What reaction conditions and reagents are used to make an aqueous solution of the diazonium ion $C_6H_5-N^+\equiv N\ Cl^-$ from phenylamine? (3)

b) Explain the following including appropriate equations in your answer.

   i) Solid benzenediazonium chloride, $C_6H_5-N^+\equiv NCl^-$, is not usually isolated because it is explosive. (3)

   ii) Stable solutions of diazonium ions cannot be obtained from aliphatic primary amines like propylamine. (3)

c) The benzenediazonium ion reacts with phenol in alkaline solution to form the azo dye 4-hydroxyazobenzene as shown below.

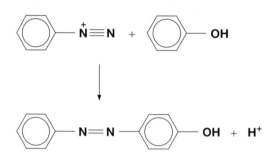

   i) What type of reagent is the diazonium ion in this reaction? (1)

   ii) Suggest two reasons why the reaction is carried out in alkaline solution. (2)

2 Describe the main reactions of amines, pointing out the similarities and differences between aliphatic amines such as butylamine and aromatic amines such as phenylamine.

Write balanced equations where appropriate. (12)

3 A series of tests were carried out on three organic compounds A, B and C. The results of the tests are described below.

State the deductions you can make from the tests on each of A, B and C.

You are not expected to identify compounds A, B and C.

a) i) A is a colourless liquid which does not mix with water. (1)

   ii) After warming a few drops of A with aqueous sodium hydroxide, the resulting solution was acidified with nitric acid. Silver nitrate solution was then added and a cream-coloured precipitate formed. (2)

b) i) B is a white solid which chars on heating, and gives off a vapour which condenses to a liquid that turns cobalt chloride paper from blue to pink. (2)

   ii) A solution of B turns universal indicator red. (1)

   iii) A solution of B reacts with aqueous sodium carbonate to produce a colourless gas which turns limewater milky. (2)

   iv) When a little of B is warmed with ethanol and one drop of concentrated sulfuric acid, a sweet-smelling product can be detected on pouring the reaction mixture into cold water. (2)

c) i) C is a liquid which burns with a very smoky, yellow flame. (1)

   ii) C does not react with sodium carbonate solution. (1)

   iii) C fizzes with sodium and gives off a gas which produces a 'pop' with a burning splint. (2)

4 The diagram below shows a series of reactions beginning with the amine, cadaverine. Cadaverine is formed when proteins decompose.

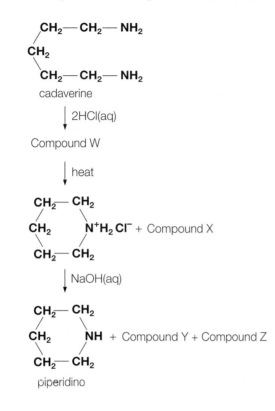

cadaverine

2HCl(aq)

Compound W

heat

$N^+H_2 Cl^-$ + Compound X

NaOH(aq)

NH + Compound Y + Compound Z

piperidino

a) i) What characteristic physical property of cadaverine would you expect to notice if you were provided with a sample of it? **(1)**

ii) What is the systematic name of cadaverine? **(1)**

iii) Draw the structural formula of compound W. **(1)**

iv) Write the name and formula of compound X. **(2)**

v) Write the formulae of compounds Y and Z. **(2)**

b) Amines are classed as primary, secondary and tertiary.

i) Describe the differences in structure between the three types of amine. **(3)**

ii) Which type(s) do cadaverine and piperidine belong to? **(2)**

c) How will the infrared spectrum of cadaverine compare with that of piperidine? Explain your answer. **(2)**

5 Amino acids and proteins

Proteins make up about 15% of the human body. There are many different protein molecules in our bodies, each able to do its own special job (Figure 5.1).

Skin, muscle and hair consist of fibrous proteins. Other proteins coil up into a globular shape and dissolve in body fluids where they act as enzymes and hormones. Proteins are polymers, and amino acids are the monomers which are used to make them.

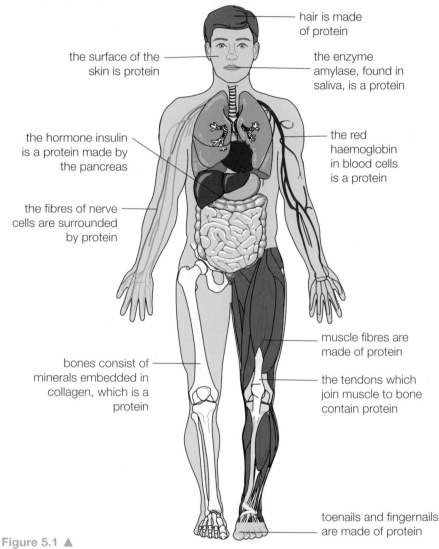

the surface of the skin is protein

hair is made of protein

the enzyme amylase, found in saliva, is a protein

the hormone insulin is a protein made by the pancreas

the red haemoglobin in blood cells is a protein

the fibres of nerve cells are surrounded by protein

bones consist of minerals embedded in collagen, which is a protein

muscle fibres are made of protein

the tendons which join muscle to bone contain protein

toenails and fingernails are made of protein

Figure 5.1 ▲
Proteins in the human body.

5.1 Amino acids

Amino acids are the compounds which join together in long chains to make proteins. They are compounds with two functional groups – the amino group, $-NH_2$; and the carboxylic acid group, $-COOH$. About 20 different amino acids are found widely in naturally occurring proteins. Some proteins contain thousands of amino acid units.

Structures and names

The structures and names of six naturally occurring amino acids are shown in Figure 5.2. The simplest amino acid is glycine, $H_2N–CH_2–COOH$.

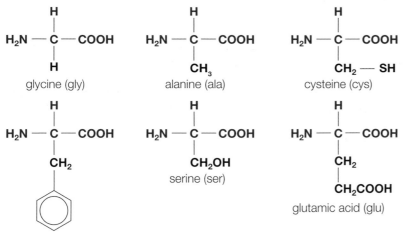

Figure 5.2 ◄
Six of the amino acids which occur in proteins.

Notice in Figure 5.2 that all six structures have the amino group attached to the carbon atom next to the carboxylic acid group. This is the case with all the amino acids that occur naturally. The carbon atom next to the carboxylic acid group is sometimes described as the alpha (α) carbon atom, or the 2-carbon atom in systematic names. So, all the amino acids in proteins are α-amino acids (2-amino acids) and their general formula can be written as $RCH(NH_2)COOH$.

R stands for the sidegroups in different amino acids (Table 5.1). The common names and R groups of several other amino acids are shown on a data sheet on the Dynamic Learning Student website.

Common name	Abbreviated name	R sidegroup
glycine	gly	$H-$
alanine	ala	CH_3-
cysteine	cys	$HS-CH_2-$
phenylalanine	phe	$C_6H_5-CH_2-$
aspartic acid	asp	$HOOC-CH_2-$

Table 5.1 ▲
The R sidegroups in some amino acids.

As many of the natural amino acids have complex structures, it is simpler and more convenient to use their common names rather than systematic names. These common names are sometimes abbreviated to a 3-letter code, which is usually the first three letters in the name. So, H_2NCH_2COOH is normally called 'glycine' rather than 2-aminoethanoic acid and its abbreviated name is 'gly'.

5.2 The acid–base properties of amino acids

As amino acids carry an amino group, $-NH_2$, and a carboxylic acid group, $-COOH$, they show both the basic properties of primary amines and the acidic properties of carboxylic acids.

Zwitterions and isoelectric points

In aqueous solution, carboxylic acid groups ionise producing hydrogen ions, $H^+(aq)$; at the same time amino groups are basic and attract hydrogen ions (protons). As a result of this, amino acids form ions in aqueous solution (Figure 5.3). However, the ions formed are unusual in that they have both positive and negative charges. Chemists call them zwitterions, from the German word 'zwei' meaning two.

Data

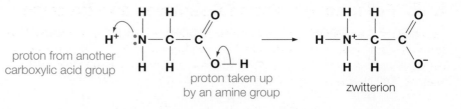

Figure 5.3 ▶
Glycine forming a zwitterion.

An amino acid will form zwitterions only at a particular pH. If the pH is too high, the solution is too alkaline. In these conditions, OH⁻ ions will remove H⁺ ions from the zwitterions forming negative ions (Figure 5.4). On the other hand, if the pH is too low then the solution is too acidic. In this case, H⁺ ions react with the zwitterions producing positive ions (Figure 5.4).

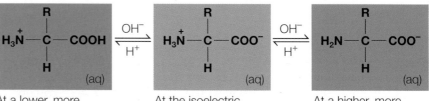

At a lower, more acidic pH, a positive ion forms.

At the isoelectric point, the zwitterion forms.

At a higher, more alkaline pH, a negative ion forms.

Figure 5.4 ▲
The ions formed by an amino acid at different pH values.

Definitions

A **zwitterion** is an ion with both a positive and a negative charge.

The **isoelectric point** of an amino acid is the pH value at which it exists as a zwitterion.

Amino acids can therefore exist in three forms depending on the pH – a cation form, a zwitterion form and an anion form. However, at one particular pH, virtually all the molecules of the amino acid will be in the zwitterion form and this pH value is called the isoelectric point.

Notice from Figure 5.4 that the net charge on an amino acid molecule will vary with the pH. The net charge will be positive in acid solutions and negative in alkaline solutions. At the isoelectric point, the positive and negative charges balance and the net charge on the zwitterion is zero.

All amino acids form zwitterions along the lines described above, but their isoelectric points may differ because of the different character of their R groups. In fact, some amino acids, like glutamic acid, have two –COOH groups and others have two –NH₂ groups which influences their isoelectric point significantly.

The movement of H⁺ ions from the –COOH group of an amino acid to its –NH₂ group will occur in solution and hence before a solid amino acid crystallises out. This means that amino acids also exist as zwitterions in the solid state. This ionic character of amino acids accounts for their high solubility in water and their high melting points.

Test yourself

3 The relative molecular masses of butylamine, $CH_3(CH_2)_3NH_2$, propanoic acid, CH_3CH_2COOH, and glycine, H_2NCH_2COOH, are very similar. But glycine (m.p. 262 °C) is a solid at room temperature whereas butylamine (m.p. −49 °C) and propanoic acid (m.p. −21 °C) are liquids. Why is this?

4 a) Write equations to show the reactions of alanine with:
  i) dilute hydrochloric acid
  ii) aqueous sodium hydroxide.
 b) How do the products (from alanine) of these two reactions differ from the zwitterions of alanine at its isoelectric point?

5 Why do zwitterions of amino acids exist just as readily in the solid state as they do in aqueous solution?

5.3 From amino acids to peptides and proteins

Tutorial

Peptides are compounds made by linking amino acids together in chains. The simplest example is a dipeptide with just two amino acids linked together by a peptide bond. Figure 5.5 shows the formation of a peptide bond between alanine and glycine to form the dipeptide, 'ala–gly'.

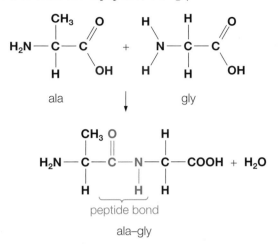

ala   gly

ala–gly

peptide bond

Figure 5.5 ◄
The formation of a peptide bond between two amino acids.

For chemists, the peptide bond is simply an example of the amide bond. However, the tradition in biochemistry is to call it a 'peptide bond'.

Notice in Figure 5.5 that when a peptide linkage forms between amino acid molecules, a molecule of water is eliminated at the same time. This is an example of a condensation reaction.

Further condensation reactions can occur between the dipeptide and other amino acid molecules to produce polypeptides and eventually proteins. This is what happens when proteins are synthesised from amino acids in our bodies. The overall process is an example of condensation polymerisation (Section 6.3).

Polypeptides are long-chain peptides. There is no agreed dividing line between peptides and polypeptides, or between polypeptides and proteins. However, some chemists do make a distinction between polypeptides and the longer amino acid chains in proteins. They restrict the definition of polypeptides to chains with 10 to 50 or so amino acids.

The hydrolysis of peptides and proteins

Digestive enzymes in the stomach and small intestine catalyse the hydrolysis of peptide bonds, splitting proteins into polypeptides and then polypeptides into amino acids. Chemists can achieve the same result by hydrolysing the peptide bond in proteins and peptides with suitable enzymes or by heating in acidic or alkaline solution. Heating alone will start to hydrolyse some of the peptide links.

When proteins and peptides are hydrolysed by refluxing with concentrated hydrochloric acid, the product contains the cation forms of the α-amino acids. These are converted to the α-amino acids on dilution with water (Figure 5.6).

If proteins and peptides are hydrolysed by refluxing with sodium hydroxide solution, the product contains carboxylates – these are anion forms of the amino acids (Figure 5.7) in which the carboxylic acid group, –COOH, exists as a carboxylate ion, –COO⁻.

> **Definitions**
>
> A **condensation reaction** is one in which molecules join together by splitting off a small molecule, such as water or hydrogen chloride.
>
> **Condensation polymerisation** involves a series of condensation reactions between the functional groups of monomers to produce a polymer.

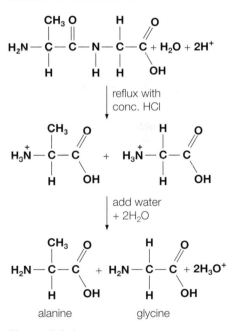

reflux with conc. HCl

add water + 2H₂O

alanine   glycine

Figure 5.6 ▲
Hydrolysing a peptide with acid to produce α-amino acids.

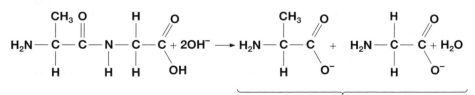

carboxylate ions

Figure 5.7 ▲
Hydrolysing a peptide with alkali to produce carboxylates.

Test yourself

www
Data

6 Draw the structures of the two dipeptides that can be produced from serine and phenylalanine.

7 Show that splitting a dipeptide into two amino acids is an example of hydrolysis.

8 a) Identify the functional groups in the sweetener, aspartame (Figure 5.8).

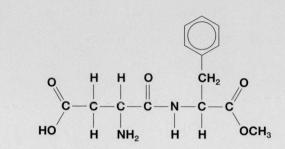

Figure 5.8 ▲
The structure of aspartame (Nutrasweet).

b) How does aspartame differ from a dipeptide?

c) Suggest a reason why aspartame cannot be used to sweeten food that will be cooked.

d) Why do you think that soft drinks sweetened with aspartame carry a warning for people with the genetic disorder which means that they must not consume phenylalanine?

Activity

The structure of proteins

A protein molecule consists of one or more polypeptide chains. Chemists describe the structure of proteins at four different levels.

● The **primary structure** of a protein is the sequence of amino acids in the polypeptide chain or chains. This includes any disulfide bridges, –S–S–, formed by oxidation of the HS– groups between neighbouring cysteine units.

● The **secondary structure** describes the repeating patterns in the structure of sections of the polypeptide chains. X-ray diffraction methods have shown that helices and pleated sheets are common repeating structures in proteins. Fibrous proteins, such as α-keratin in hair and wool, have helical chains of amino acids held together by hydrogen bonds (Figure 5.9).
Stringy α-keratin in silk fibres forms pleated sheets of parallel polypeptide chains held together side-by-side with hydrogen bonds.

● The **tertiary structure** describes the overall 3D folding and shape of a protein. This is held together by hydrogen bonds and other weak interactions between the R groups. Proteins tend to fall into two groups in terms of their tertiary structure:

    Fibrous proteins – long molecules forming fibres of structural material such as α-keratin in hair and collagen in muscle fibres.

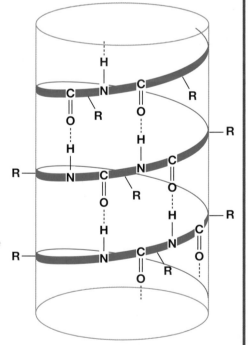

Figure 5.9 ▲
The alpha helix is an important example of the secondary structure in some proteins.

Globular proteins – compact, well-folded molecules such as enzymes and protein hormones.

● The **quaternary structure** describes the linking between chains in proteins with two or more polypeptide chains. For example, haemoglobin molecules in blood consist of four chains fitting together tightly to form a compact globular assembly.

These four levels of description for the structure of proteins are illustrated in Figure 5.10.

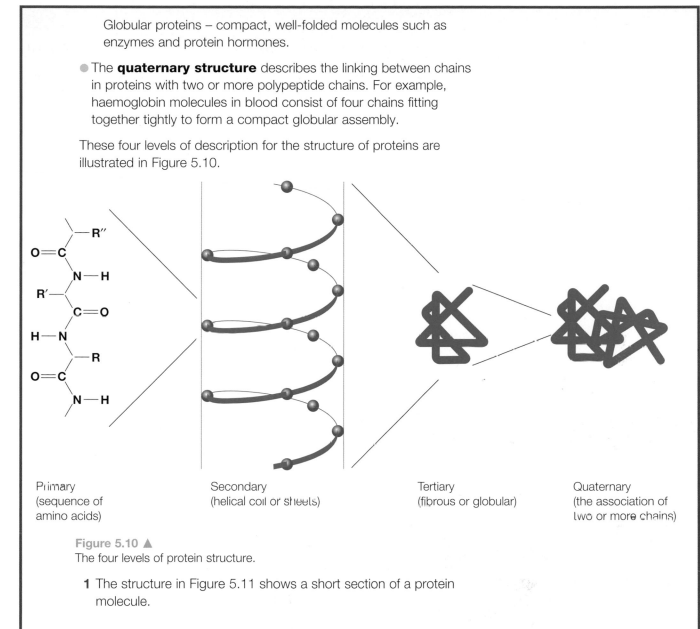

Primary (sequence of amino acids)

Secondary (helical coil or sheets)

Tertiary (fibrous or globular)

Quaternary (the association of two or more chains)

Figure 5.10 ▲
The four levels of protein structure.

1 The structure in Figure 5.11 shows a short section of a protein molecule.

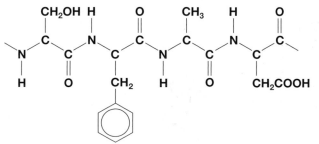

Figure 5.11 ▲

a) Identify the amino acids that are joined to make this section of a protein.

b) Which of these amino acids have sidechains that:

i) are non-polar **ii)** are polar **iii)** can ionise?

Data

From amino acids to peptides and proteins

55

2 Write an equation to show how the HS– groups on neighbouring cysteine units in a protein can be oxidised to form a disulfide bridge. (Use [O] to represent the oxidising agent.)

3 Describe the way in which hydrogen bonds hold the helices together in fibrous proteins such as α-keratin.

4 Haemoglobin, the oxygen carrier in blood, is a protein with a relative molecular mass of 66 000.

    a) Write one word to describe the tertiary structure of haemoglobin.

    b) Assuming that the average mass of an amino acid unit in proteins is equal to that of an aspartic acid unit, calculate the approximate number of amino acid molecules that are needed to produce one molecule of haemoglobin.

5 How does hydrogen bonding explain:

    a) the solubility of many proteins in water

    b) the precise 3D structure of those enzymes which are proteins

    c) the elasticity of natural protein fibres such as wool and silk?

6 Biochemists talk about enzymes being 'denatured' by strong acids, strong bases or by a rise in temperature.

    a) What do you think 'denatured' means?

    b) Suggest a reason for the loss of catalytic activity when an enzyme is denatured by acids, bases or a rise in temperature.

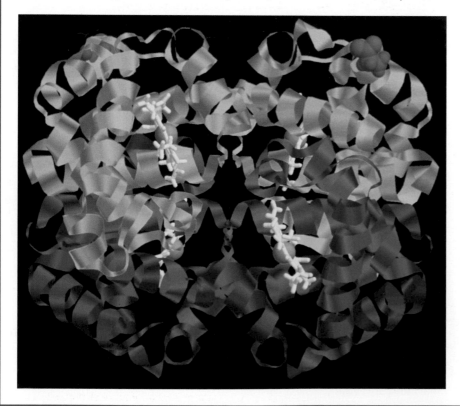

Figure 5.12 ◄
A computer graphic of a haemoglobin molecule showing the quaternary structure. Each of the four protein chains (blue and yellow) also carries a haem group (white).

5.4 Isomerism in amino acids – mirror image molecules

Every molecule has a mirror image. Generally, the mirror image of a molecule can be turned around to show that it is identical to the original molecule.

Sometimes, however, it turns out that a molecule and its mirror image are not quite the same. The molecule and its mirror image cannot be superimposed.

A molecule is chiral if, like one of your hands, it cannot be superimposed on its mirror image. The word 'chiral' (pronounced *kiral*) comes from the Greek for 'hand'.

Chirality and optical isomerism

Chiral molecules are asymmetric. This means that they have mirror image forms which are not identical. The commonest chiral compounds are organic molecules in which there is a carbon atom attached to four different atoms or groups. Look closely at the two molecules of alanine in Figure 5.13. The two molecules each have the same four different atoms or groups attached to their central carbon atom – a CH_3 group, an NH_2 group, a COOH group and an H atom. Can you see that it is impossible to superimpose the mirror images of alanine? No matter how you turn the molecules around, you cannot get the two to look identical with groups and atoms in the same position in space.

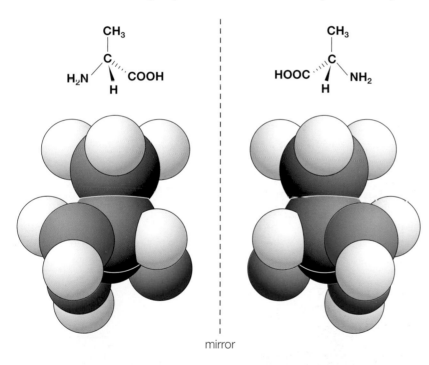

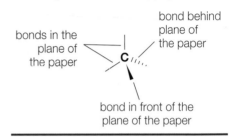

Note

Chemists have a convention for drawing 3D molecules on paper.

bonds in the plane of the paper

bond behind plane of the paper

bond in front of the plane of the paper

Figure 5.13 ◄
Molecules of alanine are chiral. It is not possible to superimpose the two mirror image molecules.

The two forms of alanine behave identically in all their chemical reactions and all their physical properties – except for their effect on polarised light. This optical property is the only way of telling the two forms of alanine apart. So, chemists call them optical isomers. The term 'enantiomers' is also used to describe mirror image molecules which are optical isomers. The word 'enantiomer' comes from a Greek word meaning 'opposite'.

Amino acid structures

All the natural amino acids which occur in proteins, except glycine, have a central carbon atom attached to four different groups. So, except for glycine, all these amino acids have chiral molecules which can exist as mirror images (Figure 5.14).

Definitions

Asymmetric molecules are molecules with no centre, axis or plane of symmetry. Asymmetric molecules are chiral and exist in mirror image forms.

Optical isomers are non-superimposable mirror images with a chiral centre consisting of a carbon atom to which four different groups or atoms are attached.

Any carbon atom with four different groups or atoms attached to it is asymmetric and chiral.

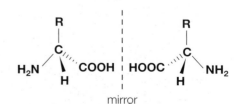

Figure 5.14 ▲
Mirror image forms of all naturally occurring amino acids, except glycine.

57

9 Identify the chiral objects in Figure 5.15.
10 With the help of molecular models, decide which of the following molecules are chiral: NH_3, CH_2Cl_2, CH_2ClBr, $CH_3CHClBr$, $CH_3CHOHCOOH$.
11 Explain why the amino acid glycine is not chiral.

Figure 5.15 ▲

Optical isomerism and polarised light

A light beam becomes polarised after passing through a sheet of polaroid, the material used to make sunglasses. The polaroid prevents vibrations of the light waves in all but one plane. So, in polarised light all the waves are vibrating in the same plane (Figure 5.16).

Figure 5.16 ▶
Ordinary light and polarised light.

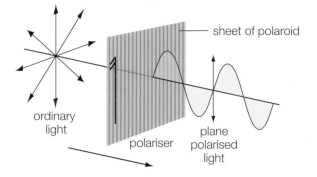

As stated above, light is said to be plane polarised after passing through a sheet of polaroid. If the polarised light is then directed at a second sheet of polaroid, all the polarised beam passes through if the second sheet of polaroid is aligned in the same way as the first (Figure 5.17a). However, no light gets through if the second sheet is rotated through 90° relative to the first sheet (Figure 5.17b).

Figure 5.17 ▶
The effect of a second sheet of polaroid on polarised light.

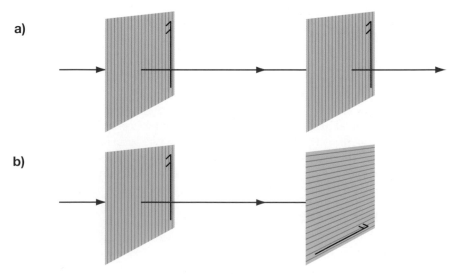

When polarised light passes through a solution of just one form of a chiral compound, it rotates the plane of polarisation. One isomer rotates the plane of polarised light clockwise. This is named the (+)isomer. The other isomer rotates the plane of polarised light anticlockwise, and this is named the (−)isomer. The direction of rotation of the plane polarised light (clockwise or anticlockwise) is that viewed by an observer looking towards the source of light. For accurate results, chemists measure the rotations with monochromatic light (light of one colour or frequency) in an instrument called a polarimeter (Figure 5.18).

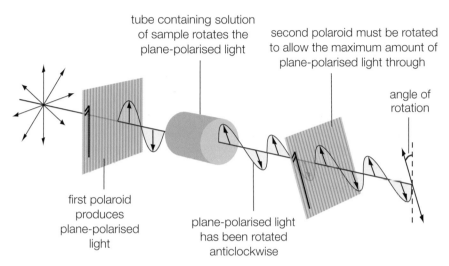

tube containing solution of sample rotates the plane-polarised light

second polaroid must be rotated to allow the maximum amount of plane-polarised light through

angle of rotation

first polaroid produces plane-polarised light

plane-polarised light has been rotated anticlockwise

Figure 5.18 ▲
The effect of passing plane-polarised light through a solution of a chiral compound.

Test yourself

12 How could you distinguish between the two mirror image forms of an amino acid by experiment?
13 Which of the following alcohols are chiral: butan-1-ol, butan-2-ol, pentan-1-ol, pentan-2-ol, pentan-3-ol?
14 Use the Data sheet: 'Common names and R sidegroups of some amino acids' on the Dynamic Learning Student website to help you to draw the structural formula of isoleucine. Put an asterisk on those atoms which are chiral centres in isoleucine.
15 The chemists who synthesise new drugs must pay close attention to chirality. Dextropropoxyphene, for example, is a painkiller. The molecule has two asymmetric carbon atoms. Its mirror image is useless for treating pain, but it is a useful ingredient in cough mixtures.
   Redraw the structure of dextropropoxyphene (Figure 5.19) and indicate the chiral centres with asterisks.

Data

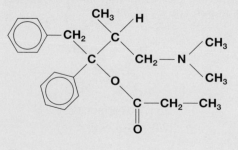

Figure 5.19 ▲
Dextropropoxyphene.

5.5 Stereoisomerism

If two molecules have the same molecular formula, but a different arrangement of their atoms, they are isomers. The isomers are different compounds with different physical properties and, in most cases, different chemical properties. Isomers and isomerism occur most commonly with carbon compounds because of the way in which carbon atoms can form chains and rings.

There are two ways in which the atoms can be arranged differently in isomers:

● The atoms are joined together in a different order forming different structures. This is called structural isomerism (Figure 5.20).

Figure 5.20 ▶
A simple example of structural isomerism.

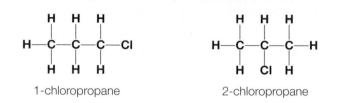

1-chloropropane   2-chloropropane

● The atoms are joined together in the same order, but they occupy different positions in space. This is called stereoisomerism.

Figure 5.21 shows how the two different types of isomerism are further divided. Structural isomerism can be divided into three different types – chain, position and functional group isomerism, which we explored in Section 10.5 of *OCR Chemistry for AS*.

Figure 5.21 ▶
A 'family tree' showing the relationships between different forms of isomerism.

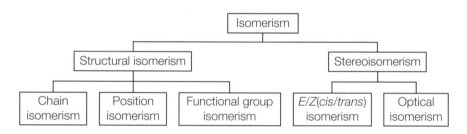

Definitions

In many cases, such as 1,2-dibromoethene in Figure 5.22 and but-2-ene, the Z-isomer may also be described as the *cis*-isomer and the E-isomer as the *trans*-isomer. However, this is not always the case. For example, in 2-bromobut-2-ene, the E-isomer is the *cis*-isomer and the Z-isomer is *trans*.

There are two different types of stereoisomerism – E/Z (*cis/trans*) isomerism, which we met in Section 12.2 in *OCR Chemistry for AS*, and optical isomerism. In both forms of stereoisomerism, the stereoisomers have the same molecular formula and the same structural formula, but different 3D shapes in which their atoms occupy different positions in space.

E/Z isomerism occurs in alkenes and other compounds with C=C double bonds. These isomers are labelled E and Z or *cis* and *trans*. In the Z-isomer, the atoms with higher atomic mass attached to each carbon atom in the double bond are on the same side of the double bond. In the E-isomer, the atoms with higher atomic mass attached to each carbon atom in the double bond are on opposite sides of the double bond (Figure 5.22).

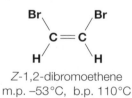   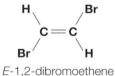

Z-1,2-dibromoethene   E-1,2-dibromoethene
m.p. –53°C, b.p. 110°C   m.p. –9°C, b.p. 108°C

Figure 5.22 ▲
E/Z isomers of 1,2-dibromoethene are distinct compounds with different melting points and different boiling points.

Test yourself

16 Which of the following compounds have *E/Z* isomers:
but-1-ene; but-2-ene; 1,2-dichloroethane; 1-chloroprop-1-ene;
2-chloroprop-1-ene; 3 chloroprop-1-ene?

17 Look at the isomers of 1,2-dibromoethene in Figure 5.22. Why do you think
the *Z*-isomer has a higher boiling point than the *E*-isomer?

18 The female silk moth secretes a pheromone called bombycol (Figure 5.23) which
attracts the male silk moth strongly. Chemists are interested in pheromones
because they offer an alternative to pesticides for controlling insect pests. By
baiting insect traps with pheromones, it is possible to capture large numbers of
insects before they mate (Figure 5.24).

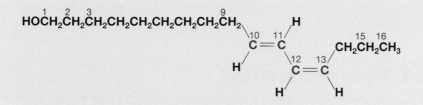

Figure 5.23 ▲
The structure of bombycol, the sex attractant for silk moths.

a) Are the groups across the double bonds in bombycol *E* or *Z*?
b) How many different *E/Z* isomers are there with the structural formula shown
in Figure 5.23?
c) Write the systematic name of bombycol, assuming that the straight-chain
alkane with 16 carbon atoms is called hexadecane.
d) Why are there no stereoisomers for bombycol?

Figure 5.24 ▲
Silk moths (male right and female lower)
with eggs on a discarded cocoon.

REVIEW QUESTIONS

Extension questions

1 An incomplete structure of the dipeptide
threonylisoleucine is shown below.

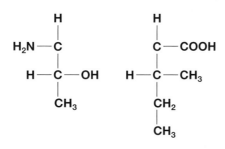

a) i) Redraw the structure of the dipeptide inserting
the missing peptide link. (2)

ii) On your structure, circle all the chiral
centres. (3)

b) What does the presence of a chiral centre tell you
about a compound? (1)

c) Draw the structures of the products obtained when
the dipeptide is refluxed with:

i) excess concentrated hydrochloric acid (2)

ii) excess sodium hydroxide solution. (2)

2 The technique of electrophoresis allows a solution of
amino acids to be separated by observing their relative
movements on chromatography paper under the
influence of an applied voltage.

a) At pH 3, glycine molecules migrate towards the
cathode. At pH 6 (the isoelectric point) glycine
molecules show no movement; but at pH 11 glycine
molecules migrate towards the anode. Explain these
observations. (7)

b) When lysine, $H_2N(CH_2)_4CH(NH_2)COOH$,
undergoes electrophoresis, it moves faster towards
the cathode at pH 3 than it moves towards the
anode at pH 11, even though the voltage remains
constant. Why is this? (4)

3 Explain the term stereoisomerism and describe the
different types of stereoisomerism, illustrating your
answer with suitable examples. (15)

6 Polymers

Polymers are long-chain molecules. Natural polymers include proteins, rubber and carbohydrates such as starch and cellulose. Synthetic polymers include those such as polythene and pvc produced by the addition polymerisation of compounds with carbon–carbon double bonds, and others such as polyesters and polyamides formed by condensation polymerisation.

The first synthetic polymers were produced more by good luck than good management. Nowadays, chemists are capable of developing new polymers with specific properties by applying the theories of bonding and structure. In many respects, polymers have changed the way we live, but the big disadvantage of most of them is that they are not biodegradable.

6.1 Polymer chemistry

Polymer chemistry is the study of the synthesis, structure and properties of polymers. It is a branch of chemistry that has developed rapidly since Leo Baekeland first discovered Bakelite in 1905 (Section 1.12). People were very excited about Bakelite, which could be used instead of ceramics and wood in the home and in industry. This first thermosetting polymer was discovered well before chemists understood the structure of big molecules.

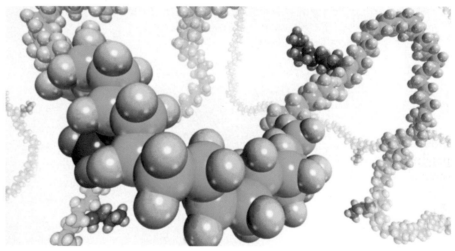

Figure 6.1 ▶
A false-colour computer graphic of low-density polythene showing the branches which prevent the chains from packing close together. Carbon atoms are coloured green and pink. Hydrogen atoms are blue and orange.

It was not until 1922 that a German chemist, Hermann Staudinger, published his theory about large molecules. Staudinger suggested that substances like rubber and cellulose consist of long-chain molecules and he had to fight hard to persuade other chemists to accept his ideas. Today his theory is taken for granted.

One person who was convinced by Staudinger's theory was the American industrial chemist Wallace Carothers. In 1931, Carothers wrote an article introducing the terms addition polymerisation and condensation polymerisation. Carother's research team at the Du Pont chemical company produced synthetic rubber, neoprene, by addition polymerisation. Then, in 1935, the team synthesised nylon – the first completely synthetic condensation polymer.

The 1930s were probably the most important years in the development of polymers and the plastics industry. During this period polythene, pvc, polystyrene and Perspex all came onto the market. Since then, research and development in the second half of the twentieth century has led to the production of many new and specialised polymers including Teflon (ptfe), the polyamide Kevlar and biodegradable polymers.

Figure 6.2 ▲
A false-colour electron micrograph of Gore-tex. The pink outer layers are nylon. The yellow and white layers consist of Teflon (ptfe). Magnification is ×160. Gore-tex is used to line outdoor wear such as anoraks and hiking boots because it is waterproof but allows perspiration to evaporate.

Figure 6.3 ◀
Expanded polystyrene has low density and it is an excellent thermal insulator. It is used for packaging fragile goods as it absorbs shocks. Its correct name is poly(phenylethene).

Definitions

Polymerisation is a process in which many small molecules (monomers) join up in long chains by addition or condensation reactions.

In **addition polymerisation**, the polymers form by addition reactions of monomers containing double bonds.

In **condensation polymerisation**, the polymers form by condensation reactions in which small molecules, such as water, are split off between the functional groups of the monomers.

6.2 Addition polymerisation

Addition polymerisation is a process for making polymers from compounds containing double bonds. The most important addition polymers are formed from compounds of general formula $CH_2=CHX$, in which the nature of X determines the properties of the polymer.

Ethene, for example, in which X is H, polymerises to form poly(ethene), commonly called polythene (Figure 6.4).

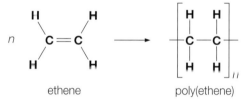

ethene   poly(ethene)

Figure 6.4 ◀
The formation of poly(ethene) from ethene.

Other widely used addition polymers include poly(propene), poly(phenylethene) – better known as polystyrene, poly(tetrafluoroethene) – often abbreviated to ptfe, and poly(chloroethene) – usually called pvc. In these addition polymers, the repeat unit in the polymer chain has the general structure shown below.

Figure 6.5 ◀
Inside the domes at the Eden Project in Cornwall, scientists have created the varying climatic conditions required by plants growing in different parts of the world. These domes consist of interconnecting steel pentagons and hexagons glazed with etfe – this is an addition polymer made by polymerising a mixture of the two monomers, ethene and tetrafluoroethene. The polymer is lightweight and lets through the ideal spectrum of light for plants to photosynthesise.

Another important addition polymer, developed in recent years as a water-soluble plastic, is poly(ethenol) – sometimes called polyvinyl alcohol. 90–98% of poly(ethenol) is composed of the following repeat unit.

Poly(ethenol) is used to make plastic bags which dissolve in water. These are ideal for use as hospital laundry bags which can be handled without touching any infected contents. When washing begins, the bags dissolve in the water and the laundry is washed.

Making addition polymers

One technique for making addition polymers using an initiator involves a radical chain reaction at high temperature and pressure. The initiator is often a peroxo compound, or an organic peroxide such as benzoyl peroxide. These peroxo compounds and peroxides act as a source of free radicals to initiate addition polymerisation (Figure 6.6).

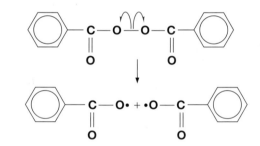

Using the symbol RO• for a free radical, the addition polymerisation can be followed through the stages of initiation, propagation and termination as shown in Figure 6.7.

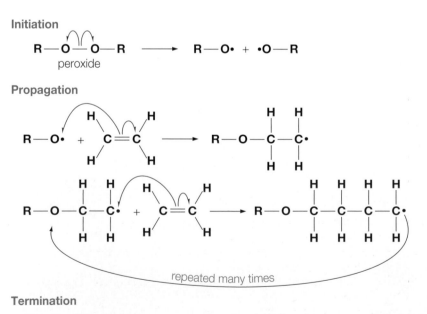

An alternative method that speeds up the polymerisation of alkenes such as ethene and propene is to use Ziegler–Natta catalysts. These catalysts enable the production of addition polymers at relatively low temperatures and pressures. The catalysts are combinations of titanium(IV) chloride and aluminium alkyls (such as triethyl aluminium) in a hydrocarbon solvent.

There is very little chain branching in the polymers so the poly(ethene) chains produced by this method can pack more closely together forming the high-density form of poly(ethene).

Figure 6.8 ◄
Extruding poly(ethene) to make plastic sheeting for the building industry. A high-pressure, high-temperature process with a peroxide initiator produces low-density poly(ethene) with branched chains. A low-pressure, low-temperature process with a Ziegler–Natta catalyst produces high-density poly(ethene) in which the polymer chains have very few branches and pack much closer.

Test yourself

1 Draw two repeat units of the polymer chain formed from each of the monomers below and write the systematic IUPAC name of the polymer.

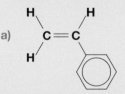

a)

b) propenamide,

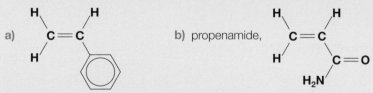

2 Identify the following polymers and write the name and displayed formulae of their monomers.

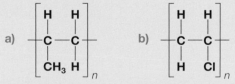

a)

b)

3 Explain the terms 'homolytic fission' and 'radical' using the action of benzoyl peroxide as an initiator for your example.

4 The paste supplied with DIY wood fillers often contains phenylethene. The paste is supplied with a small tube of hardener.
   a) Why is the hardener supplied in a separate tube and only mixed with the paste shortly before use?
   b) Suggest a chemical name for the hardener.
   c) What factors will determine how quickly the wood filler sets?

5 Why is poly(ethenol) soluble in water, unlike poly(ethene) which is insoluble?

Activity

Covering the O₂

The O₂ Dome at Greenwich, sometimes called 'the O₂', provided an important focus for celebrations of the Millennium in 2000. The huge structure is a triumph for science and engineering. Its construction would have been impossible without the availability of a tough, lightweight, inert and non-flammable material for the roof.

Figure 6.9 ▲
The O₂ at Greenwich, London.

The roof of the O₂ has an area of about 150 000 square metres. It is covered by 144 panels of ptfe-coated fibreglass supported by a network of steel cables suspended from 12 masts which reach to a height of 100 metres. The correct systematic name for ptfe is poly(tetrafluoroethene). However, it is better known by its trade name Teflon – it is also used to coat non-stick saucepans and skis. Teflon is manufactured by polymerising tetrafluoroethene with a small amount of ammonium peroxodisulfate.

1 a) Draw the displayed formula of tetrafluoroethene and a short section of the ptfe polymer showing two repeat units.

b) Why is the polymer called ptfe?

2 Explain fully why ammonium peroxodisulfate is used in the synthesis of ptfe.

3 Predict the conditions used to synthesise ptfe.

4 Describe the general shape of ptfe molecules and the forces that hold these molecules together.

5 Poly(tetrafluoroethene) is an ideal material to cover the roof of the O₂ because its strong C–F bonds are resistant to chemical attack. What other properties does ptfe have that make it ideal for the O₂?

6 Suggest two advantages that ptfe-coated fibreglass has over ordinary glass to form the roof covering of the O₂.

7 Suggest two disadvantages that ptfe-coated fibreglass has compared to ordinary glass as the roof covering of the O₂.

8 The roof of the O₂ is expected to be self-cleaning. Why is this?

6.3 Condensation polymerisation

Condensation polymers are produced by a series of condensation reactions in which small molecules such as water or hydrogen chloride are split off between the functional groups of the monomers.

Condensation reactions are sometimes described as 'addition-plus-elimination' reactions because the monomers undergo addition but this occurs only by elimination of a small molecule between each repeating unit.

There are two important classes of condensation polymers – polyesters and polyamides. When each monomer has two functional groups, polymerisation produces chains. Cross-linking is possible if one of the polymers has three functional groups.

Polyesters

Polyesters are polymers formed by condensation polymerisation between:
● either acids with two carboxylic acid groups and alcohols with at least two −OH groups
● or monomers which have both a carboxylic acid group and an −OH group.

The repeating units in the polyester chains are linked by a series of ester bonds.

The most common polyester is Terylene, used widely in fabrics. It is usually referred to simply as 'polyester'. Terylene is made by condensation reactions between benzene-1,4-dicarboxylic acid and ethane-1,2-diol (Figure 6.10). The traditional names for these two compounds are **ter**ephthalic acid and **eth**ylene glycol – hence the commercial name, Terylene. An alternative name for the polymer is polyethylene terephthalate, which gives rise to the name PET when the same polymer is used to make plastic bottles for drinks.

> **Definitions**
>
> **Polyesters** are polymers with ester links between monomer units.
>
> **Polyamides** are polymers with amide links between monomer units.

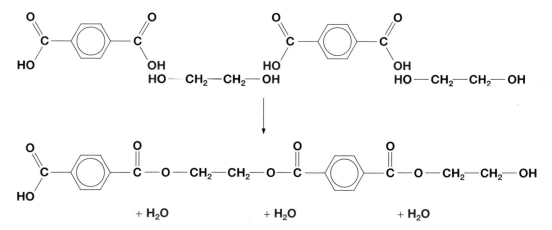

The condensation reactions shown in Figure 6.10 can be repeated again and again to produce a polymer with the repeat unit shown in Figure 6.11.

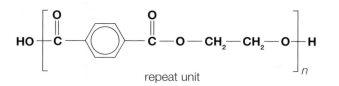

repeat unit

Figure 6.10 ▲
Condensation polymerisation to produce the polyester Terylene.

Figure 6.11 ◄
The repeat unit and structure of Terylene.

Polyesters have high tensile strength and, because of this, they are widely used as fibres in clothing and as the bonding resin in glass fibre plastics.

Perhaps the most important development in polyester chemistry in recent years concerns poly(2-hydroxypropanoic acid), commonly called poly(lactic acid) or PLA. Poly(lactic acid) is possibly the most useful and most versatile of the new biodegradable plastics. It is already used in such diverse goods as plant pots, disposable nappies and absorbable surgical sutures (stitches).

Poly(lactic acid) is manufactured by the condensation polymerisation of a single monomer which contains both a carboxylic acid group, –COOH, and an alcohol group, –OH (Figure 6.13).

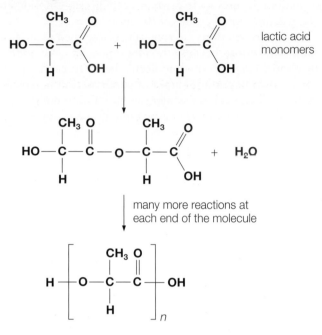

lactic acid monomers

many more reactions at each end of the molecule

Figure 6.13 ▲
The synthesis of poly(lactic acid) by condensation polymerisation.

Figure 6.12 ▲
The blazer, tie, shirt and trousers that this schoolboy is wearing may all contain polyester (Terylene). The fabrics are hard wearing, washable and relatively cheap.

Polyamides

Polyamides are polymers in which the monomers are linked by an amide bond. This is exactly the same as the amide bond in proteins, in which it is usually called the peptide bond (Figure 6.14). So, proteins and polypeptides are naturally occurring polyamides.

Earlier work in Topic 5 showed that polypeptides and proteins are synthesised in living things by condensation reactions between amino acids. In these reactions, the amine group, $-NH_2$, of one amino acid reacts with the carboxylic acid group, –COOH, of another amino acid to split out water and form an amide link (Figure 5.5).

This process is then repeated time after time to produce a polymer (protein) with tens, hundreds or, in some cases, thousands of units.

The first synthetic and commercially important polyamides were various forms of nylon. However, these were not produced from amino acids. Instead, they were formed by condensation polymerisation between diamines and dicarboxylic acids. One of the commonest forms of nylon is nylon-6,6. This is made by a condensation reaction between 1,6-diaminohexane and hexanedioic acid (Figure 6.15). The product is called nylon-6,6 because both monomers contain six carbon atoms.

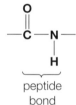

peptide bond

Figure 6.14 ▲
The amide bond is usually called the peptide bond in proteins.

Figure 6.15 ▶
Condensation polymerisation to make nylon-6,6.

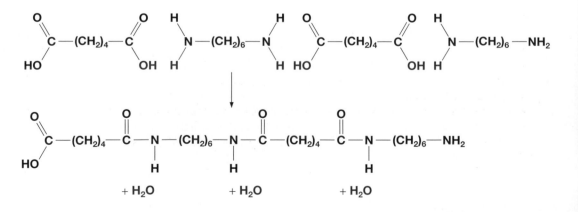

Nylon-6,6 can be produced more readily in the laboratory using the more reactive hexanedioyl dichloride in place of hexanedioic acid. Hexanedioyl dichloride reacts readily with 1,6-diaminohexane at room temperature to produce nylon-6,6. In this case, hydrogen chloride molecules are eliminated in the condensation reaction.

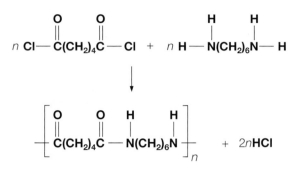

Figure 6.16 ▲
The reaction used to make nylon-6,6 in the laboratory.

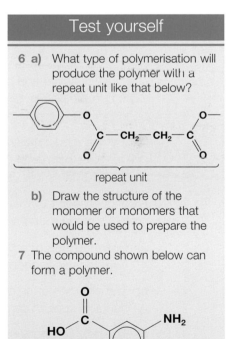

Figure 6.17 ▲
The American firm Du Pont patented nylon in February 1938. The first nylon stockings went on sale in the USA on 15 May 1940. In New York alone, four million pairs were sold in a few hours.

Although nylon is similar in structure to wool and silk, it does not have the softness of the natural fibres. But it is much harder wearing, and one of its earliest uses was as a substitute for silk in the manufacture of ladies' stockings.

Apart from their obvious use in stockings and tights, nylon fibres are used in various forms of clothing. In fact, about 75% of the UK nylon consumption goes on clothing, but its uses are many and varied. Nylon is used to make ropes that don't rot, machine bearings that don't wear out and it is mixed with wool to make durable carpets.

Nylon is the collective name for polymers with aliphatic hydrocarbon sections linked by amide bonds. They are aliphatic polyamides in which the polar amide bonds are fixed and inflexible, but the non-polar hydrocarbon sections are free to flex, rotate and twist. So, as the hydrocarbon sections become longer we would expect the nylon polymers to become more flexible with weaker bonding between the molecules.

This suggests that the properties of polyamides can be modified by changing the length and nature of the hydrocarbon sections. Chemists have followed up these ideas to develop polyamides in which the hydrocarbon sections are aromatic rather than aliphatic. These polymeric **ar**omatic **amid**es are described as aramids. Aramids, such as Kevlar (Figure 6.18), are extremely strong, rigid, fire-resistant and lightweight.

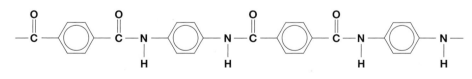

Figure 6.18 ▲
A section of the polymer chain in Kevlar.

Test yourself

8 State two similarities and two differences between the structure of nylon-6,6 and the structure of a protein.
9 Identify the types of intermolecular forces which act between the polymer chains in:
   a) poly(ethene)
   b) nylon.

Test yourself

6 a) What type of polymerisation will produce the polymer with a repeat unit like that below?

repeat unit

   b) Draw the structure of the monomer or monomers that would be used to prepare the polymer.
7 The compound shown below can form a polymer.

   a) Identify the functional groups involved in forming the polymer.
   b) What type of polymerisation will the monomer undergo?
   c) What other product forms during polymerisation?
   d) Draw a short length of the polymer chain showing two repeat units.

Activity

Modelling and synthesising polyamides

Experiments show that nylons with longer hydrocarbon sections to their chains are more flexible than those with shorter sections. Kevlar is similar to nylon-6,6 but with benzene rings rather than aliphatic chains linked by the amide group. The repetition of benzene rings in its structure makes Kevlar exceptionally strong and very inflexible compared with nylon-6,6. Because of this, it is used extensively in tyres, brakes and clutch fittings, in ropes and cables and in protective clothing (Figure 6.19).

1 Look closely at the structure of one chain of Kevlar in Figure 6.18.

   a) Explain how Kevlar is a condensation polymer of benzene-1,4-dicarboxylic acid and benzene-1,4-diamine.

   b) Weight-for-weight, Kevlar is five times stronger than steel. This exceptional strength is due to hydrogen bonding between the separate chains. Use Figure 6.18 to explain why inter-chain hydrogen bonding is so strong in Kevlar.

   c) Suggest a reason why Kevlar is made from monomers with functional groups in the 1 and 4 positions, and not from isomers with functional groups in the 1 and 2, or 1 and 3 positions.

2 Using a molecular model kit, make one repeat unit for the structure of Kevlar and explore the flexibility of the structure. (*Hint:* Use the Kekulé structure with alternating double and single bonds for the benzene ring.)

Repeat the model making and flexibility testing with one repeat unit for the structure of nylon-6,6. Why is nylon-6,6 flexible whereas Kevlar is inflexible?

3 A condensation polymer can be prepared by mixing equal amounts of the monomers in Figure 6.20 at room temperature.

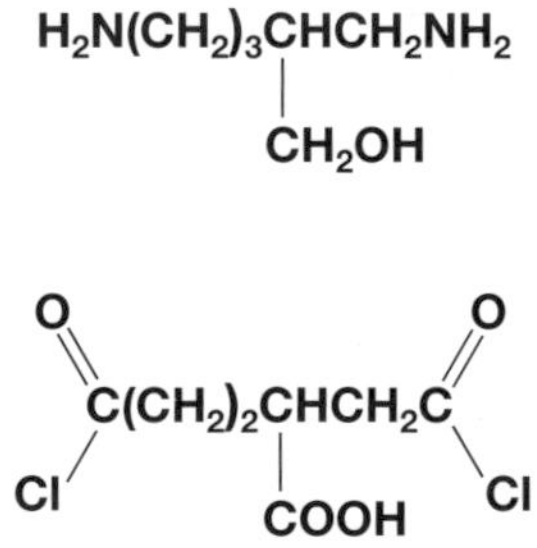

   a) Draw the structure of one repeat unit of the polymer formed from the two monomers.

   b) The polymer forms even more rapidly if the reaction mixture contains sodium carbonate. Why is this?

   c) The polymer molecules obtained at room temperature can be linked to one another (cross-linked) by a second reaction. Explain how this cross-linking can be achieved and state the conditions needed for it to happen.

   d) Explain how the choice of reaction conditions can control the extent of polymerisation and the extent of cross-linking.

Figure 6.19 ▲
This policeman is wearing a bulletproof jacket made from Kevlar.

$$H_2N(CH_2)_3CHCH_2NH_2$$
$$CH_2OH$$

$$ClOC(CH_2)_2CHCH_2COCl$$
$$COOH$$

Figure 6.20 ▲

6.4 Comparing addition and condensation polymerisation

Although both addition and condensation polymerisation result in the formation of long-chain organic molecules, known as polymers, from relatively small organic molecules, known as monomers, there are some clear differences between the two processes.

The first difference concerns the **type of reaction** involved. As its name suggests, addition polymerisation involves only addition reactions, whereas condensation polymerisation involves addition plus elimination. As monomer units join together a small molecule, usually water or hydrogen chloride, is eliminated and split off.

The second difference between addition and condensation polymerisation involves the **type of links** along the polymer chain. In addition polymers, the central chain consists of carbon atoms linked by carbon–carbon single bonds. In condensation polymers, the central chain consists of short aliphatic or aryl sections linked by

● ester groups, $-\overset{\overset{\textstyle O}{\|}}{C}-O-$ or   ● amide groups, $-\overset{\overset{\textstyle O}{\|}}{C}-\overset{\overset{\textstyle H}{|}}{N}-$

The third difference concerns the **type of monomer** involved. In addition polymerisation, the monomers have molecules with carbon–carbon double bonds. In condensation polymerisation, the monomers have molecules with at least two functional groups which may be the same or different.

A fourth difference concerns the **conditions for preparation** of the polymers. In general, addition polymerisations require an initiator together with high temperatures and high pressures, unless a catalyst is involved. In contrast, condensation polymerisations do not require initiators and usually occur at much lower temperatures and atmospheric pressure.

Polymer properties

These differences between addition and condensation polymerisation lead to considerable variation in the properties of polymers. Polymeric materials include plastics, fibres and elastomers. As polymer science has grown, chemists and material scientists have learnt how to develop new materials with particular properties.

Some of the ways of modifying the properties of polymers include:
● altering the average length of polymer chains
● changing the structure of the monomer to one with different side groups and different intermolecular forces
● varying the extent of cross-linking between chains
● selecting a monomer which produces a polymer which is biodegradable or photodegradable
● producing a co-polymer, such as etfe (Figure 6.5), which is made from two or more monomers, each of which could produce a polymer
● adding fillers and pigments
● making composites.

Definitions

Plastics are materials made of long-chain molecules, which at some stage can be moulded into shapes which are retained.

Elastomers are materials made of long-chain molecules, which can be moulded into new shapes but which spring back to their original shape when the pressure is removed.

Biodegradable materials break down due to the action of microorganisms.

Photodegradable materials break down when exposed to sunlight.

Co-polymers are polymers made from two or more monomers, each of which could produce a polymer.

Composites are materials made up of two or more recognisable constituents each of which contributes to the properties of the composite.

Figure 6.21 ◀
An electron micrograph of a glass fibre composite showing rods of glass fibre embedded in a polyester matrix. Magnification is ×660.

6.5 The hydrolysis of polyesters and polyamides

Esters and polyesters

In Topic 3, we found that an ester can be hydrolysed to form an acid and an alcohol.

Figure 6.22 ▶
The hydrolysis of a simple ester, ethyl ethanoate.

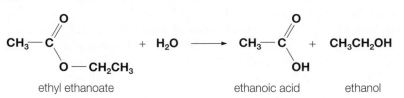

ethyl ethanoate   ethanoic acid   ethanol

Both acids and alkalis can catalyse the hydrolysis. Hydrolysis catalysed by acid is the reverse of the reaction used to synthesise esters from carboxylic acids and alcohols.

Base catalysis is generally more efficient because it is not reversible. This is because the acid reacts with the base as soon as it is produced to form its carboxylate salt, which does not react with the alcohol.

$$CH_3COOH(aq) + OH^-(aq) \rightarrow CH_3COO^-(aq) + H_2O(l)$$
ethanoic acid   ethanoate

Polyesters can be hydrolysed in a similar way to simple esters forming products with carboxylic acid and alcohol groups (Figure 6.23).

Figure 6.23 ▶
The hydrolysis of poly(lactic) acid.

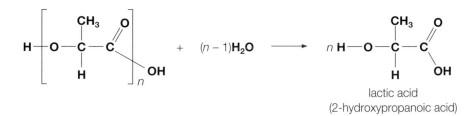

lactic acid
(2-hydroxypropanoic acid)

If the reaction is catalysed by an acid, the product is lactic acid (2-hydroxypropanoic acid). If the reaction is catalysed by a base, the lactic acid produced reacts with the base to form a salt.

$$HO–CH(CH_3)–COOH(aq) + NaOH(aq)$$
$$\rightarrow HO–CH(CH_3)–COONa(aq) + H_2O(l)$$

Polyamides

In Topic 5, we found that peptides and proteins could by hydrolysed to form amino acids, and that the hydrolysis was catalysed by both acids and bases. However, when the reaction is catalysed by acid, H^+ ions from the acid react with $-NH_2$ groups in the amino acids produced to form cations containing the $-NH_3^+$ group.

But, when the reaction is catalysed by base, ions such as OH^- from the base react with $-COOH$ groups in the amino acids produced to form carboxylate anions containing the $-COO^-$ group.

Polyamides which contain the amide group, $-\overset{\text{O}}{\underset{}{\text{C}}}-\overset{}{\underset{\text{H}}{\text{N}}}-$, like proteins, are hydrolysed in the same way.

The products are compounds containing carboxylic acid groups, $-COOH$, and amine groups, $-NH_2$. If the hydrolysis is catalysed by acid, the $-NH_2$ groups are converted to $-NH_3^+$; and if the reaction is catalysed by base, the $-COOH$ groups are converted to $-COO^-$ (Figure 6.24).

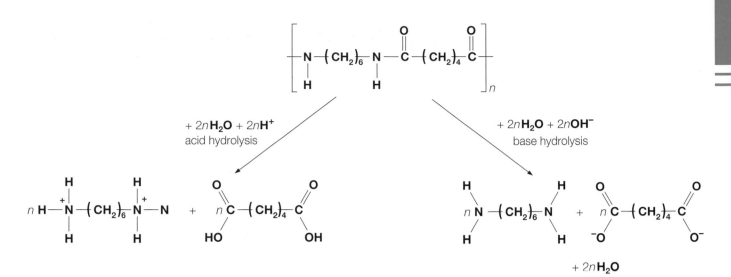

Figure 6.24 ▲
The hydrolysis of nylon-6,6 by acid and base.

Test yourself

10 A bottle made of poly(phenylethene) can be used to store dilute potassium hydroxide, but holes gradually appear in a polyester lab coat which has soaked up splashes of the same reagent. Account for the difference in the behaviour of the two polymers.

11 Suggest a reason why many polyesters and polyamides are degradable while poly(alkenes) are not.

12 a) Which type of plastic makes up most of the plastic waste from households – condensation or addition polymers?

   b) What are the implications of this when it comes to disposing of the waste?

13 Explain the difference between a co-polymer and a composite.

14 Nylon-6 contains the repeat unit shown below.

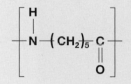

Draw the structures of the products formed when it is hydrolysed by refluxing with:

a) dilute hydrochloric acid

b) sodium hydroxide solution.

6.6 The development of degradable polymers

As it becomes more and more expensive to dump waste in landfill sites, plastics are seen as an increasing problem. The major problem with most plastic waste is that it is non-biodegradable. This means that the only choices for dealing with plastic waste are recycling and energy recovery.

Although some progress has been made, the separation, sorting and recycling of different plastics is difficult to mechanise and automate.

Modern incinerators, which burn plastic waste in order to recover the energy from its combustion, have to meet tough environmental standards. Despite these higher standards, many people remain suspicious of the emissions from incinerators and worry that they are a health risk.

Figure 6.25 ▲
The managing director of a Dutch recycling company standing in a pile of plastic bottle tops and holding a roll of recycled plastic made from them. Separation and sorting was no problem in this case!

These concerns over incineration and the difficulties in recycling have led chemists to look for other ways of minimising the waste from plastics. The most promising approach involves the development of biodegradable polymers, such as poly(lactic acid) described in the Activity on the next page.

Another important approach is the development and use of condensation polymers that are either photodegradable or readily degraded by hydrolysis.

Photodegradable condensation polymers

The C=O bond in condensation polymers can absorb the photons in radiation of a particular frequency. In some cases, sufficient energy can be captured by the polymer to facilitate its decomposition.

Hydrolysis of condensation polymers

Polyamides such as nylon and polyesters containing aromatic groups are fairly resistant to hydrolysis unless the reaction is catalysed by acid or base. But polyesters made from purely aliphatic monomers hydrolyse slowly at pH 7 without acid or base catalysts. This has led to the use of poly(glycolic) acid (Figure 6.26) for stitching internal wounds. Once the stitches (sutures) have been inserted and the surgical incision closed, the stitches dissolve slowly in the patient's tissue fluid.

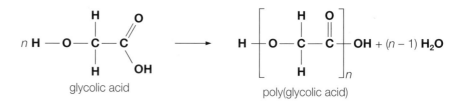

glycolic acid

poly(glycolic acid)

Figure 6.26 ▲
An equation for the synthesis of poly(glycolic acid).

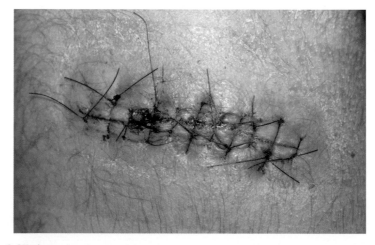

Figure 6.27 ▲
Polyamides such as nylon and aromatic polyesters are used for stitches (sutures) on external wounds. These are not degradable and have to be removed manually when the wound has healed.

Developing and using poly(lactic acid)

Poly(lactic acid) is an aliphatic, thermoplastic, biodegradable polyester (Figure 6.28). Its name is sometimes abbreviated to PLA.

Polylactic acid can be produced from renewable resources such as the sugar from canes and the starch from wheat and sweetcorn. As such, it is a sustainable alternative to oil-based plastics. PLA is more expensive to produce than its oil-based alternatives, but its cost has fallen with increased production and the increase in oil prices.

The manufacture of PLA from starch or sugar requires two stages. In the first stage, starch or sugar is converted to lactic acid by bacterial fermentation. The lactic acid then undergoes condensation polymerisation to produce PLA by heating with a catalyst of tin(II) octanoate.

Like most thermoplastics, PLA can be processed into fibres or film for a variety of uses.

Poly(lactic acid) is already used for waste sacks, compost bags, disposable plastic plates, packaging and a number of biomedical applications. These include stitches, dialysis bags and capsules containing various medicinal drugs. Packaging made from PLA will degrade to lactic acid in less than two months, but this relatively rapid breakdown is only possible in the ideal conditions of a commercial composting plant.

1 Explain what is meant by each of the following adjectives when applied to poly(lactic acid):

   a) aliphatic   **b)** thermoplastic   **c)** biodegradable.

2 Why is poly(lactic acid) described as a sustainable alternative to petroleum-based plastics?

3 Why is poly(lactic acid) becoming more financially viable in the manufacture of different goods?

4 How can poly(lactic acid) reduce the problems of plastic waste polluting the environment?

5 Draw the displayed formula of lactic acid and write its molecular formula.

6 Write an equation for the polymerisation of lactic acid to form poly(lactic acid).

7 How does poly(lactic acid) degrade when it is used to stitch an internal wound where there are no microorganisms?

8 Which do you think will degrade the faster when used for stitching internal wounds – poly(lactic acid) or poly(glycolic acid) (Figure 6.26)? Explain your answer.

9 Films of poly(lactic acid) and poly(glycolic acid) are used to coat the tablets and capsules of certain drugs. How does this help with the delivery of the drug into the body?

Figure 6.28 ▲
The skeletal formula of poly(lactic acid).

Figure 6.29 ▲
This bag is made from poly(lactic acid) – a biodegradable polymer.

REVIEW QUESTIONS

www
Extension questions

1 An elastic tape consists of 60% polyester and 40% neoprene. Neoprene is a polymer similar to synthetic rubber. It is manufactured by polymerising 2-chlorobuta-1,3-diene as in the partially-completed equation below.

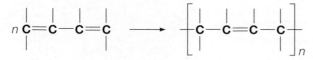

a) Copy and complete the equation above, showing the atoms or groups attached to the carbon skeletons. (2)

b) What type of polymerisation is illustrated by the manufacture of neoprene? (1)

c) What general name is given to polymers like neoprene and natural rubber? (1)

d) Polyester is manufactured by a reaction between benzene-1,4-dicarboxylic acid and ethane-1,2-diol.

   i) Draw the structural formulae of these two monomers. (2)

   ii) Draw the structural formula of the molecule which forms when one molecule of each of these monomers reacts to produce an ester. (1)

e) Why do you think that manufacturers use a mixture of polyester and neoprene in the elastic tape? (2)

f) i) What reagent could you use to show the presence of neoprene in the elastic tape? (1)

   ii) State and explain what you would observe if you used the reagent with some of the tape. (2)

g) Suggest two other properties, not covered earlier in this question, which should be considered in choosing a polymer for use in clothing. (2)

2 Short sections of the molecular structures of two polymers are shown below.

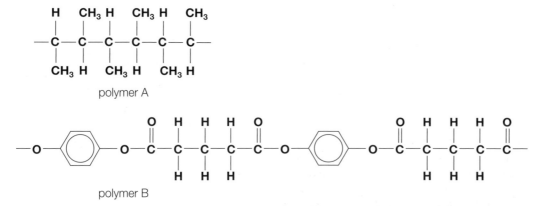

polymer A

polymer B

Figure 6.30 ▲

a) Draw the simplest repeat unit for each polymer. (2)

b) Draw and name the structural formula of the monomer used to make polymer A. (2)

c) i) Draw the structural formulae of the two monomers that could be used to make polymer B. (2)

   ii) Name one of the two monomers. (1)

d) During the last decade, degradable polymers have been developed to reduce the quantity of plastic waste that is dumped in landfill sites.

   State and explain two reasons why polymer B is more likely to be a degradable polymer than polymer A. (4)

3 Describe three differences between addition polymerisation and condensation polymerisation using poly(ethene) and nylon-6,6 as your examples. (12)

Much of the purpose and pleasure of chemistry comes from making new materials such as pigments, perfumes, drugs and dyes. This making of new materials is called synthesis. Synthesis is at the heart of much of the chemical research that goes on today. We depend on synthesis for processed foods, for our fuels, for the clothes we wear and for many of the modern materials we use everyday. Synthesis is also important to our understanding of reactions and molecular structure, particularly those of organic molecules. It is not until someone has synthesised a molecule that chemists can be confident that they have determined its structure precisely.

7.1 Organic synthesis

Many features of modern life depend on the skills of chemists and their ability to synthesise new and complex materials. New colours and fabrics for the fashion industry are synthetic organic molecules. So also are many compounds synthesised every day for testing in pharmaceutical laboratories as potential drugs to cure one disease or another. Lightweight, flat-screen computer monitors depend on liquid organic crystals. These organic compounds in the computer screen have been tailor-made by chemists so that they will respond to an electric field and affect light.

Figure 7.1 ▲
Liquid crystals photographed through a microscope using polarised light. Liquid crystals are used in the flat screens of modern computers and in the displays of calculators, digital cameras and digital watches.

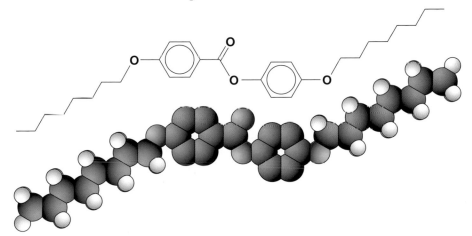

Figure 7.2 ▲
The structure of a liquid crystal molecule.

The essential job of synthetic organic chemists is to consider the proposed structure for a target molecule and then devise a way of making it from simpler, readily available starting materials. The scale of work involved and an indication of the difficulties encountered in a complex organic synthesis are illustrated by the painstaking and ingenious synthesis of chlorophyll by a team of 17 scientists led by Robert Woodward at Harvard University in 1959.

The synthesis of chlorophyll

Chlorophyll (Figure 7.3) is the green pigment in plants. Its structure was first proposed in 1940 by the famous chemist Hans Fischer. When Woodward and his team started work in 1956, they could not be sure that Fischer's proposed structure was correct.

From the start, the project was planned in great detail. The chemists read all the papers concerning previous studies of chlorophyll to ensure that no clues to a successful synthesis were missed. They drew on their understanding of the mechanisms of organic reactions to predict the likely products at each stage and suggest routes to their target molecule.

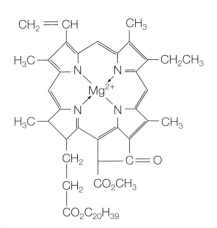

Figure 7.3 ▲
The structure of chlorophyll.

77

The synthesis of chlorophyll would have been impossible without the newer methods of separation, purification and identification that had become available. The variety of spectroscopy techniques were crucial to success. Woodward's team published their paper describing the successful synthesis of chlorophyll in 1960, opening up a new stage of research into the part that chlorophyll plays in photosynthesis.

Organic analysis

After complex molecules, such as chlorophyll, have been synthesised, chemists must use a variety of methods to analyse them in order to identify their precise composition and structure.

Traditionally, chemical tests were used to identify functional groups in organic molecules, together with combustion and quantitative analysis. Nowadays, modern laboratories rely on a range of highly sensitive automated and instrumental techniques to identify products of synthesis. These include chromatography, mass spectrometry and various kinds of spectroscopy.

7.2 Functional groups – the keys to organic molecules

Functional groups provide the key to organic molecules. A knowledge of the properties and reactions of a limited number of functional groups has opened up our understanding of most organic compounds.

A functional group is the atom or set of atoms which give a series of organic compounds their characteristic properties and reactions. Chemists often think of an organic molecule as a relatively unreactive hydrocarbon skeleton with one or more functional groups in place of one or more hydrogen atoms. The functional group in a molecule is responsible for most of its reactions. In contrast, the carbon–carbon bonds and carbon–hydrogen bonds are relatively unreactive, partly because they are both strong and non-polar.

> **Definitions**
>
> A **functional group** is the atom or set of atoms which give an organic compound its characteristic properties.

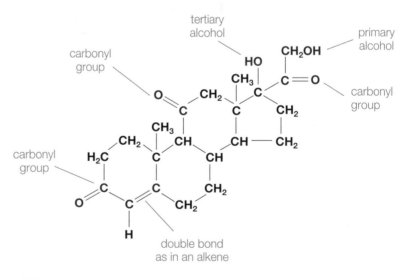

Figure 7.4 ▲
The structure of the steroid cortisone, labelled to show the reactive functional groups and the hydrocarbon skeleton.

Table 7.1 shows the major functional groups which you have met during your A-level studies, together with an example of one compound containing each group.

The characteristic properties and tests for most of these functional groups are shown on the data sheets headed 'Tests and observations on organic compounds' on the Dynamic Learning Student website.

www
Data

Functional group		Example
alcohol	–OH	propan-1-ol, $CH_3CH_2CH_2OH$
alkene	\C=C/	propene, $CH_3CH=CH_2$
halogenoalkane	–Hal	1-chloropropane, $CH_3CH_2CH_2Cl$
ether	\C—O—C/	methoxyethane, $CH_3OCH_2CH_3$
aldehyde	—C(=O)H	propanal, CH_3CH_2CHO
ketone	\C=O	propanone, CH_3COCH_3
carboxylic acid	—C(=O)CH	propanoic acid, CH_3CH_2COOH
ester	—O—C(=O)—	methyl ethanoate, CH_3OCOCH_3
amine	–NH$_2$	propylamine, $CH_3CH_2CH_2NH_2$

Table 7.1 ▲
The major functional groups

Test yourself

1 a) Write the empirical, molecular, structural, displayed and skeletal formulae of the hydrocarbon in Figure 7.5.
  b) What is the name of this compound?

Figure 7.5 ▲
Ball-and-stick and space filling models of a hydrocarbon.

2 Anaerobic respiration in muscle cells breaks down glucose to simpler compounds including the following two molecules. Identify the functional groups in these molecules.
  a) $CH_2OH–CHOH–CHO$
  b) $CH_3–CO–COOH$

3 Pheromones are messenger molecules produced by insects to attract mates or to give an alarm signal. Identify the functional groups in the pheromone below produced by queen bees.

$$\underset{}{CH_3\overset{O}{\overset{\|}{C}}CH_2CH_2CH_2CH_2CH_2}\quad\underset{H}{\overset{H}{\underset{\big|}{C}}}=\underset{COOH}{\overset{\big|}{C}}$$

DL
www
Data

Test yourself

4 Use the data sheets on the Dynamic Learning Student website headed 'Tests and observations on organic compounds' and the reaction flow charts from previous topics to predict six important properties or reactions of each of the following compounds.
  a) (–)Carvone, which is responsible for the taste of spearmint.

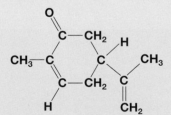

  b) The painkiller dextropropoxyphene and its mirror image which is an ingredient of cough mixtures.

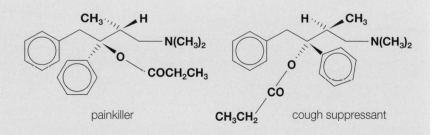

painkiller   cough suppressant

7.3 Organic routes

Organic chemists synthesise new molecules using their knowledge of functional groups, reaction mechanisms and molecular shapes – as well as the factors which control the rate and extent of chemical change.

A synthetic pathway leads from the reactants to the required product in one step or several steps. Organic chemists often start by examining the 'target molecule'. Then, they work backwards through a series of steps to find suitable starting chemicals that are available and cheap enough. In recent years, chemists have developed computer programs to help with the process of working back from the target molecule to a range of possible starting molecules.

Figure 7.6 shows an example of the systematic way in which working back can be used in synthesising one 'target molecule' from a starting molecule. In this case, the 'target molecule' is butanoic acid and the starting molecule is 1-bromobutane.

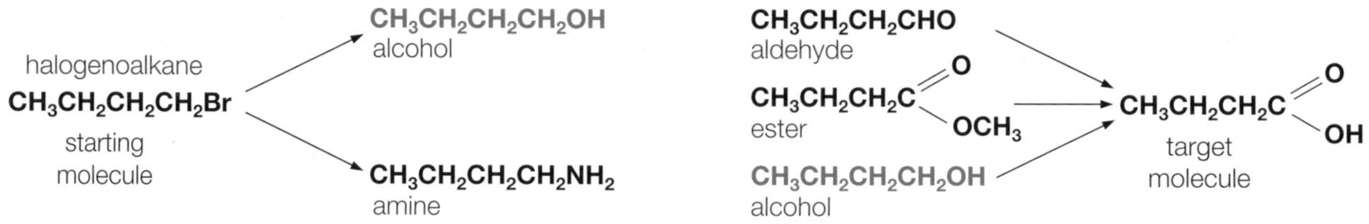

halogenoalkane
CH₃CH₂CH₂CH₂Br
starting
molecule

CH₃CH₂CH₂CH₂OH
alcohol

CH₃CH₂CH₂CH₂NH₂
amine

CH₃CH₂CH₂CHO
aldehyde

CH₃CH₂CH₂C
ester
OCH₃
O

CH₃CH₂CH₂CH₂OH
alcohol

CH₃CH₂CH₂C
target
molecule
OH
O

Figure 7.6 ▲
Working back from the target molecule to find a two-stage synthesis of butanoic acid from 1-bromobutane.

- Begin by writing down the formulae of those compounds which could be readily converted to butanoic acid, the target molecule. These include the aldehyde, butanal, the alcohol, butan-1-ol and the ester, methyl butanoate.
- Then look at your starting molecule, 1-bromobutane, to see if it could be converted to one of the compounds which would readily form butanoic acid. If necessary, write down the formulae of compounds which might be produced from 1-bromobutane. These include the alcohol, butan-1-ol and the amine, butylamine.
- With any luck, you should now see a possible two-stage synthetic route from your starting molecule to the target molecule. In this case, the route can go via butan-1-ol.
- If a two-stage route is not clear at this point, then you might need to consider a three-stage route involving the conversion of one of the products from the starting material to one of the reactants which will readily form the target material.

Figure 7.7 ▶
This photo shows a combinatorial chemistry lab. Using the computer-controlled techniques of combinatorial chemistry, vast numbers of new compounds can be made and tested in a short time.

Chemists normally seek a synthetic route which has the least number of stages and produces a high yield of the product. The larger the scale of production, the more important it is to keep the yield high so as to avoid producing large quantities of wasteful by-products.

Changing the functional groups

All the reactions in organic chemistry convert one compound to another, but there are some reactions which are particularly useful for developing synthetic routes. These useful reactions include:

- the addition of hydrogen halides to alkenes
- substitution reactions which replace halogen atoms with other functional groups such as $-OH$ or $-NH_2$
- elimination of a hydrogen halide from a halogenoalkane to introduce a carbon–carbon double bond
- oxidation of primary alcohols to aldehydes and then carboxylic acids
- reduction of carbonyl compounds to alcohols.

Activity

Converting one functional group to another

Make a copy of the flow chart in Figure 7.8. Beside each arrow, write the reagents and conditions needed for the conversion. You may need to refer to the reaction flow charts from previous topics to do this.

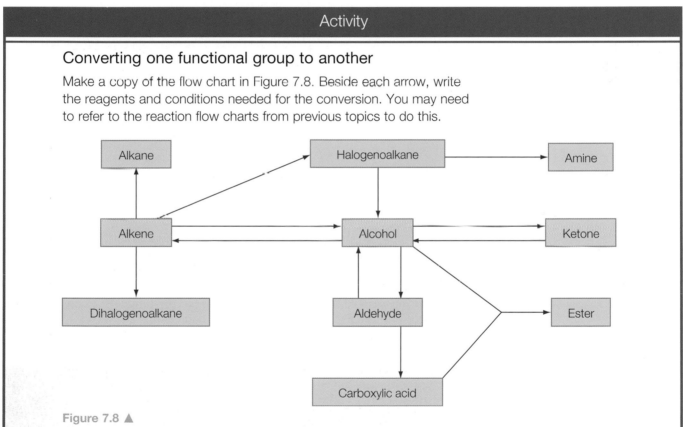

Figure 7.8 ▲
A flow diagram summarising the methods for converting one functional group to another.

Using your completed copy of Figure 7.8, suggest two-stage syntheses showing the reagents and conditions for each of the following conversions:

1 ethene to ethanoic acid

2 butan-1-ol to butan-2-ol

3 ethanol to ethyl ethanoate (using ethanol as the only carbon compound)

4 propan-2-ol to propane.

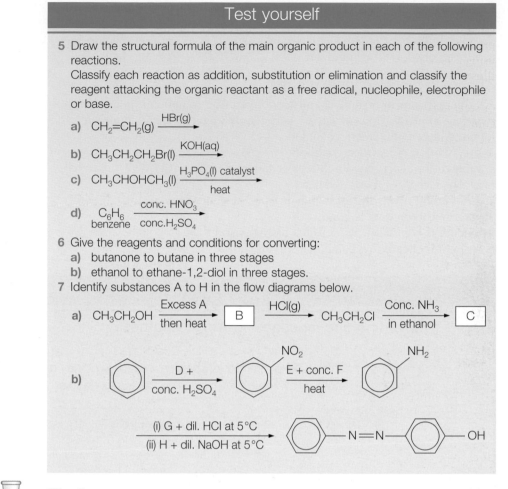

Test yourself

5 Draw the structural formula of the main organic product in each of the following reactions.
Classify each reaction as addition, substitution or elimination and classify the reagent attacking the organic reactant as a free radical, nucleophile, electrophile or base.

a) $CH_2=CH_2(g) \xrightarrow{HBr(g)}$

b) $CH_3CH_2CH_2Br(l) \xrightarrow{KOH(aq)}$

c) $CH_3CHOHCH_3(l) \xrightarrow[heat]{H_3PO_4(l) \text{ catalyst}}$

d) $\underset{benzene}{C_6H_6} \xrightarrow[\text{conc.}H_2SO_4]{\text{conc. }HNO_3}$

6 Give the reagents and conditions for converting:
a) butanone to butane in three stages
b) ethanol to ethane-1,2-diol in three stages.

7 Identify substances A to H in the flow diagrams below.

a) $CH_3CH_2OH \xrightarrow[\text{then heat}]{\text{Excess A}} \boxed{B} \xrightarrow{HCl(g)} CH_3CH_2Cl \xrightarrow[\text{in ethanol}]{\text{Conc. }NH_3} \boxed{C}$

b)

7.4 Synthetic techniques

Chemists have developed a range of practical techniques for the synthesis of solid and liquid organic compounds. These methods allow for the fact that reactions involving molecules with covalent bonds are often slow and that it is difficult to avoid side reactions which produce by-products. There are five key stages in the preparation of an organic compound.

Stage 1: Planning

The starting point of any synthesis is to choose an appropriate reaction or series of reactions as described in the last section. The next step is to work out suitable reacting quantities from the equation and decide on the conditions for reaction.

An important part of the planning stage is a risk assessment to ensure that there are no unnecessary hazards and the procedure is carried out as safely as possible.

Stage 2: Carrying out the reaction

The reactants are measured out and mixed in a suitable apparatus. Most organic reactions are slow at room temperature so it is usually necessary to heat the reactants using a flame, heating mantle or hotplate. One of the commonest techniques is to heat the reaction mixture in a flask fitted with a reflux condenser (Figure 7.9).

Organic reagents do not usually mix with aqueous reagents. So another common technique is to shake the immiscible reactants in a stoppered container.

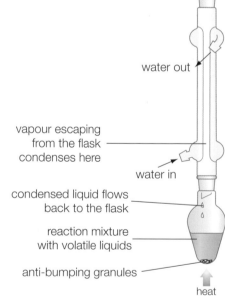

Figure 7.9 ▲
Heating in a flask with a reflux condenser prevents vapours escaping while the reaction is happening. Vapours from the reaction mixture condense and flow back (reflux) into the flask.

Stage 3: Separating the product from the reaction mixture

Chemists talk of 'working up' the reaction mixture to obtain their crude product. If the product is a solid, it can be separated ('worked up') by filtration using a Buchner or Hirsch funnel with suction from a water pump. This is illustrated in part of Figure 2.16.

Liquids can often be separated by simple distillation, fractional distillation or steam distillation. Distillation with steam at 100 °C allows the separation of compounds which decompose if heated near their boiling points. The technique only works with compounds that do not mix with water. When used to separate the products of organic preparations, steam distillation leaves behind those reagents and products which are soluble in water.

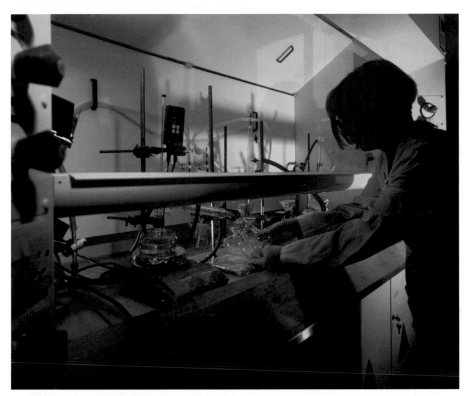

Figure 7.10 ◄
Setting up a distillation apparatus to separate chemicals synthesised during research to develop new anti-cancer drugs.

Stage 4: Purifying the product

The 'crude' product separated from the reaction mixture is usually contaminated with by-products and unused reactants. The method of purifying this 'crude' product depends on whether it is a solid or a liquid.

Purifying organic solids

The usual technique for purifying solids is recrystallisation, which is illustrated in part of Figure 2.16. The procedure for recrystallisation is based on using a solvent which dissolves the product when hot, but not when cold. The choice of solvent is usually made by trial and error. Use of a Buchner or Hirsch funnel and suction filtration speeds up filtering and facilitates recovery of the purified solid from the filter paper. The procedure is as follows:

- Dissolve the impure solid in the minimum volume of hot solvent.
- If the solution is not clear, filter the hot mixture through a heated funnel to remove insoluble impurities.
- Cool the filtrate so that the product recrystallises, leaving the smaller amounts of soluble impurities in solution.
- Filter to recover the purified product.
- Wash the purified solid with small amounts of pure solvent to wash away any solution containing impurities.
- Allow the solvent to evaporate from the purified solid in the air.

Purifying organic liquids

Chemists often begin to purify organic liquids which are insoluble in water by shaking with aqueous reagents in a separating funnel to extract impurities. This is followed by washing with pure water, drying and finally fractional distillation.

Fractional distillation separates mixtures of liquids with different boiling points. On a laboratory scale, the process takes place in a distillation apparatus which has been fitted with a fractionating column between the flask and the still-head (Figure 7.11). Separation is improved if the column is packed with inert glass beads or rings to increase the surface area so that the rising vapour can mix with the condensed liquid running back to the flask. The column is hotter at the bottom and cooler at the top. The thermometer reads the boiling point of the compound passing over into the condenser.

Figure 7.11 ▶

The apparatus for fractional distillation of a mixture of liquids.

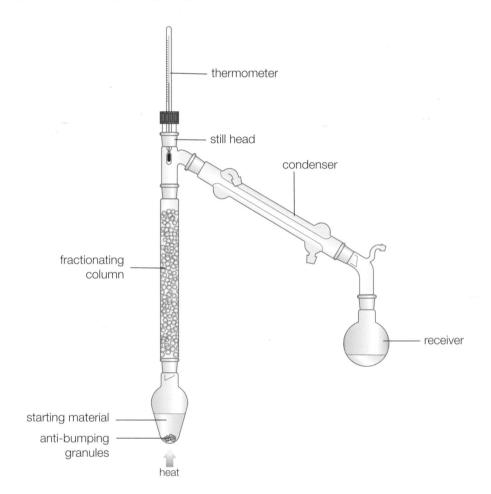

If the flask contains a mixture of liquids, the boiling liquid in the flask produces a vapour which is richer in the most volatile of the liquids present – the one with the lowest boiling point.

Most of the vapour condenses in the column and runs back. As it does so, it meets more of the rising vapour. Some of the vapour condenses and some of the liquid evaporates. In this way, the mixture evaporates and condenses repeatedly as it rises up the column. But every time it does so, the vapour becomes richer in the most volatile liquid present. At the top of the column, the vapour contains 100% of the most volatile liquid. So, during fractional distillation, the most volatile liquid with the lowest boiling point distils over first, then the liquid with the next lowest boiling point and so on.

Definitions

A **volatile liquid** evaporates easily, turning to a vapour.

Vapours are gases formed by evaporation of substances that are usually liquids or solids at room temperature.

Chemists talk about 'hydrogen gas' but 'water vapour'. Vapours are easily condensed by cooling or increased pressure because of their relatively strong intermolecular forces.

Stage 5: Measuring the yield, identifying the product and checking its purity

Measuring the yield

Comparing the *actual* yield with the yield *expected* from the chemical equation is a good measure of the efficiency of a process. The yield expected from the equation, assuming that the reaction is 100% efficient, is called the theoretical yield.

The efficiency of a synthesis, like that of other reactions, is normally calculated as a percentage yield. This is given by the relationship:

$$\text{percentage yield} = \frac{\text{actual yield of product}}{\text{theoretical yield of product}} \times 100\%$$

Worked example

a) What is the theoretical yield of glycine (2-aminoethanoic acid) from 15.5 g of 2-chloroethanoic acid?
b) What is the percentage yield if the actual yield of glycine is 7.9 g?

Notes on the method
Start by writing an equation for the reaction. This need not be a full balanced equation, so long as it includes the limiting reactant and the product in their correct molar ratio.
In this case, we must assume that any other reagents are in excess and the limiting reactant is chloroethanoic acid.

Answer
a) The equation: $ClCH_2COOH \longrightarrow H_2NCH_2COOH$

The molar mass of chloroethanoic acid, $ClCH_2COOH = 94.5 \text{ g mol}^{-1}$

The molar mass of glycine, $H_2NCH_2COOH = 75 \text{ g mol}^{-1}$

According to the equation:

1 mol of chloroethanoic acid produces 1 mol of glycine

So, 94.5 g of chloroethanoic acid produces 75 g of glycine

So, 15.5 g of chloroethanoic acid produces $\frac{75}{94.5} \times 15.5$ g of glycine

$$= 12.3 \text{ g of glycine}$$

b) Percentage yield $= \dfrac{\text{actual yield of product}}{\text{theoretical yield of product}} \times 100\%$

$$= \frac{7.9}{12.3} \times 100\%$$

$$= 64\%$$

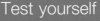

Test yourself

8 A possible two-stage synthesis of 1,2-diaminoethane first converts an alkene to a dihalogenoalkane, and then reacts this with ammonia.
a) Write out a reaction scheme for the synthesis giving reagents and conditions.
b) Calculate the mass of the alkene needed to make 2 g of the 1,2-diaminoethane assuming a 60% yield in stage 1 and a 40% yield in stage 2. Which chemicals should be in excess?
c) What hazards does the synthesis pose and what safety precautions should be taken?

Identifying the product and checking its purity

● *Qualitative tests*
Simple chemical tests for functional groups can help to confirm the identity of the product. These tests for functional groups are shown in the data sheets headed 'Tests and observations on organic compounds' on the Dynamic Learning Student website.

Data

● *Measuring melting points and boiling points*

Pure solids have sharp melting points, but impure solids soften and melt over a range of temperatures. So, watching a solid melt can often show whether it is pure or not. As databases now include the melting points of all known compounds, it is possible to check the identity and purity of a product by checking that it melts sharply, at the expected temperature.

Figure 7.12 ▶
Two methods of measuring the melting point of a solid.

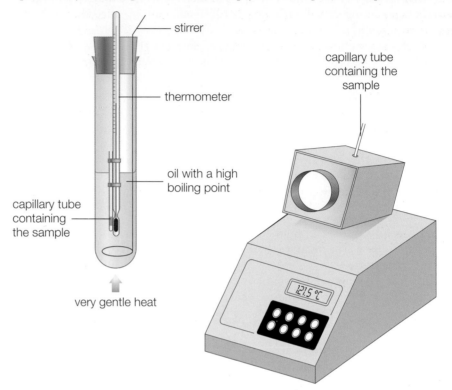

Like melting points for solids, boiling points can be used to check the purity and identity of liquids. If a liquid is pure, it should all distil over a narrow range, at the expected boiling point. The boiling point can be measured as the liquid distils over during fractional distillation.

● *Chromatography and spectroscopy*

The uses of chromatography and spectroscopy in identifying products and checking their purity are covered in Topics 8 and 9.

Test yourself

9 Give three reasons why the actual yield in an organic synthesis is always less than the theoretical yield.

10 A two-stage synthesis converts 18 g of benzene first to 22 g of nitrobenzene and then to 12 g of phenylamine.
   a) State the reagents and conditions for each stage.
   b) Calculate the theoretical yield and the percentage yield for each stage.
   c) What is the overall percentage yield?

11 Read the sub-section headed 'Purifying organic solids' in Section 7.4 again and then answer the following questions.
   a) Why should the impure solid be dissolved in the *minimum* volume of *hot* solvent?
   b) Why is the solution sometimes cooled in ice when the pure product is being recrystallised?
   c) How could you improve the evaporation of excess solvent from the purified solid in the final stage?

7.5 Stereochemical synthesis

When organic compounds are prepared synthetically in the laboratory, the product is sometimes a mixture of two optical isomers.

One process in which this can happen fairly frequently is the reaction of carbonyl compounds with H^- ions in sodium tetrahydridoborate(III), $NaBH_4$, and with cyanide ions, CN^-, in potassium cyanide. Both of these reactions with H^- and CN^- involve nucleophilic addition. The initial product in each case is an intermediate anion, which is converted to the final product containing an –OH group by adding dilute sulfuric acid (Figure 7.13).

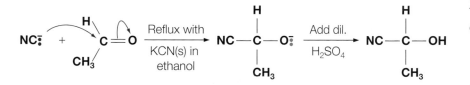

The reaction of ethanal with cyanide ions followed by dilute sulfuric acid increases the number of groups attached to the carbon atom in the carbonyl group from three to four. In this case, there are now four different groups attached to the carbon atom. This means that the final product will be a mixture of two optical isomers. As the CN^- ions can attack the flat ethanal molecule equally well from either side, the mixture will contain equal amounts of the two optical isomers. Mixtures of this kind are called racemic mixtures.

The reaction which we have just considered is used as the first stage in the two-stage laboratory synthesis of lactic acid (2-hydroxypropanoic acid) from ethanal. In the second stage, the product shown in Figure 7.13 is refluxed with the dilute acid and this converts the –CN group to a carboxylic acid group, –COOH (Figure 7.14).

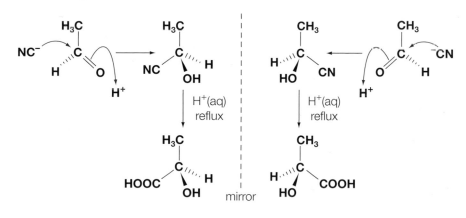

In contrast to the lactic acid produced synthetically in the laboratory, that formed in our muscles during excessive activity is the single (+) isomer. The reason for this is that the lactic acid formed in our muscles is produced naturally through processes catalysed by enzymes.

In fact, most optically active compounds in living systems are present as just one optical isomer. For example, all the glucose in living systems is the (+) isomer.

Almost all the chemical reactions in living organisms are controlled by enzymes, which are natural catalysts consisting of proteins (see Section 5.3). When enzymes act as catalysts, the reactions take place at an active site somewhere on the enzyme molecule. The shape of the active site and the functional groups around it are very stereospecific and give the enzyme its catalytic properties.

The stereospecific nature of the active site means that enzymes can usually accommodate only one particular molecule at their active site and this molecule is often only one of the optical isomers.

Figure 7.13 ◀
The nucleophilic addition of hydrogen cyanide to ethanal.

Figure 7.14 ◀
The laboratory synthesis of lactic acid (2-hydroxypropanoic acid) from ethanal produces a racemic mixture.

Figure 7.15 ▲
Paula Radcliffe winning the London Marathon in 2005. All the lactic acid in her weary muscles is the (+) isomer.

7.6 Stereochemistry and drugs

Pharmaceutical chemists seek to discover and synthesise drugs (pharmaceuticals) which will prevent diseases, cure them or, at least, alleviate the symptoms. Drugs act on molecules within the cells in our bodies, and most drugs act on proteins either in enzymes or in sensitive receptors on the surface of cells. Receptors make cells responsive to the chemicals from nerve endings and hormones.

One of the ways in which drugs act is to target the active site of a specific enzyme. Many drugs which kill harmful bacteria or stop their reproduction work by targeting enzymes. The sulfonamide drugs and penicillin antibiotics work in this way. What is crucial is that the drug affects an enzyme vital to the biochemistry of harmful bacteria, but does not damage any of the enzymes in humans.

Figure 7.16 ▶

A computer graphic of an anti-HIV drug (yellow) blocking the active site of the enzyme reverse transcriptase (green). The drug stops the HIV virus from reproducing.

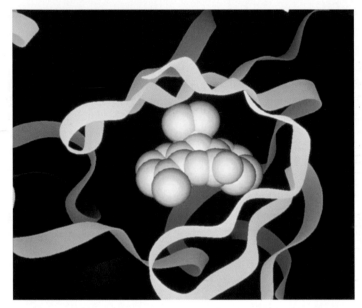

Drugs which target receptor proteins are also very important and these include the active ingredients in medicines to treat pain, heart failure, asthma and Parkinson's disease.

Chirality in drugs

Many molecules in our bodies interact selectively with the active sites in the protein structures of enzymes and receptors. These molecules are all chiral but our body chemistry works with only one of the mirror image forms. This means that most drugs are also chiral, and often the two optical isomers act on the body in different ways.

Often, one isomer is active while the other is inactive, but this is not always the case (Figure 7.17).

Figure 7.17 ▶

The optical isomers of isoleucine produce completely different tastes.

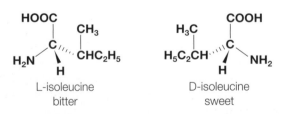

The pharmaceutical industry was alerted to the crucial importance of chirality early in the 1960s. A new drug, called thalidomide, was introduced to treat morning sickness in the first few months of pregnancy. Soon it was realised that this drug was responsible for serious malformations in babies who were born with stunted limbs.

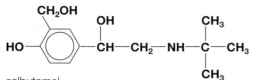

salbutamol
(used to treat asthma)

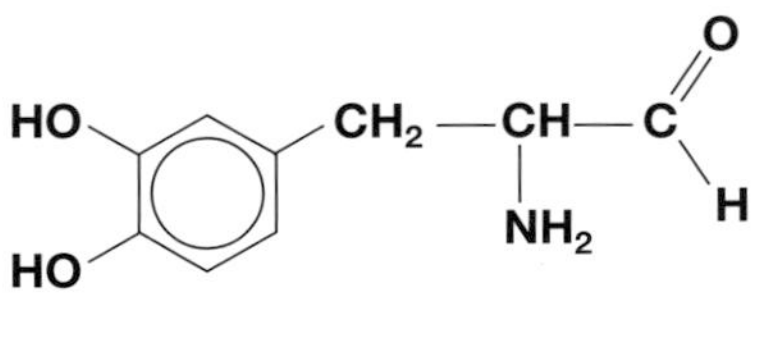

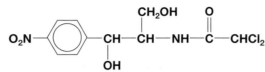

levodopa (one of the optical isomers is
used to treat Parkinson's disease)

chloramphenicol (an optical isomer is the active
antibiotic used to treat typhoid)

Figure 7.18 ▲
Drugs which are chiral.

Test yourself

12 a) Write an equation for the nucleophilic attack of ethanal by H⁻ ions in $NaBH_4$ followed by the addition of dilute sulfuric acid similar to that in Figure 7.13.
   b) In what crucial way is the product different from that in Figure 7.13?
   c) Give the name and structure of the simplest carbonyl compound which will give a chiral product with H⁻ ions followed by dilute acid.
13 Copy the molecules shown in Figure 7.18 and then identify their chiral centres with asterisks.
14 Explain in your own words, with the help of Figure 7.14, why a laboratory synthesis of a chiral compound usually produces a racemic mixture.

Activity

Thalidomide

Thalidomide first appeared in Germany in October 1957. It was marketed as a sedative with very few side-effects. The pharmaceutical company that developed thalidomide thought it was so safe that it could be prescribed to women in their first few months of pregnancy to alleviate morning sickness. No one could have imagined what would follow.

At the beginning of the 1960s, some babies were born with shortened, flipper-like limbs. The disabilities were traced to thalidomide and the drug was withdrawn, but not before an estimated 20 000 babies had been affected.

Drug testing was much less thorough in the 1950s. Tests had been conducted with thalidomide on rats and mice, but not on primates or humans. Years later, research showed that rodents metabolised thalidomide in a different way to humans.

Thalidomide is a chiral molecule (Figure 7.19) and the drug was a racemic mixture of the two isomers. Pharmacologists have since discovered that the (+) isomer is an effective and harmless sedative, while the (−) isomer is harmful to unborn babies. The adjective for this is teratogenic.

A vast amount of time and money has gone into researching the properties of thalidomide and its devastating effects on the development of limbs in the uterus.

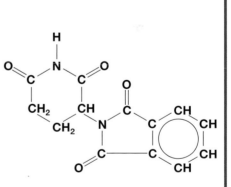

Figure 7.19 ▲
The structure of thalidomide.

Research has shown that:

- the (–) isomer blocks the development of blood vessels

- the body can convert one optical isomer of thalidomide to the other

- a few of the women with thalidomide deformities have given birth to babies with limb defects.

Today, the testing of drugs and other pharmaceutical products has become much more rigorous. However, there is still a risk that any new drug may have unforeseen side-effects.

In recent years, suggestions have been made that thalidomide would be effective in the treatment of certain cancers and in curtailing weight loss in HIV patients. This has led to rigorous clinical research trials.

1 What functional groups are present in thalidomide?

2 a) What is the molecular formula of thalidomide?

  b) What is its empirical formula?

3 Use a model-building kit to construct a molecular model of one of the isomers of thalidomide.

  a) Identify the chiral centre.

  b) Is the character of thalidomide acidic, basic or neutral? Explain your answer.

4 Thalidomide is moderately soluble in both water and non-polar solvents. Which groups in thalidomide help to make it:

  a) soluble in water

  b) soluble in non-polar solvents?

5 Why were tests of thalidomide on rodents flawed?

6 Why would the harmful effects of thalidomide still have happened even if the pure (+) isomer had been prescribed to pregnant women?

7 What conclusions can be drawn from the fact that a few children born to the first victims of thalidomide have limb deformities, even though their mothers have not taken the drug.

8 Suggest a reason why thalidomide may be effective in the treatment of certain cancers. (*Hint:* cancer cells grow faster than normal cells.)

9 Suggest three precautions that should be taken in the recent clinical research trials with thalidomide.

Figure 7.20 ▲
These technicians are preparing bottles of pills for a clinical trial.

7.7 Synthesising drugs

The testing of drugs and other pharmaceuticals is now much more thorough than it was in the 1950s and 1960s. When chiral molecules are involved, licensing authorities require pharmaceutical companies to carry out research with both isomers and to identify their individual properties. Very often this leads to a requirement to produce a single optical isomer.

This synthesis and production of pharmaceutical products which contain a single optical isomer has clear benefits for both patients and drug companies:

- it reduces the possible side-effects of the product
- it reduces the risk of companies being taken to court for negligence
- it improves pharmacological activity, and therefore reduces the quantity needed for each dose. It is therefore more economical.

However, there is one massive and very significant disadvantage. This is the increased cost of production when it is necessary to separate optical isomers with almost identical properties.

In order to overcome the problems of producing a pure single optical isomer of a pharmaceutical product, chemists have employed some very innovative techniques. These include the use of:

- enzymes or bacteria which metabolise only one of the optical isomers and introduce the required stereoselectivity
- natural chiral molecules, such as L-amino acids or D-glucose, as starting molecules
- chiral catalysts, possibly attached to a polymer support with reactants flowing over them.

In some processes, supercritical carbon dioxide is used as a substitute for organic solvents. The supercritical carbon dioxide can dissolve materials like a liquid and diffuse through solids like a gas, which it does when used to decaffeinate instant coffee.

Figure 7.21 ▲

A molecular model of ibuprofen in which some of the atoms have non-standard colours. Ibuprofen, $CH_3CH(COOH)-C_6H_4-CH_2CH(CH_3)_2$, is a chiral drug.

REVIEW QUESTIONS

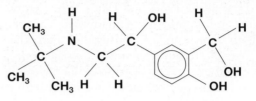

Extension questions

1 The following steps are taken from one method of synthesising ethyl ethanoate (b.p. 77 °C).

> A: Heat ethanol and ethanoic acid under reflux for about 45 minutes with a little concentrated sulfuric acid.
>
> B: Then, distil the reaction mixture collecting all the liquid which distils over below 84 °C.
>
> C: Shake the distillate with aqueous sodium carbonate solution and then discard the aqueous layer.
>
> D: Add two spatula measures of anhydrous sodium sulfate or anhydrous calcium chloride to the organic product.
>
> E: Finally, redistill the organic product collecting the liquid which boils between 75 and 79 °C.

a) Draw a diagram of the apparatus for heating under reflux in step A. **(3)**

b) State the reasons for each of the procedures in steps A to E. **(8)**

2 Salicylic acid has been used as a painkiller. Its displayed formula is shown below.

a) Identify the functional groups in salicylic acid. **(2)**

b) Write the molecular formula of salicylic acid. **(1)**

c) Draw the displayed formula of the organic product that forms when salicylic acid:

  i) is heated under reflux with ethanol and concentrated sulfuric acid **(1)**

  ii) reacts with bromine water **(1)**

  iii) is warmed with aqueous sodium hydroxide. **(2)**

3 Salbutamol is used in inhalers to relieve the symptoms of asthma. Its displayed formula is shown below.

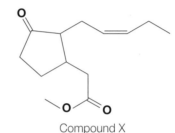

a) Identify the chiral centre in salbutamol. **(1)**

b) List three reasons why salbutamol is used as a single optical isomer in pharmaceutical products. **(3)**

c) Draw a displayed formula of the organic products which form when salbutamol is refluxed for some time with acidified potassium dichromate(VI). **(2)**

4 The skeletal formula of compound X is shown below. X is a constituent of jasmine oil and it is partly responsible for the taste and smell of black tea.

Compound X

a) What is the molecular formula of X? **(1)**

b) Name the functional groups in X. **(3)**

c) Compound X is a stereoisomer.

  i) Draw the structure of X and identify each stereochemical component with an asterisk. **(3)**

  ii) Label each of these components with the type of stereoisomerism involved. **(2)**

  iii) How many stereoisomers are there with the skeletal formula shown? Explain your answer. **(3)**

d) Point out four important factors that pharmaceutical companies must consider in their production of chiral compounds that are intended for use in medicines. **(4)**

8 Chromatography

Chromatography is very important for modern chemistry. The various techniques provide a powerful method for separating mixtures. They range from the cheap and simple method of paper chromatography to the sophisticated methods based on high-precision instruments with sophisticated detectors used in gas chromatography.

8.1 Principles of chromatography

In 1903, the Russian botanist Michel Tswett developed the technique of column chromatography to study plant pigments. He extracted the coloured chemicals from leaves. He added a sample to the top of a column of powdered chalk. Then he allowed a hydrocarbon solvent to flow through the column to separate the colours in the mixture.

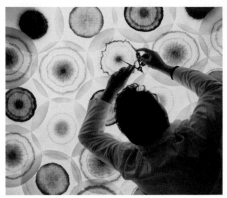

Figure 8.1 ▲
A scientist studying paper chromatograms of a range of dyes. Each of these chromatograms was made by placing a small amount of the dye at the centre of a piece of filter paper, then slowly dripping a solvent onto the centre of the paper. The solvent spread out over the paper carrying with it the chemicals in the dye at different rates.

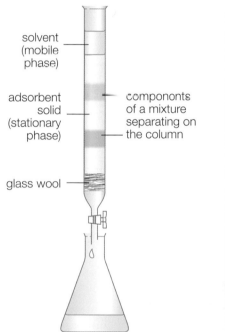

solvent (mobile phase)

adsorbent solid (stationary phase)

compononts of a mixture separating on the column

glass wool

Figure 8.2 ▲
Column chromatography. A solution of the mixture to be analysed is added to the top of the column. Then a solvent is run slowly through the column. The substances in the mixture separate and emerge at different times from the column.

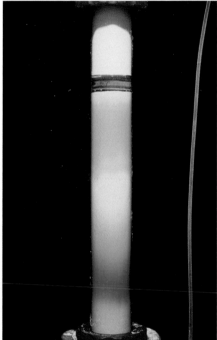

Figure 8.3 ▲
Coloured chemicals from a plant leaf separating on a chromatography column.

'Chroma' means 'colour'. The name chromatography was chosen because the technique was first used to separate coloured chemicals from mixtures. There is now a range of chromatography techniques which can be used to:

- separate and identify the components of a mixture of chemicals
- check the purity of a chemical
- identify the impurities in a chemical preparation
- purify a chemical product.

Every type of chromatography has a stationary phase and a mobile phase that flows through it. Chemicals in a mixture separate because they differ in the extent to which they mix with the mobile phase or stick to the stationary phase.

Powdered solids now used in column chromatography include silicon oxide and aluminium oxide. Both of these can adsorb chemicals onto their surfaces. The greater the tendency for molecules to be adsorbed by the stationary phase, the slower they move during chromatography.

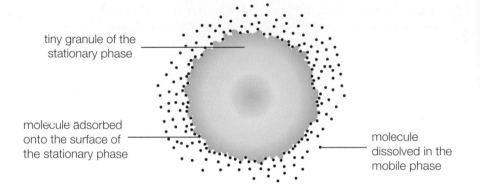

tiny granule of the stationary phase

molecule adsorbed onto the surface of the stationary phase

molecule dissolved in the mobile phase

Definitions

A sponge **absorbs** water into its pores as it soaks up the liquid. Paper is absorbent and soaks up the moving solvent during paper chromatography.

Solids can **adsorb** very thin films of liquids or gases onto their surfaces.

Figure 8.4 ▲
In column chromatography, there is an equilibrium between molecules adsorbed onto the surface of the stationary phase and molecules dissolved in the solvent.

Test yourself

1 In Michel Tswett's column chromatography method, identify:
   a) the stationary phase
   b) the mobile phase.
2 In Figure 8.2. state the colour of the component of the mixture being separated that has the greater tendency to:
   a) dissolve in the eluting solvent
   b) stick to the stationary phase.
3 Name two other techniques, other than chromatography, that can be used to determine whether a product of chemical synthesis is pure or not.

8.2 Liquid chromatography

The column chromatography developed by Michel Tswett was an example of liquid chromatography. Modern versions of the column technique continue to be widely used. Other variants include thin-layer chromatography and high-performance liquid chromatography.

Thin-layer chromatography

Thin-layer chromatography (TLC) is a another type of liquid chromatography in which the stationary phase is a thin layer of a solid, such as silicon dioxide or aluminium oxide, supported on a glass or plastic plate. As in column chromatography, the rate at which a sample moves up a TLC plate also depends on the equilibrium between adsorption on the solid and solution in the solvent. The position of equilibrium varies from one compound to another, so the components of a mixture separate.

TLC is fast, cheap and needs only a very small sample for analysis. The technique is widely used both in research laboratories and in industry. TLC can be used to quickly check that a chemical reaction is going as expected and is making the required product. After attempting to purifying a chemical, TLC can show whether or not all the impurities have been removed.

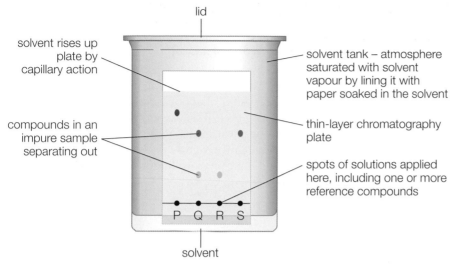

Figure 8.5 ◀
Apparatus for thin-layer chromatography. Spots of chemicals for the analysis are placed on the start line at P, Q, R and S.

Coloured compounds are easy to see on a TLC plate. However, the technique is often used with colourless compounds as well. A quick way of finding the position of colourless organic spots is to stand the plate in a covered beaker with iodine crystals. The iodine vapour stains the spots.

An alternative is to use a TLC plate impregnated with a fluorescent chemical. Under a UV-lamp the whole plate glows, except in the areas where organic compounds absorb radiation – so they show up as dark spots.

R_f values can be used to record the distances moved by chemicals in a mixture relative to the distance moved by the solvent. The values are ratios calculated using this formula where x and y are as shown in Figure 8.6:

$$R_f = \frac{\text{distance moved by chemical}}{\text{distance moved by solvent front}}$$

$$= \frac{x}{y}$$

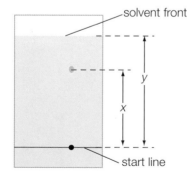

Figure 8.6 ▲
A diagram of a TLC plate showing the distances used to calculate R_f values. R_f values can help to identify components of mixtures so long as the conditions are carefully controlled. The values vary with the type of TLC plate (or paper) and the nature of the solvent.

Definition

The R_f **value** is the ratio of the distance moved by the chemical in a mixture to the distance moved by the solvent front. R_f values are used in thin-layer and paper chromatography.

Test yourself

4 Why is the start line for spotting TLC samples on a plate drawn in pencil and not with ink?
5 Why is the air inside the container of the TLC solvent saturated with the vapour of the solvent before adding the TLC plate?
6 Which of the four samples P, Q, R and S in Figure 8.5:
  a) is the mixture being analysed
  b) are reference compounds also present in the mixture
  c) is a reference compound not present in the mixture?
7 Estimate the R_f values for the yellow dye in Figure 8.5.

High-performance liquid chromatography

High-performance liquid chromatography (HPLC) is a sophisticated version of column chromatography. The technique is able to separate components in a mixture that are very similar to each other.

High performance is achieved by packing very small particles of a solid, such a silica, into a steel column (Figure 8.7). A typical column is about 10–30 cm long and has an internal diameter of about 4 mm.

The use of fine particles increases the surface area of the stationary phase. This makes the separation efficient but it means that a high-pressure pump is necessary to force the solvent through the tightly packed column. As a result, the technique is sometimes called high-pressure liquid chromatography.

Figure 8.7 ▶
A scientist checking a sample tube in front of a set of high-performance liquid chromatography columns.

An advantage of HPLC is that it is carried out at room temperature and so can analyse mixtures that decompose before they vaporise – this applies to many biological molecules. Organic molecules that break down on heating cannot be studied using gas chromatography (see Section 8.3). This makes HPLC suitable for separating biological molecules such as proteins. One important application of HPLC is to study what happens to drugs as they are metabolised in the body.

Activity

Food colours and children

The Food Standards Agency recommends that parents should avoid letting their children eat foods with some colours in them, especially if their children show signs of hyperactivity (see Section 4.5). The colours to avoid include these dyes (with their E-numbers):

● sunset yellow (E110)
● quinoline yellow (E104)
● carmoisine (E122)
● tartrazine (E102).

These colours are used in a foods such as soft drinks, sweets, cakes and ice cream.

Manufacturers must state the colours they use in the list of ingredients by giving the 'colour' and either naming the chemical or showing the E-number. Analysts can use thin-layer chromatography to check whether or not the claims made by manufacturers are correct.

Figure 8.8 ▲
Soft drinks at a party for children.

The chromatogram in Figure 8.9 shows the results of analysing the colours extracted from two soft drinks. The colours from the soft drinks are compared with reference compounds.

1 Tartrazine, sunset yellow and carmoisine are examples of azo dyes.
   a) Which functional group is present in an azo dye?
   b) How, in general, are azo dyes made?

2 Suggest a reason for carrying out this analysis by TLC rather than HPLC.

3 Which of the reference dyes is not a pure compound?

4 What is the R_f value for carmoisine under the conditions used to make this TLC plate?

5 What can you conclude from the chromatogram about:
   a) soft drink A
   b) soft drink B?

6 What advice could the analyst give to parents of a hyperactive child about the two soft drinks, based on this chromatogram?

7 What further investigations should the analyst carry out to confirm the advice given?

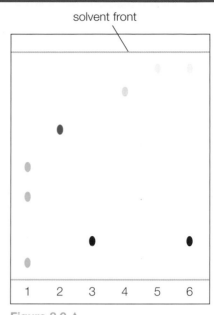

Figure 8.9 ▲
TLC plate showing the results of the analysis for two soft drinks and four dyes for reference: 1 quinoline yellow; 2 colour from soft drink A; 3 carmoisine; 4 sunset yellow; 5 tartrazine; 6 colour from soft drink B.

8.3 Gas chromatography

Gas chromatography (GC) is a sensitive technique for analysing complex mixtures. The technique is used for compounds which vaporise on heating without decomposing. This type of chromatography not only separates the chemicals from a sample, but also gives a measure of how much of each is present.

In GC the mobile phase is a gas, such as helium, which carries the mixture of volatile chemicals through a long tube containing the stationary phase. The column is coiled inside an oven. Heating the column makes it possible to analyse any chemicals that turn to vapour at the temperature of the oven.

The analyst injects a small sample into the column where it enters the oven. Volatile solids are dissolved in a solvent before injection. The chemicals in the sample turn to gases and mix with the carrier gas. The gases then pass through the column.

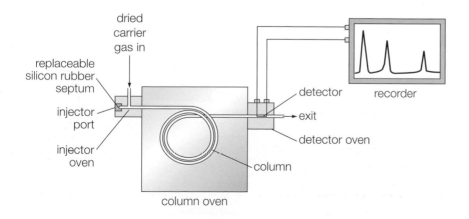

Figure 8.10 ◄
The main features of gas chromatography. The carrier gas takes the mixture of chemicals through the column where they separate. As the compounds leave the column they are detected and measured.

The components in the mixture separate as they pass through the column. After a time the chemicals emerge one by one. They pass into a detector, which sends a signal to a recorder as each compound appears. A series of peaks, one for each compound in the mixture, make up the chromatogram.

The position of a peak on a GC print-out is a record of how long it took for a particular compound to pass through the column. This is the retention time. The area underneath each peak gives an indication of the relative amounts of the compounds in the mixture. If the peaks are narrow it is good enough to measure the peak heights.

Figure 8.11 ▶
Print-out from a gas chromatography instrument.

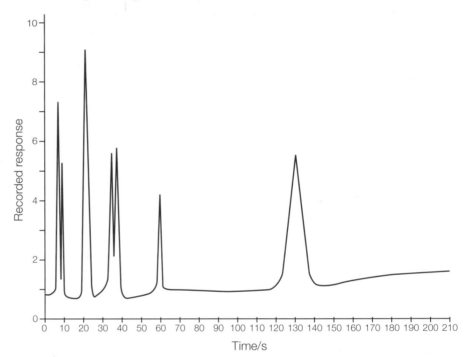

Test yourself

8 Suggest a reason for choosing helium as the carrier gas in gas chromatography.
9 Refer to Figure 8.11.
  a) How many chemicals were there in the mixture?
  b) What was the retention time of the least abundant chemical in the mixture?

Some GC instruments have capillary columns. These are 20–60 metres long with a very small internal diameter. Capillary columns are often made of silica with an outer coating of a polymer. The stationary phase is the inner surface of the column which adsorbs chemicals to a greater or lesser extent. The inner surface may be coated with a solid adsorbent or a thin film of a liquid.

Figure 8.12 ▶
A scientist changing the capillary column in the oven of a gas chromatography instrument. Capillary columns are very long, but they are so flexible that they can be wound into a tight coil.

Other GC columns are steel or glass tubes that are packed with a powder. The powder is an inert solid coated with a thin film of liquid. In these columns, the stationary phase is the liquid coating. Chemicals in the carrier gas separate in these columns because they differ in their solubility in the liquid of the stationary phase.

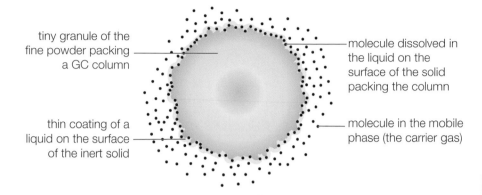

tiny granule of the fine powder packing a GC column

thin coating of a liquid on the surface of the inert solid

molecule dissolved in the liquid on the surface of the solid packing the column

molecule in the mobile phase (the carrier gas)

Figure 8.13 ▲
In some gas chromatography columns there is an equilibrium between molecules dissolved in a liquid coating on the surface of the stationary phase and molecules in the carrier gas. Chemicals separate because they differ in their relative solubility in the stationary liquid. When this type of column is used the technique is sometimes called gas–liquid chromatography (GLC).

Applications of GLC include:

- tracking down the source of oil pollution from the pattern of peaks, which acts like a fingerprint for any batch of oil
- measuring the level of alcohol in blood samples from drivers
- detecting pesticides in river water.

Test yourself

10 Why must the liquid for the stationary phase in gas–liquid chromatography have a high boiling point?
11 What are the implications of the fact that similar compounds may have very similar retention times in gas chromatography?
12 Explain why it is not possible to identify a previously unknown chemical by gas chromatography.

Activity

Forensic investigations of arson

Arsonists sometimes use flammable liquids such as petrol or paraffin to accelerate fires. Firefighters collect samples from burnt-out homes which forensic scientists can analyse in the search for clues as to how the fire started.

Suitable samples for analysis come from areas where furniture and fittings have not been completely destroyed. Useful samples include carpet underlays, soil from pot plants, bedding, clothing and material collected from underneath floor boards.

1 Suggest a reason why firefighters collect only partially burned materials for analysis.

2 Suggest a reason why soil from pot plants can provide good evidence that there have been flammable liquids present.

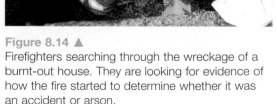

Figure 8.14 ▲
Firefighters searching through the wreckage of a burnt-out house. They are looking for evidence of how the fire started to determine whether it was an accident or arson.

Analysts use solvents to extract chemicals from the samples, and then investigate the solutions by gas chromatography. They compare the chromatograms with those from standard samples of common flammable substances.

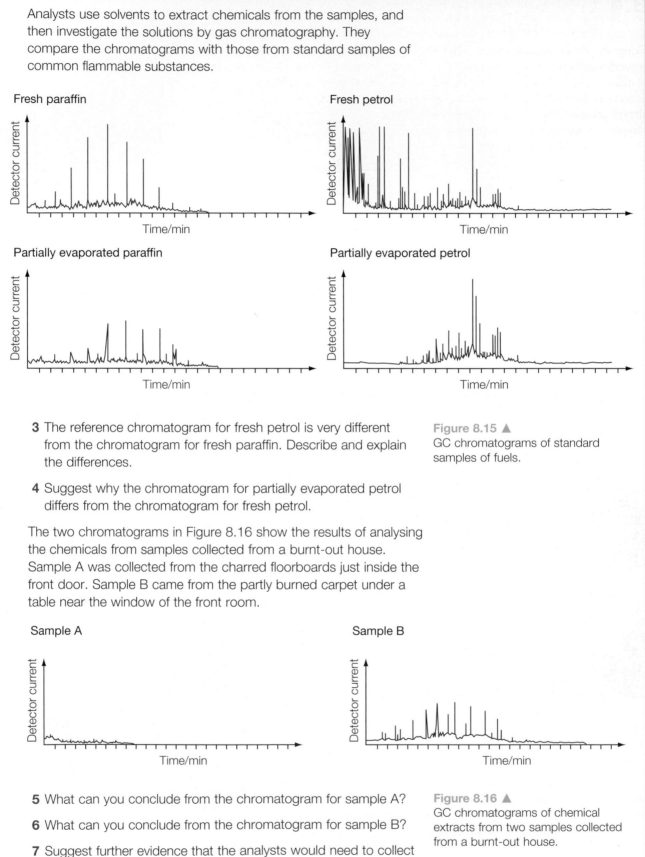

Figure 8.15 ▲
GC chromatograms of standard samples of fuels.

3 The reference chromatogram for fresh petrol is very different from the chromatogram for fresh paraffin. Describe and explain the differences.

4 Suggest why the chromatogram for partially evaporated petrol differs from the chromatogram for fresh petrol.

The two chromatograms in Figure 8.16 show the results of analysing the chemicals from samples collected from a burnt-out house. Sample A was collected from the charred floorboards just inside the front door. Sample B came from the partly burned carpet under a table near the window of the front room.

5 What can you conclude from the chromatogram for sample A?

6 What can you conclude from the chromatogram for sample B?

7 Suggest further evidence that the analysts would need to collect before deciding whether the house fire was an accident or the result of arson.

Figure 8.16 ▲
GC chromatograms of chemical extracts from two samples collected from a burnt-out house.

8.4 Chromatography combined with mass spectrometry

Coupling gas chromatography (GC) with mass spectrometry (MS) gives a very powerful method for separating, identifying and measuring complex mixtures of chemicals. The combined technique (GC–MS) is widely used in drug detection, investigation of fires and environmental monitoring, as well as in airport security. Some space probes carry tiny GC–MS systems for analysing samples collected in space or on the surface of planets such as Mars.

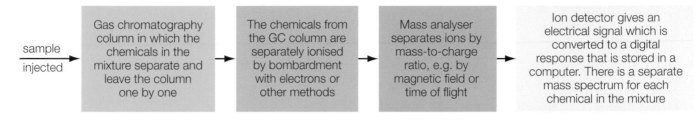

| sample injected → | Gas chromatography column in which the chemicals in the mixture separate and leave the column one by one | → | The chemicals from the GC column are separately ionised by bombardment with electrons or other methods | → | Mass analyser separates ions by mass-to-charge ratio, e.g. by magnetic field or time of flight | → | Ion detector gives an electrical signal which is converted to a digital response that is stored in a computer. There is a separate mass spectrum for each chemical in the mixture |

GC–MS overcomes some of the limitations of gas chromatography. Similar compounds often have similar retention times in GC which means that they cannot be identified by chromatography alone, even if the conditions are carefully standardised. Also, GC alone cannot identify any novel chemicals because there are no standards that can be used to determine retention times under given conditions.

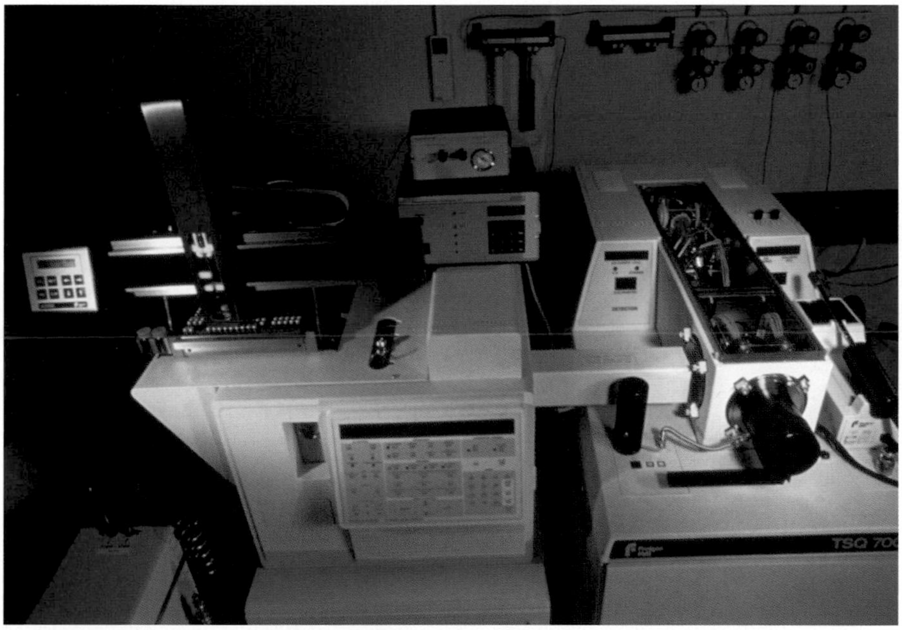

Figure 8.17 ▲
Schematic diagram showing the key features of a GC–MS system.

Figure 8.18 ▲
A gas chromatography machine (left) connected to a mass spectrometer (right) in a forensic laboratory. This equipment is sensitive enough to detect minute quantities of illegal drugs in the hair of a suspect – weeks after any drugs were taken.

GC–MS produces a mass spectrum for each of the chemicals separated on the GC column. These spectra can be used like fingerprints to identify the compounds because every chemical has a unique mass spectrum.

A computer connected to a GC–MS system stores all the data. The computer can be linked to a library of spectra of known compounds. The computer compares the mass spectrum of each chemical in a mixture to mass spectra in the library. It automatically reports a list of likely identifications along with the probability that the matches are correct.

Solving a pollution problem with GC–MS

With complex mixtures, a computer can help an analyst look for a 'needle in a haystack'. Figure 18.19 shows the chromatogram from an investigation of the air in a home where the family was feeling very sick. During the analysis by GC–MS, the computer stored 700 mass spectra as the mixture of chemicals emerged from the chromatography column.

Figure 8.19 ▼
Gas chromatogram for chemicals sampled from the air in a house. The numbers 1–700 on the time axis indicate the points at which mass spectra were recorded and stored. Underneath these numbers are the retention times.

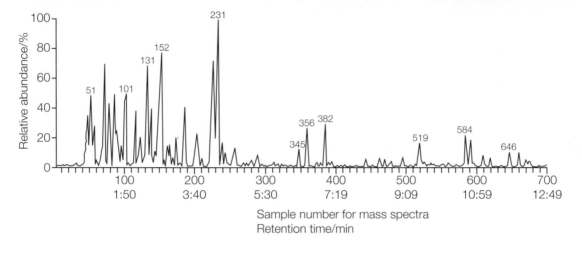

The analysts suspected that the chemicals might have come from petrol, so they asked the computer to plot a chromatogram showing only those chemicals producing a peak with mass/charge ratio of 91 in their spectra. The result is shown in Figure 18.20, which indicates that methylbenzene, ethylbenzene and three dimethylbenzenes were present in the mixture. These are all chemicals that are distinctive for the mixture of hydrocarbons found in petrol. With this evidence the investigators carried out further searches and tracked down the source of the petrol vapour.

Figure 8.20 ▼
GC–MS print out for the same sample as in Figure 18.19 – but showing only the chemicals with a prominent peak with a mass/charge ratio of 91 in their mass spectra.

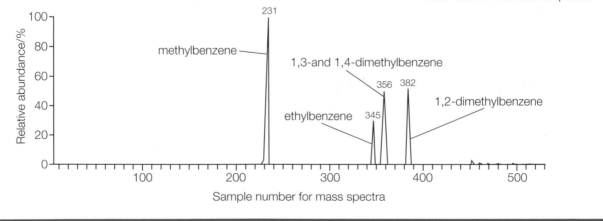

1 Why, in a mass spectrometer, does each chemical:

   a) have to be ionised

   b) pass through a region with electric and/or magnetic fields

   c) produce a spectrum with several peaks?

2 Suggest the identity of the ion fragment with a mass/charge ratio of 91 in the mass spectra of methylbenzene and related compounds.

3 How does the computer identify a chemical with a mass spectrum recorded at a particular retention time?

4 Suggest two reasons why forensic scientists find GC–MS particularly valuable.

5 HPLC can also be combined with MS. Give an example of a sample that could be analysed by HPLC–MS but not by GC–MS. Explain your choice.

REVIEW QUESTIONS

1 Draw up a table to summarise and compare three methods of chromatography, using an enlarged version of Table 8.1.   (12)

Type of chromatography	Method of separation: adsorption or relative solubility	Example of an application	Advantages	Limitations
TLC				
HPLC				
GC				

Table 8.1 ▲

2 Figure 8.21 shows the results of paper chromatography to separate amino acids. The solvent was a mixture of butan-1-ol, ethanoic acid and water.

   a) Amino acids are colourless. Suggest a method that could be used to show up the spots on the chromatogram.   (1)

   b) Why is it important to specify the type of chromatography and the solvent used?   (1)

   c) Identify the three amino acids with the help of Table 8.2.   (2)

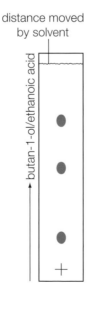

distance moved by solvent

butan-1-ol/ethanoic acid

Figure 8.21 ▶

Amino acid	R_f
alanine	0.38
arginine	0.16
glycine	0.26
leucine	0.73
tyrosine	0.50
valine	0.60

Table 8.2 ▲
R_f values for paper chromatography using a solvent which is a mixture of butan-1-ol, ethanoic acid and water.

3 Gas chromatography can be used to analyse the
chemicals formed during the production of beer. Figure
8.22 shows a GC chromatogram for a sample taken
during beer-making. The instrument was fitted with a
capillary column using a solid stationary phase. Table
8.3 gives the retention times for several relevant
compounds.

a) Suggest a reason for the trend in the retention times
for the four primary alcohols. (2)

b) Suggest a reason why 2-methylpropan-1-ol has a
shorter retention time than butan-2-ol. (2)

c) i) Use Figure 8.22 and Table 8.3 to identify the
chemicals in the beer sample. (3)

ii) How certain can you be of the answers you have
given in part a)? Which peaks were hard to
identify and why? (2)

d) The mixture was analysed by GC–MS. Figure 8.23
shows the mass spectrum of the fifth peak to emerge
from the GC column. Use this mass spectrum to
decide whether this peak is butan-2-ol or propanal.
Explain how you decide on your answer. (3)

e) How does the chemical with the shortest retention
time form during brewing? (2)

Compound	Retention time/min
methanol	19.5
ethanol	20.5
propan-1-ol	20.9
propan-2-ol	22.5
2-methylpropan-1-ol	22.7
butan-2-ol	24.6
ethanal	20.2
propanal	24.5
butanal	25.5
propanone	23.8
ethanoic acid	24.2
butanoic acid	26.2

Table 8.3 ▲

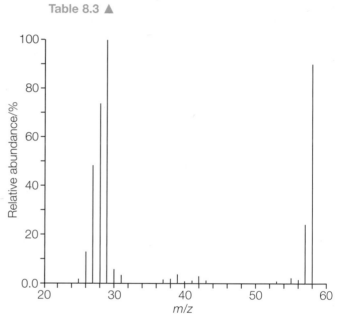

Figure 8.23 ▲

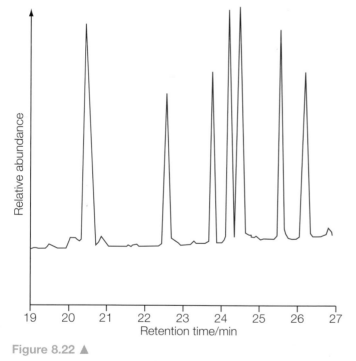

Figure 8.22 ▲

9 Spectroscopy

In a modern laboratory, organic analysis is based on a range of automated and instrumental techniques including nuclear magnetic resonance spectroscopy, mass spectrometry and infrared spectroscopy.

Figure 9.1 ◄
Using a mass spectrometer in a forensic laboratory to detect drugs in urine samples.

Spectroscopy is a term which covers a range of practical techniques for studying the composition, structure and bonding of compounds. Spectroscopic techniques are now the essential 'eyes' of chemistry.

9.1 Nuclear magnetic resonance spectroscopy

Nuclear magnetic resonance spectroscopy (NMR) is a powerful analytical technique for finding the structures of carbon compounds. The technique is used to identify unknown compounds, to check for impurities and to study the shapes of molecules.

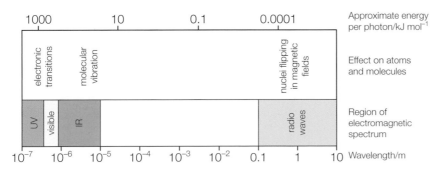

Figure 9.2 ◄
The uses of the electromagnetic spectrum in spectroscopy.

This type of spectroscopy studies the behaviour of the nuclei of atoms in magnetic fields. It is limited to those nuclei that behave like tiny magnets because they have a property called spin – in common organic compounds, the only nuclei to do this are those of carbon-13 atoms, ^{13}C, and of hydrogen atoms, ^1H. The nuclei of the much commoner carbon-12, oxygen-16 and nitrogen-14 atoms do not show up in NMR spectra.

Figure 9.3 ▶
Diagram of an NMR spectrometer showing the key features of the technique.

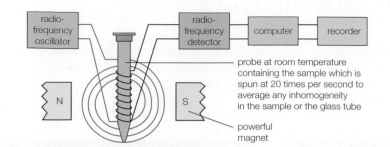

When placed in a very strong magnetic field, the magnetic nuclei can line up either in the same direction as or in the opposite direction to an external magnetic field. There is a small energy jump when the nuclei flip from one alignment to the other. The size of the energy jump corresponds to the energies of quanta of radiowaves.

The tube with the sample is supported in a strong magnetic field. The operator turns on a source of radiation at radio frequencies. The radio-frequency detector records the intensity of the signal from the sample as the oscillator emits pulses of radiation across a range of wavelengths.

The sample is dissolved in a solvent. Also in the solution is some tetramethylsilane (TMS), which is a standard reference compound that produces a single, sharp absorption peak well away from the peaks produced by samples for analysis.

Each peak corresponds to one or more magnetic atoms in a particular chemical environment. Nuclei in different parts of a molecule experience slightly different magnetic fields in an NMR machine. This is because they are shielded to a greater or lesser extent from the field applied by the spectrometer by the tiny magnetic fields associated with the electrons of neighbouring bonds and atoms.

The recorder prints out a spectrum that has been analysed by computer to show peaks wherever the sample absorbs radiation strongly. The zero on the scale is fixed by the absorption of magnetic atoms in the reference chemical. The distances of the sample peaks from this zero are called their chemical shifts (δ).

Carbon-13 NMR

Carbon-13 NMR relies on the magnetic properties of the carbon-13 isotope. Carbon-13 makes up only about 1% of all naturally occurring carbon atoms but this is enough for a signal to be detected in an NMR machine.

Figure 9.4 shows the carbon-13 NMR spectrum for ethanol. Spectra of this kind are available from the Spectral Database System (SDBS) for Organic Compounds at the National Institute of Materials and Chemical Research in Japan.

Figure 9.4 ▶
Carbon-13 NMR spectrum for ethanol dissolved in $CDCl_3$.

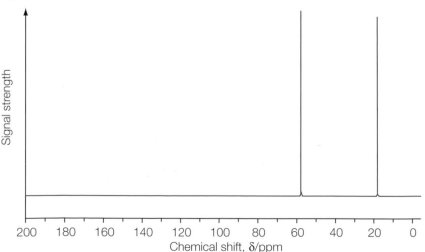

There are two peaks in the carbon-13 NMR spectrum for ethanol. This reflects the fact that there are two carbon atoms in an ethanol molecules and they are in different chemical environments. The carbon in the CH_3 group is attached to 3 hydrogen atoms and a carbon atom. The carbon in the CH_2 group is attached to 2 hydrogen atoms, a carbon atom and an oxygen atom.

Spectra of the type shown in Figure 9.4 are usually recorded with the sample in solution. The chosen solvent is commonly $CDCl_3$. Molecules of $CDCl_3$ contain one carbon atom and they produce a line in carbon-13 spectra which is easy to recognise. This line is usually removed from the spectra in databases such as SDBS to avoid any confusion. The line produced by the solvent is not shown in any of the carbon-13 spectra in this book.

The chemical shifts are measured relative to the TMS peak at the zero mark – but this peak is also generally removed from the spectra in databases for clarity.

Figure 9.5 illustrates the principles of carbon-13 NMR in a more complex example. Here too, every carbon atom, or group of carbon atoms, in a chemically distinct environment gives a separate peak in the NMR spectrum.

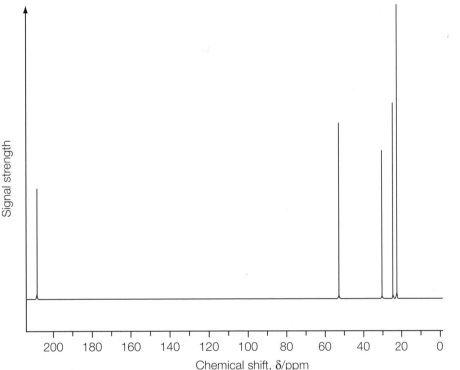

Figure 9.5 ◄
Carbon-13 NMR spectrum for 4-methylpentan-2-one dissolved in $CDCl_3$.

There are six carbon atoms in 4-methylpentan-2-one but only five peaks in the carbon-13 NMR spectrum. The reason is shown in Figure 9.6. The carbon atoms of two of the methyl groups (E) in the molecule are in exactly the same environment, so they give rise to only one peak. The other four carbon atoms, including the carbon atom in the third methyl group (A), are in slightly different environments and give rise to separate peaks.

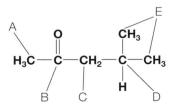

Figure 9.6 ◄
The structure of 4-methylpentan-2-one labelled to show the five different environments for the six carbon atoms. The two carbon atoms labelled E are in exactly the same chemical environment.

Generally, carbon atoms attached to electronegative atoms, such as oxygen, show the largest chemical shifts. Chemists have found that it is possible to draw up tables to show the likely range of values for the chemical shifts of carbon-13 atoms in different environments. For example, carbon-13 atoms in alkanes typically give chemical shifts in the range 10–35 ppm while carbon atoms in the carbonyl groups of aldehydes and ketones give chemical shifts in the range 190–200 ppm.

> **Note**
>
> You are only expected to interpret carbon-13 NMR spectra in which each chemical environment for carbon atoms is represented by a single peak. Also note that you cannot draw any conclusions by looking at the size of the peaks in these spectra. Carbon-13 NMR differs from proton NMR in these two ways.

www
Data

Test yourself

4 Predict the number of peaks in the carbon-13 NMR spectrum of:
  a) pentane
  b) propyl ethanoate
  c) pentanal.
5 Predict the number of peaks in the carbon-13 NMR spectrum for
  a) benzene
  b) methylbenzene.
6 Explain how you could distinguish between propanal and propanone by inspection of the carbon-13 NMR spectra of the two compounds.
7 Refer to the data sheet showing chemical shifts for carbon-13 NMR. To what extent does the data show that the presence of electronegative atoms increases the chemical shift values?
8 Use the data sheet showing chemical shift values to suggest which carbon atoms give rise to which peaks in the spectrum of:
  a) ethanol (Figure 9.4)
  b) 4-methylpentan-2-one (Figure 9.5).

Proton NMR

Proton NMR relies on the magnetic properties of the hydrogen-1 isotope. As with carbon-13 NMR, the number of main peaks in the spectrum shows how many different chemical environments there are for hydrogen atoms. Also, the values for the chemical shifts are a useful indication of the types of chemical environment for the hydrogen atoms corresponding to each peak.

Even more information can be deduced from a proton NMR spectrum because it is possible to work out the number of hydrogen atoms in each environment. In a proton NMR spectrum, the area under a peak is proportional to the number of nuclei.

An NMR instrument is set up to integrate the curve and work out the ratios. Sometimes the results of the calculation are shown by an integration trace such as the blue line shown in the spectrum for methyl ethanoate in Figure 9.8 – this shows the proton NMR spectrum for methyl ethanoate. This is a low-resolution spectrum which shows the main peaks but no fine detail.

Figure 9.7 ▲
A researcher adding a sample to a nuclear magnetic resonance spectrometer.

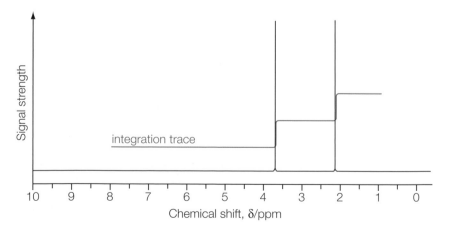

Figure 9.8 ▲
Proton NMR spectrum of methyl ethanoate in CDCl$_3$.

Alternatively, the instrument's computer prints a number below each peak that is a measure of the relative area under the curve – as shown for the spectrum in Figure 9.9.

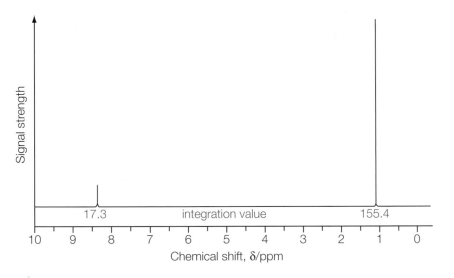

Figure 9.9 ◄
Proton NMR spectrum of a compound $C_5H_{10}O$ in $CDCl_3$.

> **Definition**
>
> **Integration** is a mathematical technique that works out the area under a curve. The ratios of the results of integrating the peaks in a proton NMR spectrum show the relative numbers of hydrogen atoms in each chemical environment.

Proton NMR spectra, like carbon-13 NMR spectra, are usually recorded with the sample in solution. It is important that the solvent does not contain hydrogen atoms that would give peaks with chemical shifts similar to those in the sample. One option is to use a solvent that contains no hydrogen atoms, such as tetrachloromethane, CCl_4. The other is to use a solvent in which atoms of the hydrogen-1 isotope have been replaced by deuterium atoms – a compound that is often used is $CDCl_3$. Deuterium atoms produce peaks in regions of the spectrum well away from the chemical shifts for proton NMR.

The reference chemical for proton NMR is again tetramethylsilane (TMS). There are twelve hydrogen atoms in a molecule of TMS but they all have the same chemical environment. TMS provides a single strong peak which marks the zero on the scale of chemical shifts

Test yourself

9 NMR based on hydrogen nuclei is sometimes called ¹H-NMR, and sometimes proton NMR. Show that these are equivalent names.

10 Refer to the proton NMR spectrum in Figure 9.8 and the data sheet of chemical shifts from the Dynamic Learning Student website.
   a) Explain why there are two peaks in the spectrum.
   b) Use the chemical shift values to decide which hydrogen atoms give rise to each peak.
   c) Show that the integration trace is as you would expect for methyl ethanoate.

11 Refer to the proton NMR spectrum in Figure 9.9 and the data sheet of chemical shifts.
   a) How many different chemical environments are there for hydrogen atoms in $C_5H_{10}O$?
   b) Use the integration values under each peak to work out the ratios of hydrogen atoms in each environment.
   c) Use your answers to parts **a)** and **b)** and chemical shift values to suggest a structure for this compound.
   d) Describe two chemical tests that could be used to confirm the presence of the main functional group in this molecule. State what you would do and what you would expect to observe.

12 With the help of the data sheet of chemical shifts, sketch the low-resolution NMR spectrum you would expect for:
   a) butanone
   b) 2-methylpropan-2-ol.

www
Data

Spectroscopy

www
Data

Test yourself

13 Use the Data sheet: 'NMR chemical shifts' from the Dynamic Learning Student website to suggest a structure for the aromatic hydrocarbon with the proton NMR spectrum shown in Figure 9.10.

14 Sketch the high-resolution NMR spectrum you would expect to observe with:
   a) propane
   b) ethoxyethane.

Coupling

At high resolution, it is possible to produce proton NMR spectra with more detail that provide even more information about molecular structures. The spins of protons connected to neighbouring carbon atoms interact with each other. Chemists call this interaction spin–spin coupling and they find that the effect is to split the peaks into a number of lines.

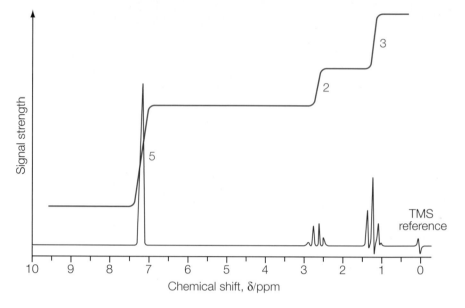

Figure 9.10 ▲
High-resolution proton NMR spectrum for an aromatic hydrocarbon. Note the extra peaks compared with the low-resolution spectrum.

In simple examples, the '$n + 1$' rule makes it possible to work out the numbers of coupled protons. A peak from protons bonded to an atom that is next to an atom with two protons splits into three lines. A peak from protons bonded to an atom which is next to an atom with three protons splits into four lines.

number of equivalent protons causing splitting	splitting pattern and relative intensity of the peaks
1	1 1
2	1 2 1
3	1 3 3 1
4	1 4 6 4 1

Figure 9.11 ▲
Pascal's triangle predicts the pattern of peaks and the relative peak heights.

Labile protons

Hydrogen bonding affects the properties of compounds that have molecules containing hydrogen atoms attached to highly electronegative atoms such as oxygen or nitrogen. These molecules can exchange protons rapidly as they move from one electronegative atom to another. Chemists describe these protons as labile.

Labile protons do not couple with protons linked to neighbouring atoms. This means that the NMR peak for a proton in an −OH group appears as a single peak in a high-resolution spectrum.

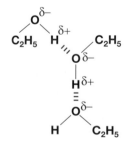

Figure 9.12 ▲
Hydrogen bonding in ethanol.

Definition

An atom (or compound) is **labile** if it quickly and easily moves (or reacts).

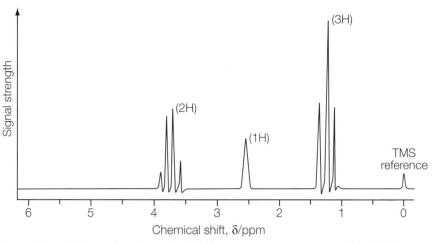

Figure 9.13 ◄
The high-resolution NMR spectrum of ethanol. Note that there is no coupling between the proton in the –OH group and the protons in the next-door –CH_2 group.

A useful technique for detecting labile protons is to measure the NMR spectrum in the presence of deuterium oxide (heavy water), D_2O. Deuterium nuclei can exchange rapidly with labile protons. Deuterium nuclei do not show up in the proton NMR region of the spectrum and so the peaks of any labile protons disappear.

Chemical shift	Number of lines	Integration ratio
1.2	triplet	3
2.4	quartet	2
11.7	singlet	1

Table 9.1 ▲

Test yourself

15 Write an equation to show the reversible exchange of deuterium and hydrogen nuclei between ethanol and deuterium oxide.
16 Account for the splitting pattern shown by the peaks in the proton NMR spectrum of ethanol in Figure 9.13.
17 Table 9.1 shows the main features of the high-resolution NMR spectrum of a compound containing carbon, hydrogen and oxygen. The peak with a chemical shift of 11.7 disappears in the presence of D_2O. Deduce the structure of the compound.

NMR in medicine

In medicine, magnetic resonance imaging (MRI) uses NMR to map hydrogen nuclei in the human body, especially in water and lipids. A computer translates the information from a body scan into 3D images of the soft tissue and internal organs, which are normally transparent to X-rays.

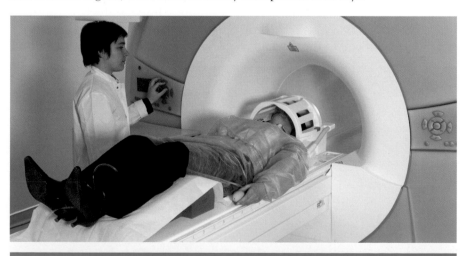

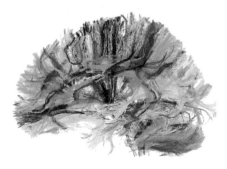

Figure 9.14 ◄
Researcher preparing a test subject for scanning in an advanced magnetic resonance imaging machine.

Figure 9.15 ▲
A coloured 3D MRI scan of a normal human brain. The front of the brain is on the left. The coloured lines indicate the many neural pathways that exist in the brain.

Test yourself

18 Suggest a reason why doctors and radiographers refer to 'MRI scanning' rather than to 'NMR imaging' even though the technologies used in medicine and chemical research are essentially the same.

9.2 Combined techniques

Analytical chemists use a combination of techniques to identify organic compounds and determine their structures.

- Mass spectrometry gives the relative molecular mass of a compound and can suggest a likely structure for a compound.
- Infrared spectroscopy shows the presence of particular functional groups by detecting their characteristic vibration frequencies.
- Nuclear magnetic resonance techniques help to detect carbon atoms and groups with hydrogen atoms in particular environments in molecules.

Mass spectrometry

Mass spectrometry is used to determine the relative molecular masses and molecular structures of organic compounds. In this way it can be used to identify unknown compounds.

The combination of gas–liquid chromatography with mass spectrometry is of great importance in modern chemical analysis (see Section 8.4). First, gas chromatography separates the chemicals in an unknown mixture, such as a sample of polluted water; then mass spectrometry detects and identifies the components.

All mass spectrometers have the components shown in Figure 9.16.

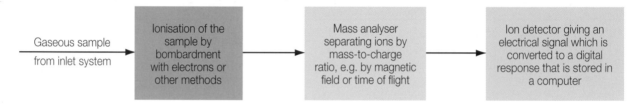

Figure 9.16 ▲
Schematic diagram to show the key features of a mass spectrometer.

There are five main types of mass spectrometer. They differ in the method used to separate ions with different mass-to-charge ratios. One type uses an electric field to accelerate ions into a magnetic field which then deflects the ions onto the detector. A second type accelerates the ions and then separates them by their flight time through a field-free region. A third type, the so-called transmission quadrupole instrument, is now much the most common because it is very reliable, compact and easy-to-use. It varies the fields in the instrument in a subtle way to allow all ions with a particular mass-to-charge ratio to pass through to the detector at the same time.

Figure 9.17 ▶
The smaller instrument on the right is a mass spectrometer being used to analyse samples from the gas chromatography instrument on the left.

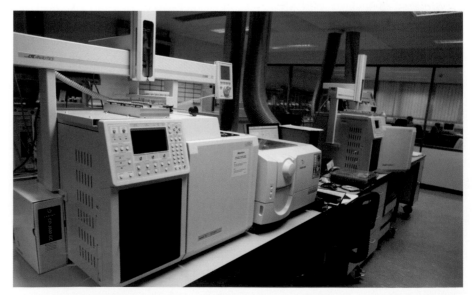

Inside a mass spectrometer there is a high vacuum. This allows ionised atoms and molecules from the chemical being tested to be studied without interference from atoms and molecules in the air.

In a mass spectrometer, a beam of high-energy electrons bombards the molecules of the sample. This turns them into ions by knocking out one or more electrons.

Bombarding molecules with high-energy electrons not only ionises them but usually splits them into fragments. As a result, the mass spectrum consists of a 'fragmentation pattern'.

Molecules break up more readily at weak bonds or at bonds which give rise to stable fragments. The highest peaks correspond to positive ions which are relatively more stable, such as tertiary carbocations or ions such as RCO$^+$ (the acylium ion) or the fragment $C_6H_5^+$ from aromatic compounds.

After ionisation and fragmentation, the charged species are separated to produce the mass spectrum, which distinguishes the fragments on the basis of their mass-to-charge ratios. When analysing molecular compounds, the peak of the ion with the highest mass is usually the whole molecule ionised. So the mass of this 'parent ion', M$^+$, is the relative molecular mass of the compound.

Chemists study mass spectra with these ideas in mind and as a result can gain insight into the structure of new molecules. They identify the fragments from their masses and then piece together likely structures with the help of evidence from other methods of analysis such as infrared spectroscopy and NMR spectroscopy.

Chemists have also built up a very large database of mass spectra of known compounds for use in analysis. Chemists regard the spectra in a database as a set of 'fingerprints' for identifying chemicals. The computer of a mass spectrometer is programmed to search the database to find a good match between the spectrum of a compound being analysed and a spectrum in the database.

Analysing mass spectra

When analysing molecular compounds, the peak of the ion with the highest mass is usually the whole molecule ionised. So the mass of this parent ion is the relative molecular mass of the compound.

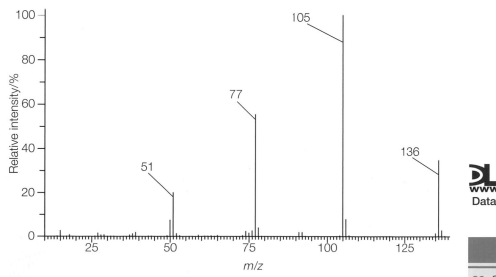

Figure 9.18 ▲
Mass spectrum of methyl benzenecarboxylate (methyl benzoate). The pattern of fragments is characteristic of this compound.

> **Definition**
>
> A **carbocation** is an unstable intermediate in which a carbon atom carries a positive charge. A carbocation with the charge on a tertiary carbon atom is more stable than one with the charge on a secondary carbon atom, which in turn is more stable than one with the charge on a primary carbon atom.

> **Test yourself**
>
> 19 An organic molecule, M, can be represented as a combination of two parts: m_1 and m_2. Draw a diagram to represent the ionisation and then fragmentation of the molecule, and explain why only one of the two fragments shows up in the mass spectrum.

Data

> **Test yourself**
>
> 20 Suggest the identity of the peaks labelled in the mass spectrum shown in Figure 9.18.

The presence of isotopes shows up in spectra of organic compounds that contain chlorine or bromine atoms. Chlorine has two isotopes, ^{35}C and ^{37}C. Chlorine-35 is three times more abundant than chlorine-37. If a molecule contains one chlorine atom, the molecular ion shows as two peaks separated by 2 mass units. The peak with the lower value of m/z is three times higher than the peak with the higher value.

Bromine consists largely of two isotopes, ^{79}Br and ^{81}Br, which are roughly equally abundant. If a molecule contains one bromine atom, the molecular ion shows up as two peaks separated by 2 mass units with roughly equal intensity.

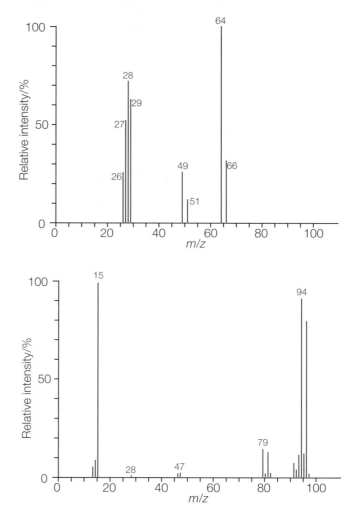

Figure 9.19 ▲
Mass spectra of two compounds containing halogen atoms.

Data

Test yourself

21 Account for these facts about the mass spectrum of dichloroethene:
    a) it includes three peaks at m/z values of 96, 98 and 100 with intensities in the ratio 9 : 6 : 1
    b) it includes two peaks at m/z values 61 and 63 with intensities in the ratio of 3 : 1.

22 One of the mass spectra in Figure 9.19 is bromomethane and the other is chloroethane. Match the spectra to the compounds, and identify as many fragments in the spectra as you can.

Test yourself

23 Figure 9.20 shows the mass spectra of two isomers, benzenecarboxylic acid (benzoic acid) and 3-hydroxybenzenecarbaldehyde (3-hydroxybenzaldehyde).
  a) Match the compounds to the spectra and give your reasons.
  b) Identify the peaks at 77 and 105 in the top spectrum.
  c) Identify the peaks at 39 and 93 in the bottom spectrum.

DL
www
Data

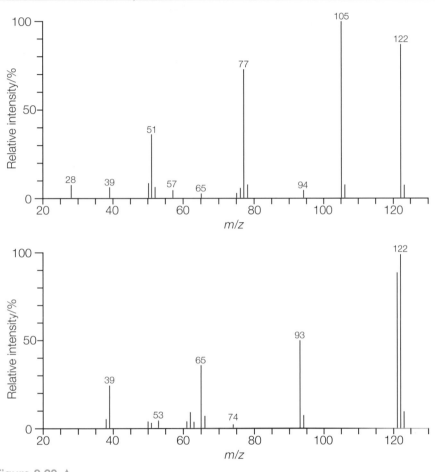

Figure 9.20 ▲
Two mass spectra.

Infrared spectroscopy

Most compounds absorb infrared (IR) radiation. The wavelengths of the radiation they absorb correspond to the natural frequencies at which vibrating bonds in the molecules bend and stretch. However, it is only molecules that change their polarity as they vibrate which interact with IR.

Figure 9.21 ◄
The essential features of a modern single-beam IR spectrometer.

Spectroscopists have found that it is possible to correlate absorptions in the region 4000–1500 cm⁻¹ with the stretching or bending vibrations of particular bonds. As a result, an infrared spectrum gives valuable clues to the presence of functional groups in an organic molecule.

Definition

An **absorption spectrum** is a plot showing how strongly a sample absorbs radiation over a range of frequencies. Absorption spectra from infrared spectroscopy give chemists valuable information about the composition and structure of chemicals.

Spectroscopy

The important correlations between different bonds and observed absorptions are shown in Figure 9.22. Hydrogen bonding broadens the absorption peaks of –OH groups in alcohols, and even more so in carboxylic acids.

Wavenumber ranges

4000 cm⁻¹	2500 cm⁻¹	1900 cm⁻¹	1500 cm⁻¹	650 cm⁻¹

C—H **O—H** **N—H** single bond stretching vibrations	**C≡C** **C≡N** triple bond stretching vibrations	**C=C** **C=O** double bond stretching vibrations	fingerprint region

Molecules with several atoms can vibrate in many ways because the vibrations of one bond affect others close to it. The complex pattern of vibrations can be used as a 'fingerprint' to be matched against the recorded IR spectrum in a database.

Note

Most organic molecules contain C–H bonds. As a result, most organic compounds have a peak at around 3000 cm⁻¹ in their IR spectrum

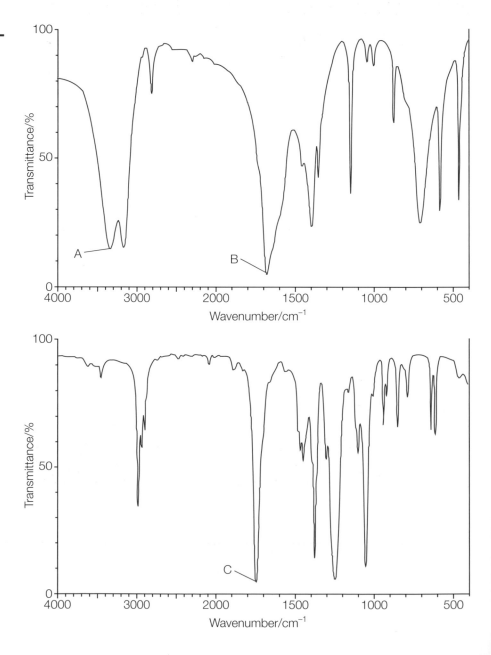

Figure 9.23 ▶
Two IR spectra.

Test yourself

24 Figure 9.23 shows the infrared spectra of ethyl ethanoate and ethanamide. Use the Data sheet: 'Characteristic IR absorptions in organic molecules' from the Dynamic Learning Student website to work out:
   a) which bonds give rise to the peaks marked with letters
   b) which spectrum belongs to which compound.

25 Compound P is a liquid which does not mix with water. Its molecular formula is C_7H_6O and it has an infrared spectrum with strong sharp peaks at $2800\,cm^{-1}$, $2720\,cm^{-1}$ and $1700\,cm^{-1}$ with a weaker absorption peak between 3000 and $3100\,cm^{-1}$. Oxidation of P gives a white crystalline solid Q with a strong broad IR absorption band in the region 2500–$3300\,cm^{-1}$ and another strong absorption at 1680–$1750\,cm^{-1}$.
   a) Suggest possible structures for P and Q.
   b) What chemical tests could you use to check on your suggestions?

DL
www
Data

Activity

Analysing a perfume chemical

Jasmine blossom is a source of chemicals used in perfumes. Analysis of an extract from the blossom by gas chromatography shows that it can contain over 200 compounds. Two of the compounds in the mixture are mainly responsible for the smell of the blossom. One of these chemicals is jasmone, which has the empirical formula $C_{11}H_{16}O$.

The structure of jasmone has been studied by mass spectrometry, IR spectroscopy and NMR with the results shown in Figures 9.24 to 9.26.

Figure 9.24 ▲
A harvester gathering jasmine flowers for the French perfume industry.

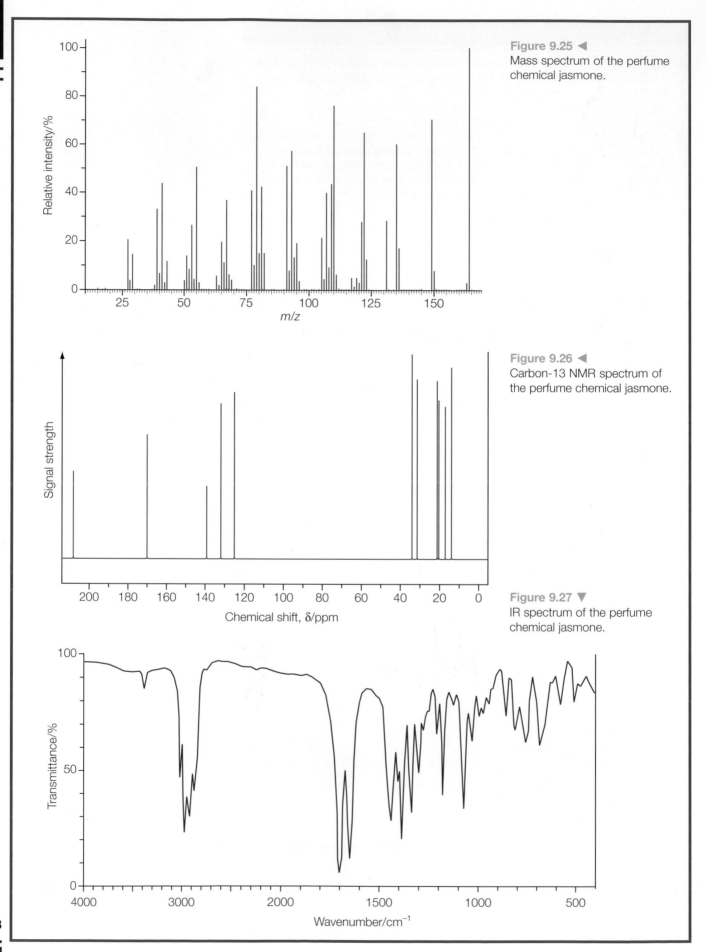

Figure 9.25 ◄
Mass spectrum of the perfume chemical jasmone.

Figure 9.26 ◄
Carbon-13 NMR spectrum of the perfume chemical jasmone.

Figure 9.27 ▼
IR spectrum of the perfume chemical jasmone.

1 Why is gas chromatography a suitable technique for separating the compounds in natural perfume chemicals?

2 **a)** Use the mass spectrum of jasmone to determine its relative molecular mass.

   b) What is the molecular formula of jasmone?

   c) How many double bonds and/or rings are there in the molecule?

3 Refer to the carbon-13 NMR spectrum in Figure 9.26.

   a) How many different environments for carbon atoms are there in the molecule?

   b) Use the data sheet of NMR chemical shifts on the Dynamic Learning Student website to suggest which chemical environments for carbon are in the molecule.
   Data

   c) What can you conclude about the structure of the molecule from the spectrum?

4 Refer to the IR spectrum in Figure 9.27 and the data sheet of characteristic IR absorptions in organic molecules from the Dynamic Learning Student website. The peak at 1650 cm^{-1} indicates the presence of C=C. What other parts of your answers to question **3** are confirmed by the spectrum?
   Data

5 Suggest a possible structure for jasmone that is consistent both with the information from the spectra and with the fact that the full name of the compound is *cis*-jasmone.

6 Describe what you would expect to observe if you tested a sample of *cis*-jasmone with:

   a) a solution of bromine in an organic solvent

   b) Tollens' reagent

   c) 2,4-dinitrophenylhydrazine reagent.

REVIEW QUESTIONS

1 Predict the number of peaks you would expect in the carbon-13 NMR spectra of each of the four isomeric alcohols with the molecular formula $C_4H_{10}O$. **(4)**

2 Two isomeric ketones with the molecular formula $C_5H_{10}O$ have the mass spectra shown below.

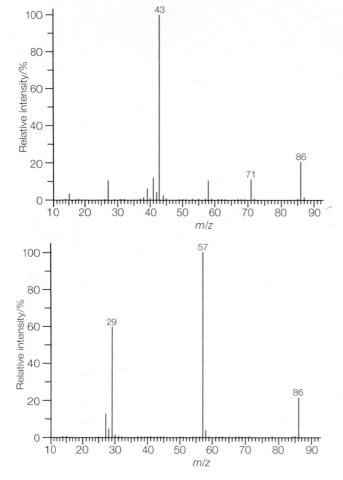

3 Identify the compound containing only carbon, hydrogen and oxygen that gives rise to the mass, NMR and IR spectra below. Draw the displayed formula of the compound and name it. Give your reasoning and show how you can account for the key features in the three spectra. **(10)**

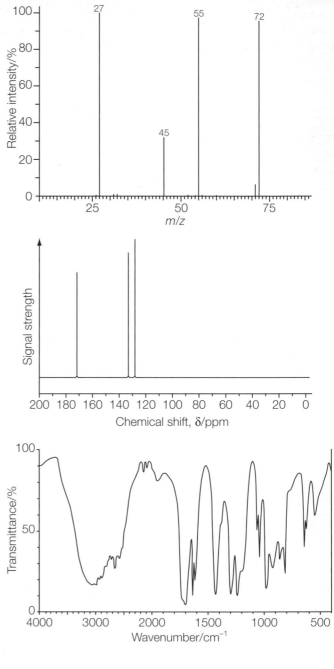

a) Draw the skeletal formula of the two ketones and name them. **(2)**

b) Why do both spectra have peaks at m/z values of 86? (2)

c) i) Suggest possible identities for the four fragments in the two spectra with m/z values of 29, 43, 57 and 71. **(4)**

   ii) Hence show which spectrum belongs to which compound. **(1)**

d) Use the data table showing chemical shifts from the Dynamic Learning Student website to predict the appearance of:

   i) the carbon-13 NMR spectrum of pentan-2-one **(3)**

   ii) the proton NMR spectrum of pentan-3-one. **(4)**

Data 1   Data 2   Data 3

Unit 5

Equilibria, energetics and elements

Reaction kinetics is the study of the rates of chemical reactions. Several factors influence the rate of chemical change including the concentration of the reactants, the surface area of solids, the temperature of the reaction mixture and the presence of a catalyst. Chemists have found that they can learn much more about reactions by studying these effects quantitatively. They can then set up models to simulate the data and make predictions about the impact of changing the conditions.

Chemists apply these models to drug design and to the formulation of medicines to make sure that patients receive treatments that are effective for some time without causing harmful side-effects. The models can also account for the damage arising from pollutants in the atmosphere and help chemists to suggest ways of reducing or preventing the problems.

Figure 10.1 ▲
Understanding the factors which determine the rate and direction of chemical change is essential to the design of productive, safe and profitable chemical processes.

10.1 Measuring reaction rates

Balanced chemical equations tell us nothing about how quickly the reactions occur. In order to get this information, chemists have to do experiments to measure the rates of reactions under various conditions.

The amounts of the reactants and products change during any chemical reaction – products form as reactants disappear. The rates at which these changes happen give a measure of the rate of reaction.

Chemists define rate of reaction as the change in concentration of a product, or a reactant, divided by the time taken for the change. Usually the rate is not constant but varies as the reaction proceeds. The first step in analysing the results of an experiment is to plot a concentration–time graph. The gradient (or slope) of the graph at any point gives a measure of the rate of reaction at that time.

Definition

The **rate of reaction** measures the rate of formation of a product or the rate of removal of a reactant:

$$\text{rate} = \frac{\text{change in measured property}}{\text{time}}$$

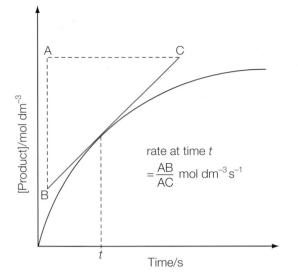

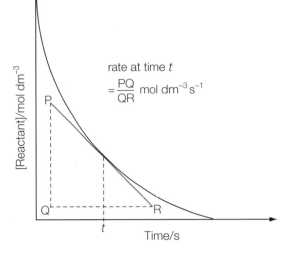

Figure 10.2 ▲
Concentration–time graph for the formation of a product. The rate of formation of product at time *t* is the gradient of the curve at that time.

Figure 10.3 ▲
Concentration–time graph for the disappearance of a reactant. The rate of loss of reactant at time *t* is the gradient of the curve at that time.

Test yourself

1 Each of the following factors can change the rate of a reaction. Give an example of a reaction to illustrate each one:
   a) the concentration of reactants in solution
   b) the pressure of gaseous reactants
   c) the surface area of a solid
   d) the temperature
   e) the presence of a catalyst.
2 How does the collision theory account for the effects of altering each of the factors a) to e) in question 1?
3 In a study of the hydrolysis of an ester, the concentration of the ester fell from $0.55\,mol\,dm^{-3}$ to $0.42\,mol\,dm^{-3}$ in 15 seconds. What was the average rate of reaction in that period?
4 The gaseous oxide N_2O_5 decomposes to NO_2 gas and oxygen.
   a) Write a balanced equation for the reaction.
   b) If the rate of disappearance of N_2O_5 is $3.5 \times 10^{-4}\,mol\,dm^{-3}\,s^{-1}$, what is the rate of formation of NO_2?

Definition

Writing the formula of a chemical in square brackets is the usual shorthand for **concentration in mol dm^{-3}**. For example, [A] represents the concentration of A in $mol\,dm^{-3}$.

Practical methods

Ideally, chemists look for methods for measuring reaction rates that do not interfere with the reaction mixture, as shown in Figures 10.4–10.6.

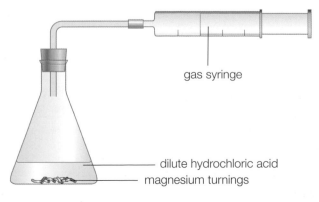

gas syringe

dilute hydrochloric acid
magnesium turnings

Figure 10.4 ◄
Following the course of a reaction over time by collecting and measuring the volume of a gas formed.

How fast?

Figure 10.5 ▶
Using a colorimeter to follow the formation of a coloured product or the removal of a coloured reactant.

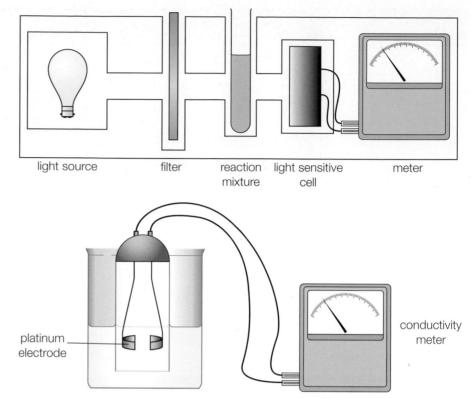

light source   filter   reaction mixture   light sensitive cell   meter

Figure 10.6 ▶
Using a conductivity cell and meter to measure the changes in electrical conductivity of the reaction mixture as the number or nature of the ions changes.

platinum electrode

conductivity meter

However, sometimes it is necessary to withdraw samples of the reaction mixture at regular intervals and analyse the concentration of a reactant or product by titration, as illustrated in Figure 10.7.

Figure 10.7 ▶
Following the course of a reaction that involves an acid by removing measured samples of the mixture at intervals, stopping the reaction by cooling in an ice bath, and then determining the concentration of the sample by titration. Further samples are taken at regular intervals.

DL
www
Practical guidance

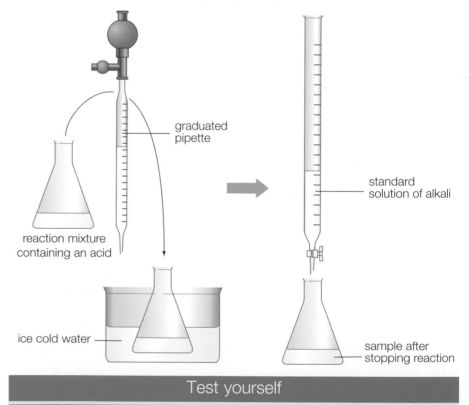

graduated pipette

reaction mixture containing an acid

standard solution of alkali

ice cold water

sample after stopping reaction

Test yourself

5 Suggest a suitable method for measuring the rate of each of these reactions:
  a) $Br_2(aq) + HCOOH(aq) \rightarrow 2HBr(aq) + CO_2(g)$
  b) $CH_3COOCH_3(l) + H_2O(l) \rightarrow CH_3COOH(aq) + CH_3OH(aq)$
  c) $C_4H_9Br(l) + H_2O(l) \rightarrow C_4H_9OH(l) + H^+(aq) + Br^-(aq)$

Activity

Investigating the effect of concentration on the rate of a reaction

Bromine oxidises methanoic acid in aqueous solution to carbon dioxide. The reaction is catalysed by hydrogen ions:

$Br_2(aq) + HCOOH(aq) \rightarrow 2Br^-(aq) + 2H^+(aq) + CO_2(g)$

The reaction can be followed using a colorimeter.

Table 10.1 shows some typical results. The concentration of methanoic acid was kept constant throughout the experiment by having it present in large excess.

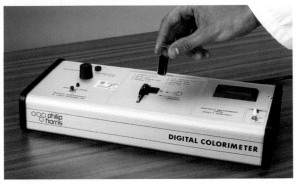

Figure 10.8 ▲
A colorimeter can be used to follow the changes in concentration of coloured chemicals during a reaction.

1 Explain why it is possible to follow the rate of this reaction using a colorimeter.

2 Suggest a suitable chemical to use as the catalyst for the reaction.

3 Explain the purpose of adding a large excess of methanoic acid.

4 Plot a graph of concentration against time using the results in Table 10.1.

5 Draw tangents to the graph and measure the gradient to obtain values for the rate of reaction at two points during the experiment. Use the values at 100 s and 500 s. (Remember when calculating the gradients that the bromine concentrations are 1000 times smaller than the numbers in the table.)

6 Table 10.2 shows values for the reaction rate obtained by drawing gradients at other times on the concentration–time graph. Plot a graph of rate against concentration using the two values you calculated in question **4** and the values in Table 10.2.

Time/s	Concentration of bromine/10^{-3} mol dm^{-3}	Rate of reaction from gradients to the concentration time graph/10^{-5} mol dm^{-3} s^{-1}
50	8.3	2.9
200	5.0	1.7
300	3.5	1.2
400	2.5	0.8

Table 10.2 ▲
Rate values obtained by measuring gradients of tangents to the concentration–time graph. Note that the bromine concentrations are multiplied by 100 000. The actual rate at 300 seconds, for example, was 1.2×10^{-5} mol dm^{-3} s^{-1}.

Time/s	Concentration of bromine/10^{-3} mol dm^{-3}
0	10.0
10	9.0
30	8.1
90	7.3
120	6.6
180	5.3
240	4.4
360	2.8
480	2.0
600	1.3

Table 10.1 ▲
Results of an experiment to investigate the rate of reaction of bromine with methanoic acid. Note that the bromine concentrations are multiplied by 1000. The actual bromine concentration at 90 seconds, for example, was 0.0073 mol dm^{-3}.

7 How does the bromine concentration change with time?

8 How does the rate of reaction change with time?

9 How does the rate of reaction depend on the bromine concentration?

125

10.2 Rate equations

Chemists have found that they can summarise the results of investigating the rate of a reaction in the form of a rate equation. A rate equation shows how changes in the concentrations of reactants affect the rate of a reaction.

Take the example of a general reaction in which x moles of A react with y moles of B to form products:

$$xA + yB \rightarrow products$$

The equation which describes how the rate varies with the concentrations of the reactants takes this form:

$$rate = k[A]^n[B]^m$$

where [A] and [B] represent the concentrations of the reactants in moles per cubic decimetre (litre).

The powers n and m are the reaction orders. The reaction above is order n with respect to A and order m with respect to B. The overall order is $(n + m)$.

The rate constant, k, is only constant at a particular temperature. The value of k varies with temperature (see Section 10.3). The units of the rate constant depend on the overall order of the reaction, as shown in Table 10.3.

> **Note**
>
> A rate equation cannot be deduced from a balanced equation – it has to be found by experiment. In this general example, the values of n and m in the rate equation may or may not be the same as the values of x and y in the balanced equation for the reaction.

Overall order	Units of the rate constant
zero	$mol\,dm^{-3}\,s^{-1}$
first	s^{-1}
second	$mol^{-1}\,dm^3\,s^{-1}$

Table 10.3 ▲

> **Definitions**
>
> In a **rate equation**, such as rate $= k[A]^m[B]^n$, the k is the **rate constant**. The powers n and m are the **orders** of the reaction with respect to the reactants A and B that appear in this equation. The **overall order** of the reaction is $(n + m)$.

Worked example

The decomposition of ethanal to methane and carbon monoxide is second order with respect to ethanal. When the concentration of ethanal in the gas phase is $0.20\,mol\,dm^{-3}$, the rate of reaction is $0.080\,mol\,dm^{-3}\,s^{-1}$ at a certain temperature. What is the value of the rate constant at this temperature?

Notes on the method
Start by writing out the rate equation based on the information given. There is no need to write the equation for the reaction because the rate equation cannot be deduced from the balanced chemical equation.

Substitute values in the rate equation, including the units as well as the values. Then rearrange the equation to find the value of k. Check that the units are as expected for a second order reaction.

Answer

The rate equation: $\qquad\qquad\qquad rate = k[ethanal]^2$

Substituting: $\quad 0.080\,mol\,dm^{-3}\,s^{-1} = k \times (0.20\,mol\,dm^{-3})^2$

Rearranging: $\qquad\qquad k = \dfrac{0.080\,mol\,dm^{-3}\,s^{-1}}{(0.20\,mol\,dm^{-3})^2}$

Hence, $\qquad\qquad\qquad\qquad k = 2.0\,mol^{-1}\,dm^3\,s^{-1}$

Test yourself

6 The rate of decomposition of di(benzenecarbonyl) peroxide is first order with respect to the peroxide. Calculate the rate constant for the reaction at 107 °C if the rate of decomposition of the peroxide at this temperature is $7.4 \times 10^{-6}\,mol\,dm^{-3}\,s^{-1}$ when the concentration of peroxide is $0.02\,mol\,dm^{-3}$.

7 The hydrolysis of the ester methyl ethanoate in alkali is first order with respect to the ester and first order with respect to hydroxide ions. The rate of reaction is $0.000\,69\,mol\,dm^{-3}\,s^{-1}$, at a given temperature, when the ester concentration is $0.05\,mol\,dm^{-3}$ and the hydroxide ion concentration is $0.10\,mol\,dm^{-3}$. Write out the rate equation for the reaction and calculate the rate constant.

First order reactions

A reaction is first order with respect to a reactant if the rate of the reaction is proportional to the concentration of that reactant. The concentration term for this reactant is raised to the power 1 in the rate equation:

rate = $k[X]^1 = k[X]$

This means that doubling the concentration of the chemical X leads to a doubling of the rate of reaction. The rate of reaction is proportional to the concentration of the reactant – this means that a plot of rate against concentration gives a straight line passing through the origin.

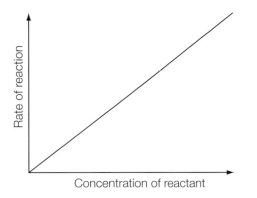

Rate of reaction

Concentration of reactant

Figure 10.9 ◄
Variation of reaction rate with concentration for a first order reaction. The graph is a straight line through the origin, showing that the rate is proportional to the concentration of the reactant.

One of the easier ways to spot a first order reaction is to plot a concentration–time graph and then work out the time taken for the concentration to fall by half. At a constant temperature, the half-life of a first order reaction is the same wherever it is measured on a concentration–time graph.

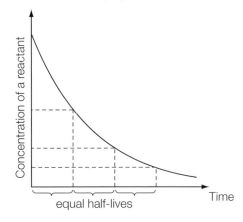

Concentration of a reactant

equal half-lives

Time

Figure 10.10 ▲
Variation of concentration of a reactant plotted against time for a first order reaction. The half-life for a first order reaction is a constant, so it is the same wherever it is read off the curve. It is independent of the initial concentration.

Test yourself

8 Refer to your answers to the activity in Section 10.1.
  a) From your rate–concentration graph, what is the order of the reaction of bromine with methanoic acid with respect to bromine?
  b) i) Determine three values for half-lives for the reaction from your concentration–time graph.
     ii) Are your values consistent with your answer to that in part a)?
9 Explain how the rate constant can be found from a rate–concentration graph such as that in Figure 10.9.

Definition

The **half-life** of a reaction is the time for the concentration of one of the reactants to fall by half.

Second order reactions

A reaction is second order with respect to a reactant if the rate of the reaction is proportional to the concentration of that reactant squared. This means that the concentration term for this reactant is raised to the power 2 in the rate equation. At its simplest, the rate equation for a second order reaction takes the form:

$$\text{rate} = k[\text{reactant}]^2$$

This means that doubling the concentration of X increases the rate by a factor of four.

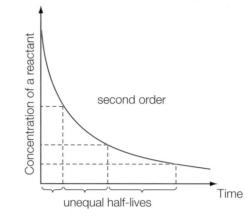

Figure 10.11 ▲

Variation of concentration of a reactant plotted against time for a second order reaction. The half-life for a second order reaction is not a constant. The time for the concentration to fall from c to $c/2$ is half the time for the concentration to fall from $c/2$ to $c/4$. The half-life is inversely proportional to the starting concentration.

The variation of rate with concentration for a second order reaction can be found, as before, by drawing tangents to the curve of the concentration–time graph. However, a rate–concentration graph is not a straight line for a second order reaction, but instead is a curve as shown in Figure 10.12.

> **Note**
>
> It can be shown mathematically that for a second order reaction, with a rate equation in the form rate = $k[A]^2$, a plot of $\frac{1}{[A]_t}$ against time is a straight line, where $[A]_t$ is the concentration of reactant A at time t. The slope of the line is equal to the value of the rate constant, k.

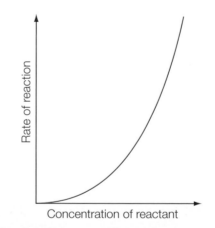

Figure 10.12 ▶
A concentration–time graph for a second order reaction.

Test yourself

10 The rate of reaction of 1-bromopropane with hydroxide ions is first order with respect to the halogenoalkane, and first order with respect to hydroxide ions.
   a) Write the rate equation for the reaction
   b) What is the overall order of reaction?
   c) What are the units of the rate constant?

Zero order reactions

At first sight, it seems odd that there can be zero order reactions. A reaction is zero order with respect to a reactant if the rate of the reaction is unaffected by changes in the concentration of that reactant (Figures 10.13 and 10.14). Chemists have found a way to account for zero order reactions in terms of the mechanisms of these reactions (Section 10.4).

In a rate equation for a zero order reaction, the concentration term for the reactant is raised to the power zero:

$$rate = k[\text{reactant}]^0$$
$$= k \text{ (a constant)}$$

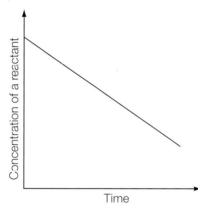

Figure 10.13 ▲
Variation of concentration of a reactant plotted against time for a zero order reaction. The gradient of this graph measures the rate of reaction. The gradient is a constant so the rate stays the same even though the concentration of the reactant is falling.

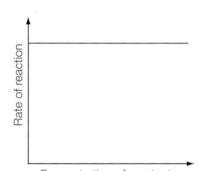

Figure 10.14 ▲
Variation of reaction rate with concentration for a zero order reaction.

The nitration of methylbenzene is an example where the conditions can be such that the reaction is zero order with respect to the aromatic compound. The methylbenzene reacts with nitronium ions formed from nitric acid (see Sections 1.6 and 1.7). The reaction creating the NO_2^+ ions is relatively slow, but as soon as the ions form they react with methylbenzene. As a result, the rate is not affected by the methylbenzene concentration.

Test yourself

11 Ammonia gas decomposes to nitrogen and hydrogen in the presence of a hot platinum wire. Experiments show that the reaction continues at a constant rate until all the ammonia has disappeared.
   a) Sketch a concentration–time graph for the reaction.
   b) Write the balanced chemical equation and the rate equation for this reaction.

The initial rate method

The most general method for determining reaction orders is the initial rate method. This is based on finding the rate immediately after the start of a reaction. This is the one point when all the concentrations are known.

The investigator makes up a series of mixtures in which all the initial concentrations are the same, except one. A suitable method is used to measure the change of concentration with time for each mixture (see Section 10.1). The results are used to plot concentration–time graphs. The initial rate for each mixture is then determined by drawing tangents to the curve at the start and calculating their gradients.

Worked example

The initial rate method was used to study the reaction:

$$BrO_3^-(aq) + 5Br^-(aq) + 6H^+(aq) \rightarrow 3Br_2(aq) + 3H_2O(l)$$

Experiment	Initial concentration of BrO$_3^-$/mol dm^{-3}	Initial concentration of Br$^-$/mol dm^{-3}	Initial concentration of H$^+$/mol dm^{-3}	Initial rate of reaction/mol dm^{-3} s^{-1}
1	0.1	0.10	0.10	1.2×10^{-3}
2	0.2	0.10	0.10	2.4×10^{-3}
3	0.1	0.30	0.10	3.6×10^{-3}
4	0.2	0.10	0.20	9.6×10^{-3}

Table 10.4 ▲

The initial rate was calculated from four graphs plotted to show how the concentration of BrO$_3^-$(aq) varied with time for different initial concentrations of reactants, with the results shown in Table 10.4.
What is:
a) the rate equation for the reaction
b) the value of the rate constant?

Notes on the method
Remember that the rate equation cannot be worked out from the balanced equation for the reaction.

First, look at the experiments in which the concentration of BrO$_3^-$ varies but the concentration of the other two reactants stays the same. How does doubling the concentration of BrO$_3^-$ affect the rate?

Then, in turn, look at the experiments in which the concentrations of first Br$^-$ and then H$^+$ vary while the concentrations of the other two reactants stay the same. How does doubling or tripling the concentration of a reactant affect the rate?

Substitute the values for any one experiment in the rate equation to find the value of the rate constant, k. Take care with the units.

www
Tutorial

Answer
From experiments 1 and 2: doubling [BrO$_3^-$]$_{initial}$ increases the rate by a factor of 2. So rate $\propto$ [BrO$_3^-$]^1

From experiments 1 and 3: tripling [Br$^-$]$_{initial}$ triples the rate. So rate $\propto$ [Br$^-$]^1

From experiments 2 and 4: doubling [H$^+$]$_{initial}$ increases the rate by a factor of 4 (2^2). So rate $\propto$ [H$^+$]^2

The reaction is first order with respect to BrO$_3^-$ and Br$^-$ but second order with respect to H$^+$.

The rate equation is: rate = k [BrO$_3^-$][Br$^-$][H$^+$]^2

Rearranging this equation, and substituting values from experiment 4:

$$k = \frac{rate}{[BrO_3^-][Br^-]\,[H^+]^2}$$

$$= \frac{9.6 \times 10^{-3}\,mol\,dm^{-3}\,s^{-1}}{0.2\,mol\,dm^{-3} \times 0.1\,mol\,dm^{-3} \times (0.2\,mol\,dm^{-3})^2}$$

$$k = 12.0\,mol^{-3}\,dm^9\,s^{-1}$$

Test yourself

12 Hydrogen gas reacts with nitrogen monoxide gas to form steam and nitrogen. Doubling the concentration of hydrogen doubles the rate of reaction. Tripling the concentration of nitrogen monoxide increases the rate by a factor of nine.
  a) Write the balanced equation for the reaction.
  b) Write the rate equation for the reaction.

13 This data refers to the reaction of the halogenoalkane 1-bromobutane (represented as RBr here) with hydroxide ions. The results are shown in Table 10.5.

Experiment	[RBr]/mol dm^{-3}	[OH$^-$]/mol dm^{-3}	Rate of reaction/mol dm^{-3} s^{-1}
1	0.020	0.020	1.36
2	0.010	0.020	0.68
3	0.010	0.005	0.17

Table 10.5▲
  a) Deduce the rate equation for the reaction.
  b) Calculate the value of the rate constant.

14 This data refers to the reaction of the halogenoalkane 2-bromo-2-methylbutane (represented as R'Br here) with hydroxide ions. The results are shown in Table 10.6.

Experiment	[R'Br]/mol dm^{-3}	[OH$^-$]/mol dm^{-3}	Rate of reaction/mol dm^{-3} s^{-1}
1	0.020	0.020	40.40
2	0.010	0.020	20.19
3	0.010	0.005	20.20

Table 10.6▲
  a) Deduce the rate equation for the reaction.
  b) Calculate the value of the rate constant.

10.3 The effect of temperature on reaction rates

Raising the temperature often has a dramatic effect on the rate of a reaction, especially reactions which involve the breaking of strong covalent bonds. This explains why the practical procedure for most organic reactions involves heating the reaction mixture. With the help of collision theory, it is possible to make predictions about the effect of temperature changes on rates.

The constant k in a rate equation is only a constant at a specified temperature. Generally, the value of the rate constant increases as the temperature rises – and this means that the rate of reaction increases.

Collision theory accounts for the effect of temperature on reaction rates by assuming that chemical changes pass through a transition state. The transition state is at a higher energy than the reactants, so there is an energy barrier or activation energy. Reactant molecules must collide with enough energy to overcome this activation energy barrier. This means that the only collisions that lead to reaction are those with enough energy to break existing bonds and allow the atoms to rearrange to form new bonds in the product molecules.

> **Definitions**
>
> A **reaction profile** is a plot which shows how the total energy of the atoms, molecules or ions changes during the progress of a change from reactants to products.
>
> A **transition state** is the state of the reacting atoms, molecules or ions when they are at the top of the activation energy barrier for a reaction step.

Figure 10.15 ◄
A reaction profile showing the activation energy for a reaction.

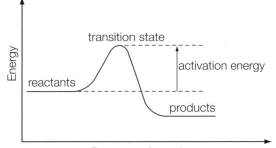

Activation energies account for the fact that reactions go much more slowly than would be expected if every collision in a mixture of chemicals led to reaction. Only a very small proportion of collisions bring about chemical change because molecules can only react if they collide with enough energy to overcome the energy barrier. At around room temperature, for many reactions, only a small proportion of molecules have enough energy to react.

The Maxwell–Boltzmann curve describes the distribution of the kinetic energies of molecules. As Figure 10.16 shows, the proportion of molecules with energies greater than the activation energy is small at around 300 K.

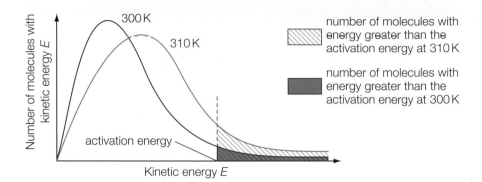

Figure 10.16 ▲
The Maxwell–Boltzmann distribution of molecular kinetic energies in a gas at two temperatures. The modal speed increases as the temperature rises. The area under the curve gives the total number of molecules in the reaction mixture. This does not change as the temperature rises so the peak height falls as the curve widens.

The shaded areas in Figure 10.16 show the proportions of molecules having at least the activation energy for a reaction at the two temperatures. This area is bigger at the higher temperature. So at a higher temperature there are more molecules with enough energy to react when they collide, and the reaction goes faster.

Test yourself

15 Why is it that many reactions have activation energies ranging between about 50 kJ mol^{-1} and 250 kJ mol^{-1}?

16 Table 10.7 shows the value of the rate constant for the reaction of benzenediazonium chloride in aqueous solution with water at four temperatures.

Temperature/K	Rate constant/10^{-5} s^{-1}
278	0.15
298	4.1
308	20
323	140

Table 10.7 ▲

  a) What do the units of the rate constant tell you about the form of the rate equation?
  b) What do the values tell you about the effect of temperature on the rate of the reaction?
  c) What is the effect of a 10 degree rise in temperature on the rate of the reaction?

17 The activation energy for the decomposition of ammonia into nitrogen and hydrogen is 335 kJ mol^{-1} in the absence of a catalyst, but 162 kJ mol^{-1} in the presence of a tungsten catalyst. Explain the significance of these values in terms of the transition-state theory.

10.4 Rate equations and reaction mechanisms

Rate equations were one of the first pieces of evidence which set chemists thinking about the mechanisms of reactions. They wanted to understand why a rate equation cannot be predicted from the balanced equation for the reaction. They were puzzled that similar reactions turned out to have different forms of rate equations.

Multi-step reactions

The key to understanding reaction mechanisms was the realisation that most reactions do not take place in one step, as suggested by a balanced equation, but in a series of steps.

It is unexpected that the decomposition of ammonia gas in the presence of a hot platinum wire is a zero order reaction. How can it be that the concentration of the only reactant does not affect the rate? A possible explanation is illustrated in Figure 10.17.

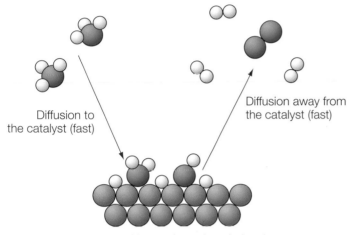

Diffusion to the catalyst (fast)

Diffusion away from the catalyst (fast)

Bonds breaking and new bonds forming. Rate determined by the surface area of the catalyst which is a constant (rate-determining)

Figure 10.17 ▲
Three steps in the decomposition of ammonia gas in the presence of a platinum catalyst.

Ammonia diffuses to the surface of the metal rapidly and is adsorbed onto the surface. This happens quickly. Bonds break and atoms rearrange to make new molecules on the surface of the metal. This is the slowest process. Once formed, the nitrogen and hydrogen rapidly break away from the metal into the gas phase.

So there is a rate-determining step that can only happen on the surface of the platinum. The rate of reaction is determined only by the surface area of the platinum, which is constant. This means that the rate of reaction is constant, so long as there is enough ammonia to be adsorbed all over the metal surface. The rate is independent of the ammonia concentration.

Hydrolysis of halogenoalkanes

Another puzzle for chemists was the discovery that there are different rate equations for the reactions between hydroxide ions and the two isomers with the formula C_4H_9Br (see questions **13** and **14** in Section 10.2).

The hydrolysis of a primary halogenoalkane, such as 1-bromobutane, is second order overall. The rate equation has the form:

$$\text{rate} = k[C_4H_9Br][OH^-]$$

Test yourself

18 Give an analogy from the everyday world to explain the idea of a rate-determining step. You could base your example on people getting their meals in a busy self-service canteen, or cars on a motorway with lots of traffic but affected by lane closures.

Figure 10.18 ▶
A one-step mechanism for the hydrolysis
of 1-bromobutane.

To account for this chemists have suggested a mechanism showing the C–Br bond breaking at the same time as the nucleophile, OH⁻, forms a C–OH bond. In this mechanism, both reactants are involved in the single, rate-determining step.

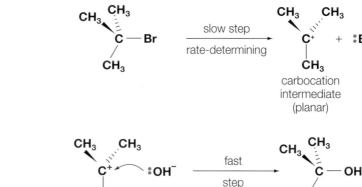

1-bromobutane   transition state   butan-1-ol

www
Tutorial

In this example of a substitution reaction, the nucleophile is the hydroxide ion. Chemists label this mechanism S_N2 – the '2' shows that there are two molecules or ions involved in the rate-determining step.

On the other hand, the hydrolysis of tertiary halogenoalkanes, such as 2-bromo-2-methylpropane, is first order overall. The rate equation has the form:

rate = $k[C_4H_9Br]$

The suggested mechanism shows the C–Br bond breaking first to form an ionic intermediate. Then the nucleophile, OH⁻, rapidly forms a new bond with carbon.

Figure 10.19 ▶
A two-step mechanism for the hydrolysis
of 2-bromo-2-methylpropane.

slow step
rate-determining

carbocation
intermediate
(planar)

fast
step

In this example of a substitution reaction, the nucleophile is also the hydroxide ion. In this case, chemists label the mechanism S_N1 – the '1' shows that there is just one molecule or ion involved in the rate-determining step. The concentration of the hydroxide ions does not affect the rate of reaction because hydroxide ions are not involved in the rate-determining step.

What these examples show is that it is generally the molecules or ions involved (directly or indirectly) in the rate-determining step that appear in the rate equation for the reaction.

Definitions

An **S_N1 reaction** is a nucleophilic substitution reaction with a mechanism that involves only one molecule or ion in the rate-determining step.

An **S_N2 reaction** is a nucleophilic substitution reaction with a mechanism that involves two molecules or ions in the rate-determining step.

www
Tutorial

Test yourself

19 Explain, in terms of bonding, why the first step in the S_N1 mechanism is slow but the second step is fast.

20 In the proposed two-step mechanism for the reaction of nitrogen dioxide gas with carbon monoxide gas, the first step is slow and the second step is fast:
$2NO_2(g) \rightarrow NO_3(g) + NO(g)$ slow
$NO_3(g) + CO(g) \rightarrow NO_2(g) + CO_2(g)$ fast
a) What is the overall equation for the reaction?
b) Suggest a rate equation which is consistent with this mechanism.
c) What, according to your suggested rate equation, is the order of reaction with respect to carbon monoxide?

Activity

A model for explaining how enzymes work

The lock-and-key model

Enzymes are natural catalysts. They are much more powerful than inorganic catalysts, and are also highly specific. Most enzymes catalyse only one reaction or one type of reaction. An example is catalase – this enzyme occurs in most living tissues where it dramatically speeds up the decomposition of hydrogen peroxide. It has no effect on any other reactions in cells.

A proposed model to explain how enzymes work is based on an analogy with a lock and a key. Enzymes are proteins. Like all proteins, they have a precise molecular shape (see Section 5.3). The lock-and-key model suggests that each enzyme molecule has an active site.

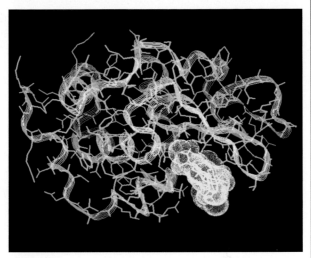

Figure 10.20 ▲
This computer graphic shows a molecule of the enzyme lysozyme. Lysozyme catalyses the hydrolysis reactions that damage the cell walls of bacteria. In this image the protein is shown in blue. The backbone is traced out by a magenta ribbon. The substrate is shown in yellow, bound to the active site.

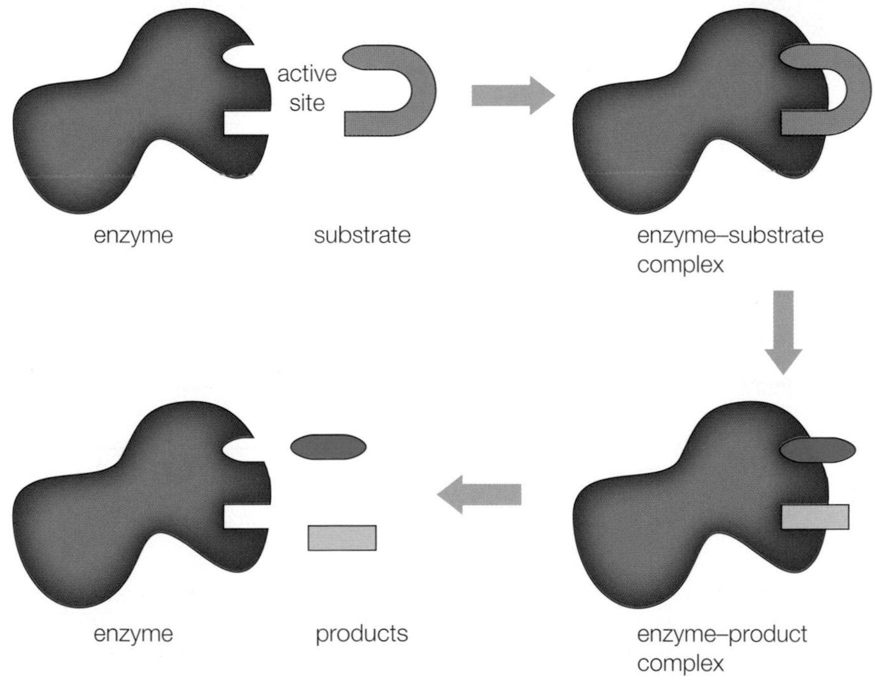

active site

enzyme   substrate   enzyme–substrate complex

enzyme   products   enzyme–product complex

Figure 10.21 ◀
A diagram to illustrate the lock-and-key model for enzyme action.

Molecules of the main reactant (the substrate) fit into the active site. Typically, the active site is a cleft formed by the folding of the protein chain where substrate molecules can be held by intermolecular forces such as hydrogen bonds.

The substrate is converted to products at the active site. These products then separate from the enzyme leaving the active site free to accept another molecule of the substrate:

enzyme (E) + substrate (S) → enzyme–substrate complex (ES)
     → enzyme–product complex (EP) → enzyme (E) + products (P)

Investigating urease

The enzyme urease speeds up the reaction of urea ($H_2N–CO–NH_2$) with water to form carbon dioxide and ammonia. Two series of experiments were carried out to investigate the rate equation for the reaction. The experiments were designed to measure the initial rate of the reaction under different conditions.

Part 1: This involved a series of runs in which the concentration of the enzyme was kept constant but the concentration of the substrate, urea, was varied from one run to the next as shown in Table 10.8.

Part 2: In a second series of runs, the concentration of the substrate, urea, was kept constant while the concentration of the enzyme, urease, was varied from one run to the next. This was done by adding different volumes of urease solution to the reaction mixture keeping the total volume constant by adding water. The results are given in Table 10.9.

Concentration of urea/mol dm^{-3}	Initial rate of reaction/ mol dm^{-3} min^{-1}
0.000	0
0.005	1.7×10^{-6}
0.010	2.3×10^{-6}
0.020	3.2×10^{-6}
0.050	4.4×10^{-6}
0.100	5.9×10^{-6}
0.200	7.2×10^{-6}
0.300	7.7×10^{-6}
0.400	8.0×10^{-6}

Table 10.8▲

Volume of urease solution/cm^3	Initial rate of reaction/ mol dm^{-3} min^{-1}
0.00	0
0.005	0.6×10^{-6}
0.10	0.8×10^{-6}
0.20	1.8×10^{-6}
0.30	3.2×10^{-6}
0.50	4.8×10^{-6}
1.00	10.4×10^{-6}
1.50	14.9×10^{-6}
2.00	19.5×10^{-6}

Table 10.9▲

1 How can the lock-and-key model explain why enzymes are highly specific?

2 Write an equation for the reaction of urea with water.

3 Plot the rate of reaction against substrate concentration for the results from part 1 of this investigation.

4 What does your graph show about the order of reaction with respect to the substrate urea when:

   a) the substrate concentration is high

   b) the substrate concentration is low?

5 Plot the rate of reaction against volume of enzyme solution for the results from part 2 of the investigation. (Note that the volume of the urease solution is a measure of the enzyme concentration.)

6 What is the order of reaction with respect to the enzyme?

7 Write the full rate equation for the reaction when:

   a) the substrate concentration is low

   b) the substrate concentration is high.

8 Show how the mechanism for the reaction of enzyme with substrate can account for your answers to questions **4**, **6** and **7**.

   $E + S \rightarrow ES \rightarrow EP \rightarrow E + P$

9 Suggest reasons why an understanding of the mechanisms of enzyme-catalysed reactions is important in the development of new drugs.

REVIEW QUESTIONS

Extension questions

1 The data in Table 10.10 refers to the decomposition of hydrogen peroxide, H_2O_2.

Time/s	$[H_2O_2]$/mol dm^{-3}
0	20.0×10^{-3}
12×10^3	16.0×10^{-3}
24×10^3	13.1×10^{-3}
36×10^3	10.6×10^{-3}
48×10^3	8.6×10^{-3}
60×10^3	6.9×10^{-3}
72×10^3	5.6×10^{-3}
96×10^3	3.7×10^{-3}
120×10^3	2.4×10^{-3}

Table 10.10▲

a) Plot a concentration–time graph for the decomposition reaction (3)

b) Read off three half-lives from the graph and show that this is a first-order reaction. (3)

c) Draw tangents to the curve in your graph at four different concentrations, and calculate the gradient of the curve at each point. (4)

d) Plot a graph of rate against concentration using your results from part c), and hence find the value for the rate constant at the temperature of the experiment. (4)

2 The results in Table 10.11 come from a study of the rate of reaction of iodine with a large excess of hex-1-ene dissolved in ethanoic acid.

Time/s	$[I_2]$/mol dm^{-3}
0	20.0×10^{-3}
1×10^3	15.6×10^{-3}
2×10^3	12.8×10^{-3}
3×10^3	11.0×10^{-3}
4×10^3	9.4×10^{-3}
5×10^3	8.3×10^{-3}
6×10^3	7.5×10^{-3}
7×10^3	6.8×10^{-3}
8×10^3	6.2×10^{-3}

Table 10.11▲

a) Plot a concentration–time graph and show that the half-life is not a constant. (5)

b) From your graph, find the rate of reaction at a series of concentrations. (3)

c) i) Use your results from part b) to plot a graph to confirm that the reaction is second order with respect to iodine. (3)

 ii) Explain how to interpret the graph you have drawn. (2)

3 Hydrogen peroxide oxidises iodide ions to iodine in the presence of hydrogen ions. The other product is water. The reaction is first order with respect to hydrogen peroxide, first order with respect to iodide ions, but zero order with respect to hydrogen ions.

a) Write a balanced equation for the reaction. (1)

b) Write the rate equation for the reaction. (2)

c) What is the overall order of the reaction? (1)

d) A proposed mechanism for the reaction involves three steps:

$$H_2O_2 + I^- \rightarrow H_2O + IO^-$$
$$H^+ + IO^- \rightarrow HIO$$
$$HIO + H^+ + I^- \rightarrow I_2 + H_2O$$

Which step is likely to be the rate-determining step and why? (2)

4 Two gases, X and Y, react according to this equation:

$$X(g) + 2Y(g) \rightarrow XY_2(g)$$

This reaction was studied at 400 K giving the results shown in Table 10.12.

Experiment number	Initial concentration of X/mol dm^{-3}	Initial concentration of Y/mol dm^{-3}	Initial rate of formation of XY$_2$/mol dm^{-3} s^{-1}
1	0.10	0.10	0.0001
2	0.10	0.20	0.0004
3	0.10	0.30	0.0009
4	0.20	0.10	0.0001
5	0.30	0.10	0.0001

Table 10.12▲

a) What is the order of the reaction with respect to:
 i) X
 ii) Y? (4)

b) Write a rate equation for the reaction of X with Y. (2)

c) Use the results of experiment 1 in Table 10.12 to calculate the value of the rate constant and give its units. (2)

d) Suggest a possible mechanism for the reaction. (3)

e) Explain why chemists are interested in determining rate equations and measuring rate constants. (5)

11 How far?

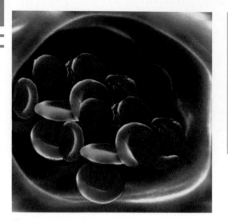

Figure 11.1 ▲
Red blood cells flowing through a blood vessel magnified 2500 times. The protein haemoglobin has just the right properties to take up oxygen in the lungs and release it to cells throughout the body. The position of equilibrium of this reversible process varies with the concentration of oxygen.

Figure 11.2 ▶
Solvent extraction is used to separate and purify chemicals. A compound dissolved in one liquid can be extracted into another liquid in which it is more soluble. After shaking the mixture in a tap funnel, the two solutions are in equilibrium but with more of the solute in one of the solvents.

All chemical reactions tend towards a state of dynamic equilibrium. Chemists have discovered a law which allows them to predict the concentrations of chemicals expected in equilibrium mixtures. This law is one of several approaches which chemists use to answer the questions 'How far?' and 'In which direction?'. An understanding of equilibrium ideas helps to explain changes in the natural environment, the biochemistry of living things and the conditions used in the chemical industry to manufacture new products.

11.1 Reversibility and equilibrium

Reversible reactions tend towards a state of balance. They reach equilibrium when neither the forward change nor the backward change is complete, with both changes still going on at equal rates. They cancel each other out and there is no overall change – this is dynamic equilibrium.

Under given conditions, the same equilibrium state can be reached either by starting with the chemicals on one side of the equation for a reaction, or by starting with the chemicals on the other side. Figures 11.3 and 11.4 illustrate this for the reversible reaction between hydrogen and iodine:

$$H_2(g) + I_2(g) \rightleftharpoons 2HI(g)$$

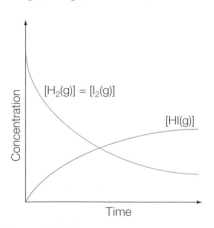

Figure 11.3▲
Reaching an equilibrium state by the reaction of equal amounts of hydrogen gas and iodine gas.

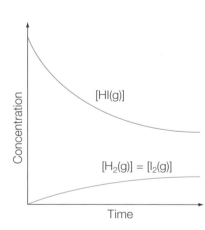

Figure 11.4▲
Reaching the same equilibrium state by the decomposition of hydrogen iodide under the same conditions as for Figure 11.3.

Test yourself

1 Explain, with the help of an example, the idea of dynamic equilibrium.
2 Describe what is happening to the molecules in the gas mixtures from time zero to the time at which each mixture reaches equilibrium as described by:
 a) Figure 11.3
 b) Figure 11.4.

The equilibrium law

The equilibrium law is a quantitative law for predicting the amounts of reactants and products when a reversible reaction reaches a state of dynamic equilibrium. In general, for a reversible reaction at equilibrium:

$$aA + bB \rightleftharpoons cC + dD$$

$$K_c = \frac{[C]^c[D]^d}{[A]^a[B]^b}$$

This is the form for the equilibrium constant, K_c, when the concentrations of the reactants and products are measured in moles per cubic decimetre. [A], [B] and so on are the equilibrium concentrations, sometimes written as $[A]_{eqm}$ and $[B]_{eqm}$ to make this clear.

The concentrations of the chemicals on the right-hand side of the equation appear on the top line of the expression. The concentrations of reactants on the left appear on the bottom line. Each concentration term is raised to the power of the number in front of its formula in the balanced equation.

Worked example

Calculate the value of K_c for the reaction which forms an ester from ethanoic acid and ethanol (see Section 3.3) from this data.

$$CH_3COOH(l) + C_2H_5OH(l) \rightleftharpoons CH_3COOC_2H_5(l) + H_2O(l)$$

When 0.50 mol of $CH_3COOH(l)$ is dissolved in 0.5 dm³ of an organic solvent with 0.09 mol of $C_2H_5OH(l)$ and allowed to come to equilibrium at 293 K, the amount of the ester, $CH_3COOC_2H_5(l)$, formed at equilibrium is 0.086 mol.

Practical guidance (www)

Notes on the method
- Write down the equation.
- Underneath write first the initial amounts, and then write the amounts at equilibrium.
- Use the equation to calculate the amounts not given.
- Calculate the equilibrium concentrations given the volume of the solution.
- Substitute the values and units in the expression for K_c.

Answer

Equation:

$$CH_3COOH(l) + C_2H_5OH(l) \rightleftharpoons CH_3COOC_2H_5(l) + H_2O(l)$$

Initial amounts/mol	0.50	0.09	0	0

At equilibrium:
- amount given/mol: 0.086
- amounts calculated/mol:

(0.50 − 0.086)	(0.09 − 0.086)		0.086
= 0.414	= 0.004		

Equilibrium concentrations/mol dm⁻³

0.414 ÷ 0.5	0.004 ÷ 0.5	0.086 ÷ 0.5	0.086 ÷ 0.5
= 0.828	= 0.008	= 0.172	= 0.172

$$K_c = \frac{[CH_3COOC_2H_5(l)][H_2O(l)]}{[CH_3COOH(l)][C_2H_5OH(l)]}$$

$$= \frac{0.172 \text{ mol dm}^{-3} \times 0.172 \text{ mol dm}^{-3}}{0.828 \text{ mol dm}^{-3} \times 0.008 \text{ mol dm}^{-3}}$$

$$= 4.47$$

In this example the units cancel, so K_c has no units.

3 On mixing 1.68 moles of $PCl_5(g)$ with 0.36 moles of $PCl_3(g)$ in a 2.0 dm^3 container and allowing the mixture to reach equilibrium, the amount of PCl_5 in the equilibrium mixture was 1.44 mol. Calculate K_c for the reaction $PCl_5(g) \rightleftharpoons PCl_3(g) + Cl_2(g)$.

4 $K_c = 170 \, \text{mol}^{-1} \, \text{dm}^3$ at 298 K for the equilibrium system $2NO_2(g) \rightleftharpoons N_2O_4(g)$. If a 5 dm^3 flask contains 1.0×10^{-3} mol of NO_2 and 7.5×10^{-4} mol of N_2O_4, is the system at equilibrium? Is there any tendency for the concentration of NO_2 to change and, if so, will it increase or decrease?

Equilibrium constants and balanced equations

An equilibrium constant always applies to a particular chemical equation and can be deduced directly from the equation.

There are two common ways of writing the reaction of sulfur dioxide with oxygen. As a result, there are two forms for the equilibrium constant which have different values. So long as the matching equation and equilibrium constant are used in any calculation, the predictions based on the equilibrium law are the same. For:

$$2SO_2(g) + O_2(g) \rightleftharpoons 2SO_3(g) \quad \text{Equation 1}$$

$$K_c = \frac{[SO_3(g)]^2}{[SO_2(g)]^2[O_2(g)]}$$

But for:

$$SO_2(g) + \tfrac{1}{2}O_2(g) \rightleftharpoons SO_3(g) \quad \text{Equation 2}$$

$$K_c = \frac{[SO_3(g)]}{[SO_2(g)][O_2(g)]^{\frac{1}{2}}}$$

So, it is important to write the balanced equation and the equilibrium constant together.

Reversing the equation also changes the form of the equilibrium constant because the concentration terms for the chemicals on the right-hand side of the equation always appear on the top of the expression for K_c.

So, for:

$$2SO_3(g) \rightleftharpoons 2SO_2(g) + O_2(g) \quad \text{Equation 3}$$

$$K_c = \frac{[SO_2(g)]^2[O_2(g)]}{[SO_3(g)]^2}$$

5 Consider the equilibrium between sulfur dioxide, oxygen and sulfur trioxide.
   a) Show that the units for the equilibrium constant, K_c, for equation 1 are mol^{-1} dm^3.
   b) $K_c = 1.6 \times 10^6$ mol^{-1} dm^3 for equation 1 at a particular temperature, what is the value of K_c for equation 2?
   c) What is the value of K_c for equation 3?

6 Write the K_c expressions for the following equations and state the units of the equilibrium constant for each example:
   a) $CO_2(g) + H_2(g) \rightleftharpoons CO(g) + H_2O(g)$
   b) $N_2(g) + 3H_2(g) \rightleftharpoons 2NH_3(g)$
   c) $2O_3(g) \rightleftharpoons 3O_2(g)$
   d) $4PF_5(g) \rightleftharpoons P_4(g) + 10F_2(g)$

Activity

Testing the equilibrium law

The reversible reaction involving hydrogen, iodine and hydrogen iodide has been used to test the equilibrium law experimentally. In a series of six experiments, samples of the chemicals were sealed in reaction tubes and then heated at 731 K until the mixtures reached equilibrium. Four of the tubes started with different mixtures of hydrogen and iodine. Two of the tubes started with just hydrogen iodide.

Once the tubes had reached equilibrium, they were rapidly cooled to stop the reactions. Then the contents of the tubes were analysed to find the compositions of the equilibrium mixture. The results for six of the tubes are shown in Table 11.1.

Tube	Initial concentrations/mol dm^{-3}			Equilibrium concentrations/mol dm^{-3}		
	[H$_2$(g)]	[I$_2$(g)]	[HI(g)]	[H$_2$(g)]	[I$_2$(g)]	[HI(g)]
1	2.40×10^{-2}	1.38×10^{-2}	0	1.14×10^{-2}	0.12×10^{-2}	2.52×10^{-2}
2	2.40×10^{-2}	1.68×10^{-2}	0	0.92×10^{-2}	0.20×10^{-2}	2.96×10^{-2}
3	2.44×10^{-2}	1.98×10^{-2}	0	0.77×10^{-2}	0.31×10^{-2}	3.34×10^{-2}
4	2.46×10^{-2}	1.76×10^{-2}	0	0.92×10^{-2}	0.22×10^{-2}	3.08×10^{-2}
5	0	0	3.04×10^{-2}	0.345×10^{-2}	0.345×10^{-2}	2.35×10^{-2}
6	0	0	7.58×10^{-2}	0.86×10^{-2}	0.86×10^{-2}	5.86×10^{-2}

Table 11.1 ▲

1 Write the equation for the reversible reaction to form hydrogen iodide from hydrogen and iodine.

2 Show that the equilibrium concentration of:

  a) hydrogen in tube 1 is as expected given the value of $[I_2(g)]_{eqm}$

  b) hydrogen iodide in tube 2 is as expected given the value of $[I_2(g)]_{eqm}$.

3 Explain why $[H_2(g)]_{eqm} = [I_2(g)]_{eqm}$ in tubes 5 and 6.

4 For each of the tubes work out the value of:

  a) $\dfrac{[HI(g)]_{eqm}}{[H_2(g)]_{eqm}[I_2(g)]_{eqm}}$

  b) $\dfrac{[HI(g)]^2_{eqm}}{[H_2(g)]_{eqm}[I_2(g)]_{eqm}}$

  c) Enter your values in a table and comment on the results.

5 What is the value of K_c for the reaction of hydrogen with iodine at 731 K?

11.2 Equilibrium constants and the direction of change

If the value of an equilibrium constant is large then the position of equilibrium is over to the right-hand side of the equation. Broadly speaking, if K_c is about 100 or larger at a given temperature then the products predominate.

Conversely, if the value of the equilibrium constant is small then the position of equilibrium is over to the left-hand side of the equation. If K_c is about 0.01 or smaller at a given temperature then the reactants predominate.

If the value of K_c is close to 1, then there are significant quantities both of reactants and of products present at equilibrium.

It is very important to keep in mind that equilibrium constants say nothing about the time it takes for a reaction mixture to reach equilibrium. The system may reach equilibrium rapidly or slowly – the value of K_c says nothing about the rate of change.

For example, the value of K_c for the reaction of hydrogen with chlorine to make hydrogen chloride is about 10^{31} at room temperature, but in the absence of a catalyst or ultraviolet light there is no reaction.

> **Note**
>
> Changing any or all of the concentrations does not alter the value of the equilibrium constant, so long as the temperature stays constant. Changing the pressure changes the concentration of molecules in a gas. This does not affect the value of the equilibrium constant either.

Test yourself

7 What can you conclude about the direction and extent of change in each of these examples?
   a) $Zn(s) + Cu^{2+}(aq) \rightleftharpoons Zn^{2+}(aq) + Cu(s)$ $K_c = 1 \times 10^{37}$ at 298 K
   b) $2HBr(g) \rightleftharpoons H_2(g) + Br_2(g)$ $K_c = 1 \times 10^{-10}$ at 298 K
   c) $N_2(g) + 3H_2(g) \rightleftharpoons 2NH_3(g)$ $K_c = 2.2$ at 623 K
8 In general, if the equilibrium constant for a forward reaction is large what will be the size of the equilibrium constant for the reverse of the reaction?

The effect of changing concentrations on systems at equilibrium

The equilibrium law makes it possible to explain the effect of changing the concentration of one or more of the chemicals in an equilibrium mixture.

An example is the equilibrium involving chromate(VI) and dichromate(VI) ions in water:

$$2CrO_4^{2-}(aq) + 2H^+(aq) \rightleftharpoons Cr_2O_7^{2-}(aq) + H_2O(l)$$
yellow   orange

At equilibrium:

$$K_c = \frac{[Cr_2O_7^{2-}(aq)]}{[CrO_4^{2-}(aq)]^2[H^+(aq)]^2}$$

where these are equilibrium concentrations.

In dilute solution, $[H_2O(l)]$ is constant so it does not appear in the equilibrium law expression.

Adding a few drops of concentrated acid increases the concentration of $H^+(aq)$ on the left-hand side of the equation.

This briefly upsets the equilibrium. For an instant after adding acid:

$$\frac{[Cr_2O_7^{2-}(aq)]}{[CrO_4^{2-}(aq)]^2[H^+(aq)]^2} < K_c$$

The system restores equilibrium as chromate(VI) ions react with hydrogen ions to produce more of the products. There is very soon a new equilibrium – and once again:

$$\frac{[Cr_2O_7^{2-}(aq)]}{[CrO_4^{2-}(aq)]^2[H^+(aq)]^2} = K_c$$

Figure 11.5▲
On the left, a yellow solution of chromate(VI) ions in water. On the right, a solution of chromate(VI) ions in water after adding a few drops of strong acid – the solution has turned orange as more dichromate(VI) ions form.

but now with new values for the various concentrations.

Chemists sometimes say that adding the acid makes the 'position of equilibrium shift to the right'. The effect is visible here because the yellow colour of the chromate(VI) ions turns to the orange colour of dichromate(VI) ions. This is as le Chatelier's principle predicts. The advantage of using K_c is that it makes quantitative predictions possible.

Test yourself

9 Show that it is reasonable to assume that the concentration of water is constant in dilute aqueous solutions by calculating the concentration of water in a $0.1 \, mol \, dm^{-3}$ solution of a solute.

10 Describe and explain the effect of adding alkali to a solution of dichromate(VI) ions.

11 a) Use the equilibrium law to predict and explain the effect of adding pure ethanol to an equilibrium mixture of ethanoic acid, ethanol, ethyl ethanoate and water:

$$CH_3COOH(l) + C_2H_5OH(l) \rightleftharpoons CH_3COOC_2H_5(l) + H_2O(l)$$

   b) Show that your prediction is consistent with le Chatelier's principle.

12 Use the equilibrium law to predict the effect of the following changes on an equilibrium mixture of hydrogen, carbon monoxide and methanol:

$$2H_2(g) + CO(g) \rightleftharpoons CH_3OH(g)$$

   a) adding more hydrogen to the gas mixture at constant total pressure
   b) compressing the mixture to increase the total pressure.

The effect of temperature changes on systems at equilibrium

Le Chatelier's principle predicts that raising the temperature makes the equilibrium shift in the direction which is endothermic. For example, for the reaction that produces sulfur trioxide during the manufacture of sulfuric acid, raising the temperature lowers the percentage of sulfur trioxide at equilibrium.

$$2SO_2(g) + O_2(g) \rightleftharpoons 2SO_3(g) \quad \Delta H = -98 \, kJ \, mol^{-1}$$

The equilibrium shifts to the left as the temperature increases because this is the direction in which the reaction is endothermic.

Note

If ΔH for a forward reaction is negative, then ΔH for the reverse reaction will have the same magnitude but the opposite sign. So, if a forward reaction is exothermic, then the reverse reaction is endothermic.

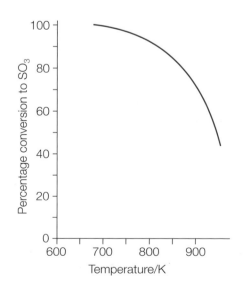

Figure 11.6▲
The effect of raising the temperature on the equilibrium between SO_2, O_2 and SO_3.

How far?

Note

The value of an equilibrium constant for an exothermic reaction decreases as the temperature increases.

The value of the equilibrium constant for an endothermic reaction increases as the temperature increases.

Figure 11.7▲
Tubes containing mixtures of $N_2O_4(g)$ and $2NO_2(g)$. The tube in the middle is at room temperature; the tube on the left in hot water; and the tube on the right in iced water.

The reason that temperature changes cause a shift in the position of equilibrium is that the value of the equilibrium constant changes. This is illustrated by the values in Table 11.2.

Temperature/K	K_c/mol^{-1} dm^3
293	9.9×10^{25}
500	1.0×10^{12}
700	1.7×10^6

Table 11.2▲
Values of K_c at three temperatures for the equilibrium $2SO_2(g) + O_2(g) \rightleftharpoons 2SO_3(g)$.

Test yourself

13 Show that the values in Table 11.2 are consistent with predictions for the equilibrium based on le Chatelier's principle.

14 The values of K_c for the equilibrium $N_2O_4(g) \rightleftharpoons 2NO_2(g)$ are 1.44 mol dm^{-3} at 400 K and 41 mol dm^{-3} at 500 K.
   a) What is the effect of increasing the temperature on the position of equilibrium?
   b) How can your answer to part a) account for the appearance of the gas mixtures in Figure 11.7?
   c) What is the sign of ΔH for the reaction?

15 For the reaction between hydrogen and iodine to form hydrogen iodide, the value of K_c is 794 at 298 K but 54 at 700 K. What can you deduce from this information?

The effect of catalysts on systems at equilibrium

Catalysts speed up reactions but are not used up as they do their job. It is important to note that while a catalyst speeds up the rate at which a reaction gets to an equilibrium state, it has no effect on the final position of equilibrium. In other words, a catalyst provides a faster route to the same equilibrium state. The alternative route with a catalyst has a lower activation energy, but speeds up the forward and back reactions to the same extent so that the dynamic equilibrium is unchanged.

www
Tutorial

Figure 11.8▶
Crystals of palladium seen under an electron microscope. Palladium is a rare and precious metal which is used to catalyse hydrogenation reactions.

City smog and equilibrium

Smog is a problem on still, sunny days in cities with many motor vehicles. Smog starts with the release of nitric oxide (NO) from motor vehicles. The NO reacts with oxygen and ozone in the air to form nitrogen dioxide (NO_2). In sunlight, NO_2 decomposes to form NO and free oxygen atoms, O. The oxygen atoms combine with oxygen molecules to form ozone, O_3. Ozone alone is a serious pollutant, but it can lead to further harm when it mixes with unburnt hydrocarbons. The ozone reacts with hydrocarbons to form a complex mixture of irritant chemicals which, in the absence of any wind, builds up to create photochemical smog.

Nitrogen in the air is usually inert but inside the cylinders of a petrol engine the temperature is over 2000 K. Under these conditions, nitrogen reacts with oxygen to form some NO. Data about the reversible decomposition of NO is given in Table 11.3.

Figure 11.9 ▲
Photochemical smog over Hong Kong, China.

Temperature/K	$\Delta H^{\ominus}$/kJ mol^{-1}	K_c
298	−43.16	2.2×10^{30}
900	−43.22	2.5×10^{9}
2300	−43.20	605

Table 11.3 ▲
Data for the reversible reaction $2NO \rightleftharpoons N_2(g) + O_2(g)$.

1 Why is city smog described as 'photochemical smog'?

2 Show that the trend in values for K_c in Table 11.3 is as expected from the values of the enthalpy change for the reaction.

3 Why does the size of the enthalpy change vary so little with temperature?

4 Calculate the equilibrium concentration of NO present in a 1 dm^3 steel cylinder containing 0.04 mol of N_2 and 0.01 mol of O_2 at equilibrium:

 a) at 2300 K

 b) at 298 K.

5 Explain why the NO formed in a car engine actually does cause pollution when it leaves the hot cylinder and enters the cold air, despite your answer to question **4 b)**.

6 How are oxides of nitrogen removed from the exhausts of petrol engines?

REVIEW QUESTIONS

1 a) A flask contains an equilibrium mixture of hydrogen gas ($0.01 \, mol \, dm^{-3}$), iodine gas ($0.01 \, mol \, dm^{-3}$) and hydrogen iodide gas ($0.07 \, mol \, dm^{-3}$) at a constant temperature. Calculate K_c for the reaction of hydrogen with iodine to form hydrogen iodide at this temperature. **(3)**

   b) Enough hydrogen is added to the mixture in part a) to suddenly double the hydrogen concentration in the flask to $0.02 \, mol \, dm^{-3}$. After a while, the mixture settles down with a new iodine concentration of $0.007 \, mol \, dm^{-3}$ at the same temperature as before.

      i) What are the new concentrations of hydrogen and hydrogen iodide? **(2)**

      ii) Show that the new mixture is at equilibrium. **(2)**

   c) Why does a sudden doubling of the hydrogen concentration affect the position of equilibrium? **(2)**

2 At 298 K the value of K_c for the following equilibrium is 10^{10}:

$$Sn^{2+}(aq) + 2Fe^{3+}(aq) \rightleftharpoons Sn^{4+}(aq) + 2Fe^{2+}(aq)$$

   a) i) Write the expression for K_c. **(2)**

      ii) What are the units of K_c for this reaction? Explain your answer. **(2)**

   b) What is the value of K_c for:

      i) $Sn^{4+}(aq) + 2Fe^{2+}(aq) \rightleftharpoons Sn^{2+}(aq) + 2Fe^{3+}(aq)$

      ii) $\frac{1}{2}Sn^{2+}(aq) + Fe^{3+}(aq) \rightleftharpoons \frac{1}{2}Sn^{4+}(aq) + Fe^{2+}(aq)$? **(4)**

3 At 473 K, the value of K_c for the decomposition of PCl_5 is $8 \times 10^{-3} \, mol \, dm^{-3}$.

$$PCl_5(g) \rightleftharpoons PCl_3(g) + Cl_2(g) \quad \Delta H = +124 \, kJ \, mol^{-1}$$

   a) Write the expression for K_c for the reaction. **(1)**

   b) What is the value of K_c for the reverse reaction at 473 K, and what are its units? **(2)**

   c) A sample of pure PCl_5 is heated to 473 K in a vessel containing no other chemicals. At equilibrium the concentration of PCl_5 is $5 \times 10^{-2} \, mol \, dm^{-3}$. What are the equilibrium concentrations of PCl_3 and Cl_2? **(3)**

   d) Explain how the concentrations of PCl_5, PCl_3 and Cl_2 change in the equilibrium mixture if:

      i) more PCl_5 is added **(2)**

      ii) the pressure is increased **(2)**

      iii) the temperature is increased. **(2)**

   e) What is the effect on the value of K_c if:

      i) more PCl_5 is added **(1)**

      ii) the pressure is increased **(1)**

      iii) the temperature is increased? **(2)**

4 Explain what is wrong with each of the following statements. To what extent, if any, are these statements true?

   a) Once a reaction mixture reaches equilibrium there is no further reaction. **(3)**

   b) Adding more of one of the reactants to an equilibrium mixture increases the yield of products because the value of K_c increases. **(3)**

   c) Adding a catalyst to make a reaction go faster can increase the amount of product at equilibrium. **(3)**

   d) Raising the temperature to make a reaction go faster can increase the amount of product at equilibrium. **(3)**

12 Acids, bases and buffers

Acids and bases are very common not only in laboratories but also in living things, in the home and in the natural environment. Acid–base reactions are reversible and are governed by the equilibrium law. This means that chemists can predict reliably and quantitatively how acids and bases behave. This is important for the supply of safe drinking water, the care of patients in hospitals, the formulation of shampoos and cosmetics – as well as the processing of food and many other aspects of life.

Chemists have several theories to explain the behaviour of acids, but the preferred theory for discussing acid–base equilibria is the Brønsted–Lowry theory. This theory describes acids as proton donors and bases as proton acceptors.

Figure 12.2▲
Polyrhachis laboriosa ants attacking an intruder from a different colony. They are about to kill the intruder by spraying a jet of methanoic acid from their abdomens. This species of ant lives in trees at the edges of tropical forests in Cameroon.

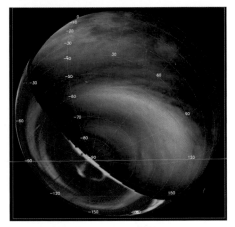

Figure 12.1▲
A composite, false-colour image produced by combining ultraviolet and infrared images from instruments on the European Space Agency's Venus Express spacecraft in July 2007. There is a very thick cloud layer at around 60 kilometres altitude around the planet. This lies between the lower and middle layers of Venus's atmosphere. Scientists now know that the upper part of this layer is composed mostly of tiny droplets of sulfuric acid.

12.1 Acids and bases

Acids

According to the Brønsted–Lowry theory, hydrogen chloride molecules give hydrogen ions (protons) to water molecules when they dissolve in water, producing hydrated hydrogen ions called oxonium ions. The water acts as a base.

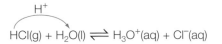

$$\overset{H^+}{\frown}$$
$$HCl(g) + H_2O(l) \rightleftharpoons H_3O^+(aq) + Cl^-(aq)$$

Figure 12.3▲
Proton transfer between hydrogen chloride molecules and water molecules. This is reversible – a proton from the oxonium ion can transfer back to the chloride ion to give hydrogen chloride and water.

Note

It is more correct to represent hydrogen ions in aqueous solution as $H_3O^+(aq)$ – however, chemists commonly use a shorter symbol for hydrated protons, $H^+(aq)$.

A **strong acid** is an acid which is fully ionised when it dissolves in water.

Monobasic acids are acids that can give away (donate) one proton per molecule. Examples are hydrochloric acid, HCl; nitric acid, HNO_3; and ethanoic acid, CH_3COOH. These are also called monoprotic acids.

Dibasic acids are acids that can give away (donate) two protons per molecule. Examples are sulfuric acid, H_2SO_4; and ethanedioic acid, $HOOC-COOH$. These are also called diprotic acids.

Hydrogen chloride is a strong acid. What this means is that it readily gives up its protons to water molecules and the equilibrium in solution lies well over to the right. Hydrogen chloride is effectively completely ionised in solution. Other examples of strong acids are sulfuric acid and nitric acid.

The typical reactions of dilute acids in water are the reactions of aqueous hydrogen ions:

- with metals: $Mg(s) + 2H^+(aq) \rightarrow Mg^{2+}(aq) + H_2(g)$
- with carbonates: $CO_3^{2-}(s) + 2H^+(aq) \rightarrow CO_2(g) + H_2O(l)$
- with bases: $O^{2-}(s) + 2H^+(aq) \rightarrow H_2O(l)$

Test yourself

1 a) What type of bond links the water molecule to a proton in an oxonium ion?
  b) Draw a dot-and-cross diagram to show the bonding in an oxonium ion.
  c) Predict the shape of an oxonium ion.
2 Write a balanced ionic equation for the reaction of 1 mol of ethanedioic acid with 2 mol of sodium hydroxide showing the displayed formulae (see Section 10.3 in *OCR Chemistry for AS*) for the acid and for the ethanedioate ion formed.
3 a) Identify the products of the reaction when concentrated sulfuric acid reacts with sodium chloride.
  b) Show that this is a proton transfer reaction
  c) Account for the fact that this reaction can give a good yield of hydrogen chloride gas.
4 Write ionic equations to show the reactions of nitric acid with:
  a) zinc   b) potassium carbonate
  c) calcium oxide   d) lithium hydroxide.

Bases

A base is a molecule or ion which can accept a hydrogen ion (proton) from an acid. A base has a lone pair of electrons, which can form a dative covalent bond with a proton.

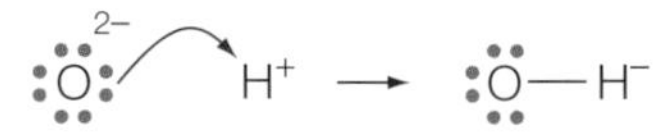

$$:\overset{..}{\underset{..}{O}}:^{2-} \quad H^+ \longrightarrow \quad :\overset{..}{\underset{..}{O}}-H^- $$

An ionic oxide, such as calcium oxide, reacts completely with water to form calcium hydroxide. The calcium ions do not change. But the oxide ions, which are powerful proton acceptors, all take protons from water molecules. The oxide ion is a strong base. Common bases include the oxide and hydroxide ions, ammonia, amines, as well as the carbonate and hydrogencarbonate ions.

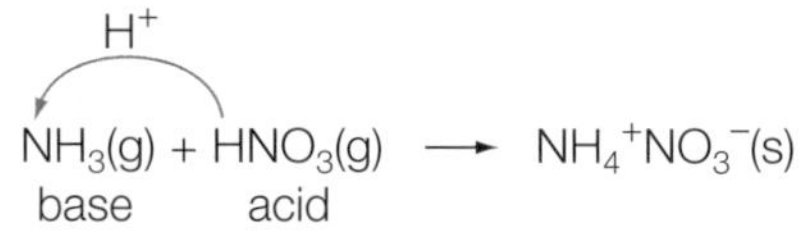

$$ \overset{H^+}{\overbrace{\qquad}} $$
$$ NH_3(g) + HNO_3(g) \longrightarrow NH_4^+NO_3^-(s) $$
$$ \text{base} \qquad \text{acid} $$

In biochemistry, the term 'base' often refers to one of the five nitrogenous bases which make up nucleotides and the nucleic acids DNA and RNA. These compounds (adenine, guanine, cytosine, uracil and thymine) are bases in the chemical sense because they have lone pairs on nitrogen atoms which can accept hydrogen ions.

Figure 12.4 ▶
Oxide ions have lone pairs of electrons which can form dative covalent bonds with hydrogen ions.

Figure 12.5 ▶
There is a lone pair on the nitrogen atom of ammonia which allows it to act as a base.

Figure 12.6 ▶
The displayed formula of adenine. This is one of the bases in DNA.

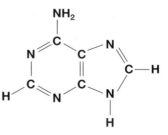

Test yourself

5 Show that the reactions between the following pairs of compounds are acid–base reactions, and identify as precisely as possible the molecules or ions which are the acid and the base in each example.
   a) MgO + HCl
   b) H_2SO_4 + NH_3
   c) NH_4NO_3 + NaOH
   d) HCl + Na_2CO_3
6 a) What type of bond links the ammonia molecule to a proton in an ammonium ion?
   b) Draw a dot-and-cross diagram to show the bonding in an ammonium ion.
   c) Predict the shape of an ammonium ion.
7 How many lone pairs of electrons are there in a molecule of adenine (Figure 12.6)?

Conjugate acid–base pairs

Any acid–base reaction involves competition for protons. This is illustrated by a solution of an ammonium salt, such as ammonium chloride, in water:

$$NH_4^+(aq) + H_2O(l) \rightleftharpoons NH_3(aq) + H_3O^+(aq)$$
$$\text{acid 1} \quad \text{base 2} \quad \text{base 1} \quad \text{acid 2}$$

In this example there is competition for protons between ammonia molecules and water molecules. On the left-hand side of the equation, the protons are held by lone pairs on the ammonia molecules. On the right-hand side, they are held by lone pairs on water molecules. The position of equilibrium shows which of the two bases has the stronger hold on the protons.

Chemists use the term 'conjugate acid–base pair' to describe a pair of molecules or ions which can be converted from one to the other by the gain or loss of a proton. The equilibrium in a solution of an ammonium salt above involves two conjugate acid–base pairs:

● NH_4^+ and NH_3
● H_3O^+ and H_2O.

Definitions

An acid turns into its **conjugate base** when it loses a proton. A base turns into its **conjugate acid** when it gains a proton.

Any pair of compounds made up of an acid and a base that can be converted from one to the other by proton transfer is a **conjugate acid–base pair**.

Test yourself

8 Identify and name the conjugate bases of these acids: HNO_3, CH_3COOH, H_2SO_4, HCO_3^-
9 Identify and name the conjugate acids of these bases: O^{2-}, OH^-, NH_3, CO_3^{2-}, HCO_3^-, SO_4^{2-}.
10 Explain and illustrate these two statements:
   a) the stronger the acid, the weaker its conjugate base
   b) the stronger the base, the weaker its conjugate acid.

12.2 The pH scale

The concentration of hydrogen ions in aqueous solutions commonly ranges from $2\,mol\,dm^{-3}$ to $1 \times 10^{-14}\,mol\,dm^{-3}$. The concentration of aqueous hydrogen ions in dilute hydrochloric acid is about $100\,000\,000\,000\,000$ times greater than the concentration of hydrogen ions in dilute sodium hydroxide solution.

Given such a wide range of concentrations, chemists find it convenient to use a logarithmic scale to measure the concentration of aqueous hydrogen ions in acidic or alkaline solutions – this is the pH scale. The definition of pH is:

$$pH = -\log[H^+(aq)]$$

Figure 12.7 ▲
A scientist measuring the pH of glacier melt water during research into air and water pollution.

Acids, bases and buffers

increasingly acidic ← → neutral ← → increasingly alkaline

Figure 12.8▲
The pH scale showing the colours of full-range indicator at the different pH values.

Note

Strictly speaking, the definition of pH is given by:

$$pH = -\log_{10}\frac{[H^+(aq)]}{1\ \text{mol dm}^{-3}}$$

because mathematically it is only possible to take logarithms of numbers and not of quantities with units. Dividing by a standard concentration of 1 mol dm^{-3} does not change the value, but does cancel the units.

www
Tutorial

Definition

Chemists use **logarithms to base 10** to handle values that range over several orders of magnitude. Logarithms to base 10 are defined such that:

- $\log 10^3 = 3$
- $\log 10^2 = 2$
- $\log 10^1 = 1$
- $\log 10^0 = 0$
- $\log 10^{-1} = -1$
- $\log 10^{-2} = -2$

In general, $\log 10^x = x$. For example, $2 = 10^{0.301}$, so $\log_{10} 2 = 0.301$.

By definition:

$$\log xy = \log x + \log y$$

and

$$\log x^n = n \log x.$$

So it follows that

$$\log\frac{1}{x} = \log x^{-1} = -\log x.$$

Worked examples

1 What is the pH of 0.020 mol dm^{-3} hydrochloric acid?

Notes on the method
Hydrochloric acid is a strong acid so it is fully ionised.
Note that 1 mol HCl gives 1 mol H$^+$(aq).
Use the log button on your calculator.
Do not forget the minus sign in the definition of pH.

Answer
$[H^+(aq)] = [HCl(aq)] = 0.020$ mol dm^{-3}
$pH = -\log(0.020) = 1.70$

2 The pH of human blood is 7.40. What is the aqueous hydrogen ion concentration in blood?

Notes on the method
$pH = -\log[H^+(aq)]$
From the definition of logarithms, this rearranges to $[H^+(aq)] = 10^{-pH}$
Use the inverse log button (10^x) on your calculator – not forgetting the minus sign in the definition of pH.

Answer
$pH = 7.4$
$[H^+(aq)] = 10^{-7.4}$
$= 4.0 \times 10^{-8}$ mol dm^{-3}

Test yourself

11 What is the pH of solutions of hydrochloric acid with these concentrations?
   a) 0.1 mol dm^{-3}
   b) 0.01 mol dm^{-3}
   c) 0.001 mol dm^{-3}
12 Calculate the pH of a 0.08 mol dm^{-3} solution of nitric acid.
13 What is the concentration of hydrogen ions in these solutions?
   a) orange juice with a pH of 3.3
   b) coffee with a pH of 5.4
   c) saliva with a pH of 6.7
   d) a suspension of an antacid in water with a pH of 10.5

The ionic product of water

There are hydrogen ions and hydroxide ions even in pure water because of the transfer of hydrogen ions between water molecules. This only happens to a very slight extent:

$$H_2O(l) + H_2O(l) \rightleftharpoons H_3O^+(aq) + OH^-(aq)$$

This can be written more simply as:

$$H_2O(l) \rightleftharpoons H^+(aq) + OH^-(aq)$$

The equilibrium constant $K_c = \dfrac{[H^+(aq)][OH^-(aq)]}{[H_2O(l)]}$

There is a very large excess of water, so $[H_2O(l)]$ = a constant, so the relationship simplifies to:

$$K_w = [H^+(aq)][OH^-(aq)]$$

where K_w is the ionic product of water.

The pH of pure water at 298 K is 7.0. So, the hydrogen ion concentration at equilibrium is given by $[H^+(aq)] = 1 \times 10^{-7}\,mol\,dm^{-3}$.

Also, in pure water $[H^+(aq)] = [OH^-(aq)]$. So, the concentration of hydroxide ions is given by $[OH^-(aq)] = 1 \times 10^{-7}\,mol\,dm^{-3}$.

Hence, the ionic product of water is given by $K_w = 1 \times 10^{-14}\,mol^2\,dm^{-6}$.

K_w is a constant in all aqueous solutions at 298 K. This makes it possible to calculate the pH of alkalis.

Worked example

What is the pH of a 0.05 mol dm^{-3} solution of sodium hydroxide?

Notes on the method
Sodium hydroxide is fully ionised in solution.
So in this solution $[OH^-(aq)] = 0.05\,mol\,dm^{-3}$ and pH $= -\log[H^+(aq)]$.

Answer
For this solution:

$$K_w = [H^+(aq)] \times 0.05\,mol\,dm^{-3}$$
$$= 1 \times 10^{-14}\,mol^2\,dm^{-6}$$

$$So\ [H^+(aq)] = \frac{1 \times 10^{-14}\,mol^2\,dm^{-6}}{0.05\,mol\,dm^{-3}}$$

$$= 2 \times 10^{-13}\,mol\,dm^{-3}$$

Hence, pH $= -\log(2 \times 10^{-13}) = 12.7$

Test yourself

14 The value of K_w varies with temperature. At 273 K its value is $1.1 \times 10^{-15}\,mol^2\,dm^{-6}$, while at 303 K it is $1.5 \times 10^{-14}\,mol^2\,dm^{-6}$.
   a) Is the ionisation of water an exothermic process or an endothermic process?
   b) What happens to the hydrogen ion concentration in pure water as the temperature increases? What happens to the pH?
   c) Does pure water stop being neutral if its temperature is above or below 298 K?
15 Calculate the pH of these solutions:
   a) 1.0 mol dm^{-3} NaOH   b) 0.02 mol dm^{-3} KOH
   c) 0.001 mol dm^{-3} Ba(OH)$_2$.

Figure 12.9 ◄
Tufa towers at Lake Mono, California. They were first exposed when the water level in the lake dropped because water was diverted, to Los Angeles, from rivers feeding the lake. These pillars of calcium carbonate were created underwater when water from underground streams rich in calcium salts mixed with the lake water, which was alkaline because it was rich in hydrogencarbonates.

Working in logarithms

The logarithmic form of equilibrium constants is particularly useful for pH calculations. Taking logarithms produces a conveniently small scale of values.

$$K_w = [H^+(aq)][OH^-(aq)] = 1 \times 10^{-14} \text{ at } 298\,K$$

Taking logarithms, and applying the rule that $\log xy = \log x + \log y$, gives:

$$\log K_w = \log[H^+(aq)] + \log[OH^-(aq)] = \log 10^{-14} = -14$$

Multiplying through by -1 reverses the signs:

$$-\log K_w = -\log[H^+(aq)] - \log[OH^-(aq)] = 14$$

Hence, $pK_w = pH + pOH = 14$, where, by analogy with pH:

- pK_w is defined as $-\log K_w$
- pOH is defined as $-\log[OH^-(aq)]$.

So, you can see that $pH = 14 - pOH$, which makes it easy to calculate the pH of alkaline solutions.

> **Note**
>
> Don't try to remember the formula $pH = 14 - pOH$. Only use it if you can work it out quickly for yourself from the definition of K_w.

Worked example

What is the pH of a $0.05\,mol\,dm^{-3}$ solution of sodium hydroxide?

Notes on the method
Sodium hydroxide, NaOH, is a strong base so it is fully ionised.
Find the values of logarithms with the log button of your calculator.

Answer
$[OH^-(aq)] = 0.05\,mol\,dm^{-3}$
$pOH = -\log 0.05 = 1.3$
$pH = 14 - pOH = 14 - 1.3 = 12.7$

12.3 Weak acids and bases

Most organic acids and bases ionise to only a slight extent in aqueous solution. Carboxylic acids (see Section 3.2) such as ethanoic acid in vinegar, citric acid in fruit juices and lactic acid in sour milk are all weak acids. Ammonia and amines (see Section 4.2) are weak bases.

Weak acids

Weak acids, such as ethanoic acid, are only slightly ionised when they dissolve in water. In a $0.1\,mol\,dm^{-3}$ solution of ethanoic acid, for example, only about 1 in a 100 molecules ionise to produce hydrogen ions:

$$CH_3COOH(aq) \rightleftharpoons CH_3COO^-(aq) + H^+(aq)$$

This means that the pH of a $0.1\,mol\,dm^{-3}$ of ethanoic acid is 2.9, and not 1 as it would be if it were a strong acid.

There is a very important distinction between acid strength and concentration – strength is the extent of ionisation; concentration is the amount, in moles, of acid in a cubic decimetre. It takes just as much sodium hydroxide to neutralise $25\,cm^3$ of a $0.1\,mol\,dm^{-3}$ solution of a weak acid as it does to neutralise $25\,cm^3$ of $0.1\,mol\,dm^{-3}$ of a solution of a strong acid such as hydrochloric acid.

Figure 12.10▲
Bacteria added to milk ferment the lactose sugar and turn it into lactic acid. The acid turns the milk into yogurt and also restricts the growth of food poisoning bacteria.

Test yourself

16 Explain why measuring the pH of a solution of an acid does not provide enough evidence to show whether the acid is strong or weak.

17 Explain why it takes the same amount of sodium hydroxide to neutralise $25\,cm^3$ of $0.1\,mol\,dm^{-3}$ ethanoic acid as it does to neutralise $25\,cm^3$ of $0.1\,mol\,dm^{-3}$ hydrochloric acid.

Weak bases

Weak bases are only slightly ionised when they dissolve in water. In a $0.1\,mol\,dm^{-3}$ solution of ammonia, for example, 99 in every 100 molecules do not react and remain as dissolved molecules. Only 1 molecule in a 100 reacts to form ammonium ions:

$$NH_3(aq) + H_2O(l) \rightleftharpoons NH_4^+(aq) + OH^-(aq)$$

As with weak acids, it is important to distinguish between strength and concentration.

Acid dissociation constants

Chemists use the equilibrium constant, K_a, for the reversible ionisation of a weak acid as a measure of its strength. Such an equilibrium constant shows the extent to which an acid dissociates into ions in solution.

A weak acid can be represented by the general formula HA, where A^- is the ion produced when the acid ionises:

$$HA(aq) \rightleftharpoons H^+(aq) + A^-(aq)$$

According to the equilibrium law, the equilibrium constant takes this form:

$$K_a = \frac{[H^+(aq)][A^-(aq)]}{[HA(aq)]}$$

In this context, the equilibrium constant, K_a, is called the acid dissociation constant. Given a value of K_a it is possible to calculate the pH of a solution of a weak acid.

Data

Test yourself

18 If a weak acid is shown as HA, what is A^- in the particular case of:
  a) hydrogen fluoride
  b) methanoic acid
  c) phenol?

Worked example

Calculate the hydrogen ion concentration and the pH of a $0.01\,mol\,dm^{-3}$ solution of propanoic acid. K_a for the acid is $1.3 \times 10^{-5}\,mol\,dm^{-3}$.

Tutorial

Notes on the method
Two approximations simplify the calculation.
1 The first assumption is that $[H^+(aq)] = [A^-(aq)]$ at equilibrium. In this example A^- is the propanoate ion $CH_3CH_2COO^-$. This assumption seems obvious from the equation for the ionisation of a weak acid, but it ignores the hydrogen ions from the ionisation of water. Water produces far fewer hydrogen ions than most weak acids so its ionisation can usually be ignored. This assumption is acceptable so long as the pH of the acid is below 6.
2 The second assumption is that so little of the propanoic acid ionises in water that $[HA(aq)] \approx 0.01\,mol\,dm^{-3}$ at equilibrium – HA represents propanoic acid here. This is a riskier assumption that has to be checked because in very dilute solutions the degree of ionisation may become quite large relative to the amount of acid in the solution. Chemists generally accept that this assumption is acceptable so long as less than 5% of the acid ionises.

Answer
$$CH_3CH_2COOH(aq) \rightleftharpoons H^+(aq) + CH_3CH_2COO^-(aq)$$

$$K_a = \frac{[H^+(aq)][CH_3CH_2COO^-(aq)]}{[CH_3CH_2COOH(aq)]}$$

$$= \frac{[H^+(aq)]^2}{0.01\,mol\,dm^{-3}}$$

$$= 1.3 \times 10^{-5}\,mol\,dm^{-3}$$

Therefore, $[H^+(aq)]^2 = 1.3 \times 10^{-7}\,\text{mol}^2\,\text{dm}^{-6}$

So, $[H^+(aq)] = 3.6 \times 10^{-4}\,\text{mol dm}^{-3}$

So, $pH = -\log[H^+(aq)]$

$= -\log(3.6 \times 10^{-4})$

$= 3.4$

Check the second assumption – in this case, less than $0.0004\,\text{mol dm}^{-3}$ of the $0.0100\,\text{mol dm}^{-3}$ of acid (4%) has ionised. In this instance, the degree of ionisation is small enough to justify the assumption that $[HA(aq)] \approx$ the concentration of un-ionised acid.

Practical guidance

One method which can, in principle, be used to measure K_a for a weak acid is to measure the pH of a solution when the concentration of the acid is known accurately. This is not a good method for determining the size of K_a because the pH values of dilute solutions are very susceptible to contamination – for example by dissolved carbon dioxide from the air.

Worked example

Calculate the K_a of lactic acid given that the pH of a $0.10\,\text{mol dm}^{-3}$ solution of the acid is 2.43.

Notes on the method
The same two approximations simplify the calculation:

1   Assume that $[H^+(aq)] = [A^-(aq)]$, where $A^-(aq)$ represents the aqueous lactate ion. Since the pH is well below 6 this is certainly justified.

2   Also assume that so little of the lactic acid ionises in water that at equilibrium $[HA(aq)] \approx 0.1\,\text{mol dm}^{-3}$. Here HA represents lactic acid. This is a riskier assumption which can be checked during the calculation.

Answer

$pH = 2.43$

$[H^+(aq)] = 10^{-2.43} = 3.72 \times 10^{-3}\,\text{mol dm}^{-3}$

$[H^+(aq)] = [A^-(aq)] = 3.72 \times 10^{-3}\,\text{mol dm}^{-3}$

In this example, less than 5% of the acid is ionised (less than 0.004 out of 0.100 mol in each cubic decimetre.)

So $[HA(aq)] \approx 0.1\,\text{mol dm}^{-3}$

Substituting in the expression for K_a:

$$K_a = \frac{[H^+(aq)][A^-(aq)]}{[HA(aq)]}$$

$$= \frac{(3.72 \times 10^{-3}\,\text{mol dm}^{-3})^2}{0.1\,\text{mol dm}^{-3}}$$

$$= 1.38 \times 10^{-4}\,\text{mol dm}^{-3}$$

Test yourself

19 Calculate the pH of a $0.01\,\text{mol}\,\text{dm}^{-3}$ solution of hydrogen cyanide given that $K_a = 4.9 \times 10^{-10}\,\text{mol}\,\text{dm}^{-3}$.

20 Calculate the pH of a $0.05\,\text{mol}\,\text{dm}^{-3}$ solution of ethanoic acid given that $K_a = 1.7 \times 10^{-5}\,\text{mol}\,\text{dm}^{-3}$.

21 Calculate K_a for methanoic acid given that the pH of a $0.050\,\text{mol}\,\text{dm}^{-3}$ solution of the acid is 2.55.

22 Calculate K_a for butanoic acid, C_3H_7COOH, given that the pH of a $0.01\,\text{mol}\,\text{dm}^{-3}$ solution of the acid is 3.42.

Working in logarithms

Chemists find it convenient to define a quantity $pK_a = -\log K_a$ when working with weak acids. This definition means that hydrocyanic acid, HCN, with a pK_a value of 9.3 is a much weaker acid than nitrous acid, HNO_2, with a pK_a value of 3.3. Books of data tabulate pK_a values.

The relationship between acid strength and pH can be expressed more simply because both are logarithmic quantities.

$$K_a = \frac{[H^+(aq)][A^-(aq)]}{[HA(aq)]}$$

The two common assumptions when using this expression in calculations are that:

- $[H^+(aq)] = [A^-(aq)]$
- $[HA(aq)] = c_A$, where c_A = the concentration of the un-ionised acid.

Substituting in the expression for K_a gives:

$$K_a = \frac{[H^+(aq)]^2}{c_A}$$

Hence, $K_a \times c_A = [H^+(aq)]^2$

Taking logarithms: $\log(K_a \times c_A) = \log [H^+(aq)]^2$

Applying the rules that $\log xy = \log x + \log y$ and that $\log x^n = n \log x$, gives:

$$\log K_a + \log c_A = 2 \times \log [H^+(aq)]$$

which, on multiplying by -1, becomes:

$$-\log K_a - \log c_A = -2 \times \log [H^+(aq)]$$

Hence, $pK_a - \log c_A = 2 \times pH$

This shows that for a solution of a weak acid which is less than 5% ionised:

$$pH = \tfrac{1}{2}(pK_a - \log c_A)$$

which rearranges to $pK_a = 2pH + \log c_A$.

Note

Do not try to remember this logarithmic form of the equilibrium law. The relationship is easy to use, but only apply it if you can derive it quickly from first principles as shown here. Do not forget that this form of the law has two built-in assumptions, so it only applies when these assumptions are acceptable.

Test yourself

23 What is the value of pK_a for methanoic acid given that $K_a = 1.6 \times 10^{-4}\,\text{mol}\,\text{dm}^{-3}$?

24 What is the value of K_a for benzoic acid given that $pK_a = 4.2$?

25 Show that the logarithmic relationship $pK_a = 2pH + \log c_A$ gives the same answers from the data as the methods used in the worked examples from pages 153 and 154.

The acid strength of halogenated carboxylic acids

Introducing a halogen atom into the structure of a carboxylic acid can have a marked effect on its acid strength. This is illustrated by the values in Table 12.1.

Acid	K_a/mol dm^{-3}	pK_a
ethanoic acid	1.7×10^{-5}	4.8
fluoroethanoic acid	2.2×10^{-3}	2.7
chloroethanoic acid	1.3×10^{-3}	2.9
iodoethanoic acid	7.6×10^{-4}	3.1
dichloroethanoic acid	5.0×10^{-2}	1.3
trichloroethanoic acid	2.3×10^{-1}	0.7
butanoic acid	1.5×10^{-5}	4.8
2-chlorobutanoic acid	1.4×10^{-3}	2.8
3-chlorobutanoic acid	8.7×10^{-5}	4.0
4-bromobutanoic acid	3.0×10^{-5}	4.5

Table 12.1▲

1 Calculate the pH of a 0.1 mol dm^{-3} solution of:

   a) butanoic acid

   b) trichlorethanoic acid.

2 **a)** What is the pattern in the acid strength of fluoro-, chloro- and iodoethanoic acids when compared with the value for ethanoic acid?

   b) Suggest an explanation for the pattern.

3 **a)** What is the pattern in the acid strength of chloro-, dichloro- and trichloroethanoic acids when compared with the value for ethanoic acid?

   b) Is the pattern consistent with your suggested explanation in question **2 b)**?

4 **a)** What is the pattern in the acid strength of the chlorinated butanoic acids when compared with the value for butanoic acid?

   b) Suggest an explanation for the pattern.

12.4 Buffer solutions

Buffer solutions contain mixtures of molecules and ions in solution which help to keep pH more or less constant. Buffer solutions help to stabilise the pH of blood, medicines, shampoos, swimming pools and of many other solutions in living things, domestic products and in the environment.

A buffer solution cannot prevent pH changes, but can even out the large swings in pH that can happen without a buffer.

Buffers are important in living organisms. For example, the pH of blood is closely controlled by buffers within the narrow range 7.35 to 7.45. Chemists use buffers when they want to investigate chemical reactions at a fixed pH.

Figure 12.11▲
Eye drops contain a buffer solution to make sure that they do not irritate the sensitive surface of the eye.

Figure 12.12▲
Many shampoos for animals, as well as for people, contain a buffer solution. They are marketed as 'pH balanced' shampoos.

Buffers are equilibrium systems which illustrate the practical importance of the equilibrium law. A typical buffer mixture consists of a solution of a weak acid and one of its salts – for example, a mixture of ethanoic acid and sodium ethanoate. There must be plenty of both the acid and its salt.

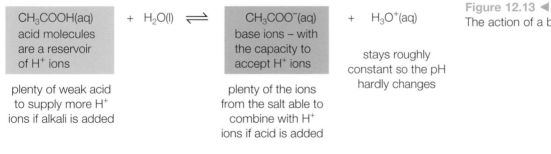

| $CH_3COOH(aq)$ acid molecules are a reservoir of H^+ ions | + $H_2O(l)$ ⇌ | $CH_3COO^-(aq)$ base ions – with the capacity to accept H^+ ions | + $H_3O^+(aq)$ |

plenty of weak acid to supply more H^+ ions if alkali is added

plenty of the ions from the salt able to combine with H^+ ions if acid is added

stays roughly constant so the pH hardly changes

Figure 12.13 ◄
The action of a buffer solution.

Le Chatelier's principle provides a qualitative explanation of the buffering action. Adding a small amount of a strong acid temporarily increases the concentration of $H^+(aq)$, so the equilibrium shifts to the left to counteract the change. Adding a small amount of a strong alkali temporarily decreases the concentration of $H^+(aq)$, so the equilibrium shifts to the right to counteract the change.

Test yourself

26 Show that the buffer solution in Figure 12.13 consists of a conjugate acid–base pair.
27 Explain why a weak acid on its own cannot make a buffer solution, but a mixture of a weak acid and one of its salts can.

The pH of buffer solutions

By choosing the right weak acid, it is possible to prepare buffers at any pH value throughout the pH scale. If the concentrations of the weak acid and its salt are the same, then the pH of the buffer is equal to pK_a for the acid. The pH of a buffer mixture can be calculated with the help of the equilibrium law.

$$K_a = \frac{[H^+(aq)][A^-(aq)]}{[HA(aq)]}$$

This rearranges to give $[H^+(aq)] = \dfrac{K_a \times [HA(aq)]}{[A^-(aq)]}$, from which the pH can be calculated.

So the equilibrium law makes it possible to calculate the pH of a buffer solution made from a mixture of a weak acid and its conjugate base.

In a mixture of a weak acid and its salt, the weak acid is only slightly ionised, while the salt is fully ionised. This means that it is often accurate enough to assume that:

- all the HA molecules come from the added acid
- all the negative ions, $A^-(aq)$, come from the added salt.

So the calculation of the hydrogen ion concentration of a buffer solution can be based on the expression:

$$[H^+(aq)] = K_a \times \frac{[acid]}{[salt]}$$

Diluting a buffer solution with water does not change the *ratio* of the concentrations of the salt and acid, so the pH does not change unless the dilution is so great that the assumptions used to arrive at this formula break down.

Worked example

www
Tutorial

What is the pH of a buffer solution containing $0.40\,\text{mol dm}^{-3}$ methanoic acid and $1.00\,\text{mol dm}^{-3}$ sodium methanoate?

Notes on the answer
Look up the value of K_a in a table of data: K_a for methanoic acid is $1.6 \times 10^{-4}\,\text{mol dm}^{-3}$.

Make the assumptions that all the methanoic acid molecules come from the added acid, and that all the methanoate ions come from the added salt.

Answer
From the information in the question, $[acid] = 0.40\,\text{mol dm}^{-3}$ and $[salt] = 1.00\,\text{mol dm}^{-3}$.

Substituting in the expression gives:

$$[H^+(aq)] = K_a \times \frac{[acid]}{[salt]}$$

$$= 1.6 \times 10^{-4}\,\text{mol dm}^{-3} \times \frac{0.40\,\text{mol dm}^{-3}}{1.00\,\text{mol dm}^{-3}}$$

$$[H^+(aq)] = 6.4 \times 10^{-5}\,\text{mol dm}^{-3}$$

So, $pH = -\log [H^+(aq)]$

$$= -\log [6.4 \times 10^{-5}]$$

$$= 4.2$$

Test yourself

28 Calculate the pH of these buffer mixtures.
  a) A solution containing equal amounts, in moles, of $H_2PO_4^-$(aq) and HPO_4^{2-}(aq). K_a for the dihydrogenphosphate(v) ion is 6.3×10^{-7} mol dm^{-3}.
  b) A solution containing 12.2 g of benzenecarboxylic acid (C_6H_5COOH) and 7.2 g of sodium benzenecarboxylate in 250 cm^3 of aqueous solution. K_a for benzenecarboxylic acid is 6.3×10^{-5} mol dm^{-3}.
  c) A solution containing 12.2 g benzenecarboxylic acid (C_6H_5COOH) and 7.2 g of sodium benzenecarboxylate in 1000 cm^3 of aqueous solution.
29 What is the ratio of the concentrations of the ethanoate ions and the ethanoic acid molecules in a buffer solution with pH = 5.4? K_a for ethanoic acid is 1.7×10^{-5} mol dm^{-3}.

Activity

Blood buffers

In a healthy person, the pH of blood lies within a narrow range (7.35–7.45). Chemical reactions in cells tend to upset the normal pH. Respiration, for example, produces carbon dioxide all the time. The carbon dioxide diffuses into the blood, where it is mainly in the form of carbonic acid, H_2CO_3. However, the blood pH stays constant because it is stabilised by buffer solutions – in particular by the buffer system based on the equilibrium between carbon dioxide, water and hydrogencarbonate ions. This is the carbonic acid–hydrogencarbonate buffer.

$$CO_2(g) + H_2O(l) \rightleftharpoons H^+(aq) + HCO_3^-(aq)$$

Proteins in blood, including haemoglobin, can also contribute to the buffering of blood pH. This is because the molecules contain both acidic and basic functional groups (see Sections 5.1 and 5.3).

Two major organs help to control the total amounts of carbonic acid and hydrogencarbonate ions in the blood. The lungs remove excess carbon dioxide from the blood and the kidneys remove excess hydrogencarbonate ions.

The brain responds to the level of carbon dioxide in the blood. During exercise, for example, the brain speeds up the rate of breathing.

The consequences can be fatal if the blood pH moves outside the normal range. Patients who have been badly burned or suffered other serious injuries are treated quickly with a drip into a vein. One of the purposes of an intravenous drip is to help to maintain the pH of the blood close to its normal value.

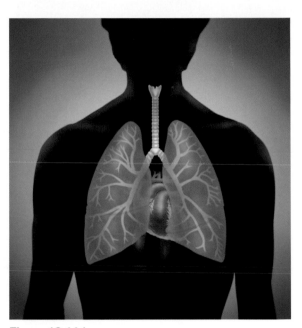

Figure 12.14 ▲
The lungs have a vital part to play in maintaining the pH of the blood.

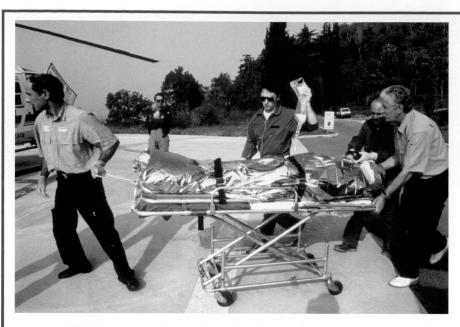

1 Write an equation to show aqueous carbon dioxide reacting with water to form hydrogen ions and hydrogencarbonate ions.

2 Explain why breathing faster and more deeply tends to raise the blood pH.

3 a) Suggest two reason why the blood pH tends to fall during strenuous exercise.

  b) Why do people breathe faster and more deeply when running?

4 a) Write the K_a expression for the equilibrium between carbon dioxide, water, hydrogen ions and hydrogencarbonate ions.

  b) In a sample of blood, the concentration of hydrogencarbonate ions is $2.5 \times 10^{-2}\,\text{mol dm}^{-3}$. The concentration of aqueous carbon dioxide is $1.25 \times 10^{-3}\,\text{mol dm}^{-3}$. The value of $K_a = 4.5 \times 10^{-7}\,\text{mol dm}^{-3}$. Use this information to calculate:

    i) the hydrogen ion concentration in the blood

    ii) the pH of the blood.

    iii) What can you conclude about the person who gave the blood sample?

5 Explain why a mixture of carbon dioxide, water and hydrogencarbonate ions can act as a buffer solution.

6 Give one example each of an acidic functional group and a basic functional group that means that a protein can help to buffer blood pH.

7 Why are blood buffers on their own unable to maintain the correct blood pH for any length of time?

8 Suggest reasons why people may need treatment to adjust their blood pH if they have been rescued after breathing thick smoke during a fire.

12.5 Acid–base titrations

The equilibrium law helps to explain what happens during acid–base titrations and it provides a basis for the selection of the right indicator for a titration.

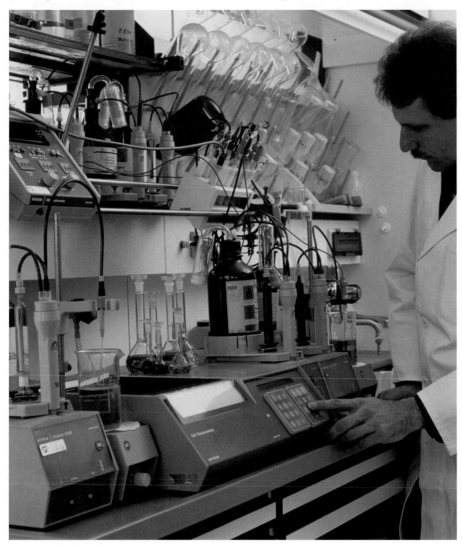

Figure 12.16 ▲
Chemist operating a computer controlled automatic titrator.

The pH changes during a titration as a solution of an alkali runs from a burette and mixes with an acid in a flask. Plotting the pH against the volume of alkali added gives a shape that is determined by the nature of the acid and the base. Usually there is a marked change in pH near the equivalence point and it is this that makes it possible to detect the end-point of the titration with an indicator.

It is common to use an indicator to find the end-point during a titration. This is the point at which the colour change of the indicator shows that enough of the solution in the burette has been added to react with the amount of the acid in the flask. In a well-planned titration, the colour change observed at the end-point corresponds exactly with the equivalence point.

The equivalence point is the point during any titration when the amount, in moles, of the reactant added from a burette is just enough to react exactly with all the measured amount of the acid in the flask as shown by the balanced equation.

An alternative method of following the course of a titration and determining the equivalence point is to use a pH meter.

Figure 12.17▲
Apparatus for measuring the changes in pH during an acid–base titration.

Activity

Titration of a strong acid with a strong base

Strong acids and strong bases are fully ionised in solution.
Figure 12.18 shows the shape of the pH curve for a titration of a strong acid, such as hydrochloric acid, with a strong base, such as sodium hydroxide.

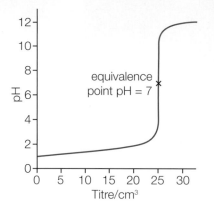

Figure 12.18◄
The pH change on gradually adding 0.1 mol dm^{-3} NaOH(aq) from a burette to 25 cm^3 of 0.1 mol dm^{-3} HCl(aq) .

1 Show that pH = 1 for a solution of 0.1 mol dm^{-3} HCl(aq).

2 Why does the pH equal 7 at the equivalence point of a titration of a strong acid with a strong base?

3 Calculate the pH of 25 cm^3 of a solution of sodium chloride after adding:

   a) 0.05 cm^3 (1 drop) of 0.1 mol dm^{-3} of HCl(aq)

   b) 0.05 cm^3 (1 drop) of 0.1 mol dm^{-3} of NaOH(aq).

   (In both instances assume that the volume change on adding the single drop is insignificant.)

4 Calculate the pH of the solution produced by adding 5 cm^3 of 0.1 mol dm^{-3} NaOH(aq) to 25 cm^3 of a solution of sodium chloride.

5 Show that your answers to questions **1**, **2** and **3** are consistent with Figure 12.18.

6 What features of the curve plotted in Figure 12.18 are important to the practical accuracy of acid–base titrations of this kind?

Titration of a weak acid with a strong base

If the acid in the titration flask is weak, then the equilibrium law applies and the pH curve up to the equivalence point can be calculated with the help of the expression for K_a.

Consider, for example, the reaction of ethanoic acid with sodium hydroxide during a titration. At the start, the flask contains the pure acid:

$$CH_3COOH(aq) \rightleftharpoons H^+(aq) + CH_3COO^-(aq)$$

The pH of the pure acid can be calculated from K_a as shown in Section 12.3. When some strong alkali runs in from the burette, some of the ethanoic acid reacts to produce sodium ethanoate. Once this has happened $[H^+(aq)] \neq [CH_3COO^-(aq)]$ and the method of calculating the pH has to change to account for this. After adding some alkali, and before reaching the end-point, the titration flask contains a buffer solution. The pH is calculated using the same method as for buffer solutions (see Section 12.4).

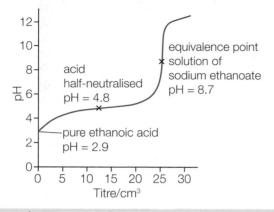

Figure 12.19 ◄
The pH change on adding 0.1 mol dm^{-3} NaOH(aq) from a burette to 25 cm^3 of a 0.1 mol dm^{-3} solution of CH$_3$COOH(aq).

Worked example

What is the pH of the mixture formed during a titration after adding 20.0 cm^3 of 0.10 mol dm^{-3} NaOH(aq) to 25.0 cm^3 of a 0.10 mol dm^{-3} solution of CH$_3$COOH(aq) if $K_a = 1.7 \times 10^{-5}$ mol dm^{-3}?

Notes on the method
The pH of the mixture can be estimated quite accurately using the equilibrium law by assuming that:

- the concentration of ethanoic acid molecules at equilibrium is determined by the amount of acid which has yet to be neutralised
- the concentration of ethanoate ions is determined by the amount of acid converted to sodium ethanoate.

This is the same as the assumptions made when calculating the pH of buffer solutions.

Answer
The total volume of the solution is 45.0 cm^3.
5.0 cm^3 of the 0.1 mol dm^{-3} ethanoic acid solution remains not neutralised and this has been diluted to a total volume of 45 cm^3 solution.

So the concentration of ethanoic acid molecules $= \dfrac{5.0 \text{ cm}^3}{45.0 \text{ cm}^3} \times 0.10 \text{ mol dm}^{-3}$

Also, the concentration of ethanoate ions $= \dfrac{20.0 \text{ cm}^3}{45.0 \text{ cm}^3} \times 0.10 \text{ mol dm}^{-3}$

So the ratio $\dfrac{[\text{acid}]}{[\text{salt}]} = \dfrac{[CH_3COOH(aq)]}{[CH_3COO^-(aq)]}$

$$= \dfrac{5.0}{20.0}$$

Substituting in the rearranged expression for the equilibrium law gives:

$[H^+(aq)] = K_a \times \dfrac{[\text{acid}]}{[\text{salt}]}$

$\qquad = 1.7 \times 10^{-5} \text{ mol dm}^{-3} \times \dfrac{5.0}{20.0}$

$\qquad = 4.25 \times 10^{-6} \text{ mol dm}^{-3}$

So, $\quad$ pH $= -\log[H^+(aq)]$

$\qquad = -\log[4.25 \times 10^{-6}]$

$\qquad = 5.4$

Note in Figure 12.19 that at halfway to the equivalence point, the added alkali has converted half of the weak acid to its salt. In this example, at this point $[CH_3COOH(aq)] = [CH_3COO^-(aq)]$.

So, $[H^+(aq)] = K_a \times \dfrac{[CH_3COOH(aq)]}{[CH_3COO^-(aq)]} = K_a$

Hence, $pH = pK_a$ halfway to the equivalence point (Figure 12.20). The pH changes rather slowly in the range of added volumes of alkali from about 5 cm³ to 20 cm³, In this range the titration flask contains a series of buffer solutions.

At the equivalence point itself, the solution contains sodium ethanoate. As Figure 12.19 shows, the solution is not neutral at this point. A solution of a salt of a weak acid and a strong base is alkaline. Sodium ions have no effect on the pH of a solution, but ethanoate ions are basic. The ethanoate ion is the conjugate base of a weak acid.

Beyond the equivalence point, the curve is determined by the excess of strong base and so the shape is the same as for Figure 2.18.

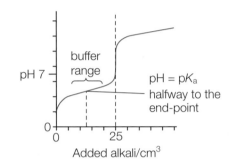

Figure 12.20▲
In the buffering range, the pH changes little on adding substantial volumes of strong alkali. Over this range the flask contains significant amounts of both the acid and the salt formed from the acid.

Titration of a strong acid with a weak base

During the titration of a strong acid with a weak base, the flask contains a strong acid at the start and the titration curve follows the same line as in Figure 12.18. In a titration of hydrochloric acid with ammonia solution, for example, the salt formed at the equivalence point is ammonium chloride.

Since ammonia is a weak base, the ammonium ion is an acid. So a solution of ammonium chloride is acidic and the pH is below 7 at the equivalence point. After the equivalence point, the curve rises less far than in Figure 12.18 because the excess alkali is a weak base and is not fully ionised.

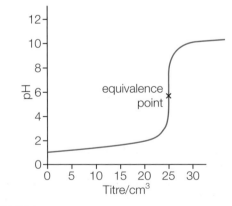

Figure 12.21▲
The pH change on gradually adding a 0.1 mol dm⁻³ solution of the weak base NH₃(aq) from a burette to 25 cm³ of a 0.1 mol dm⁻³ solution of HCl(aq), a strong acid.

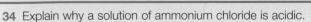

Titration of a weak acid with a weak base

In practice, it is not usual to titrate a weak acid with a weak base. As shown in Figure 12.22, the change of pH around the equivalence point is gradual and not very marked. This means that it is hard to fix the end-point precisely. If the dissociation constants of the weak acid and of the weak base are approximately equal (as is the case for ethanoic acid and ammonia) then the salt formed at the equivalence point is neutral and the pH is 7 at this point.

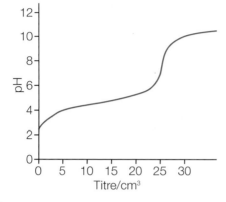

Figure 12.22 ▲
The pH change on gradually adding $0.1 \, mol \, dm^{-3} \, NH_3(aq)$ from a burette to $25 \, cm^3$ of a $0.1 \, mol \, dm^{-3}$ solution of $CH_3COOH(aq)$. Before the end-point the curve is essentially the same as in Figure 12.19, but after the end-point it is as in Figure 12.21. Note the resulting small change of pH around the equivalence point

Test yourself

35 Write a balanced equation for the neutralisation of ethanoic acid by ammonia solution.

Working with logarithms

There can be advantages from working with a logarithmic form of the equilibrium law when calculating the pH of a mixture of a weak acid and one of its salts, both in buffer solutions and during titrations.

In general, for a weak acid HA:

$$HA(aq) \rightleftharpoons H^+(aq) + A^-(aq)$$

$$K_a = \frac{[H^+(aq)][A^-(aq)]}{[HA(aq)]}$$

This rearranges to give:

$$[H^+(aq)] = K_a \times \frac{[HA(aq)]}{[A^-(aq)]}$$

Taking logs and substituting pH for $-\log[H^+(aq)]$ and pK_a for $-\log K_a$ gives:

$$pH = pK_a + \log\left(\frac{[A^-(aq)]}{[HA(aq)]}\right)$$

Note the change of sign and the inversion of the log ratio. This follows because:

$$-\log\left(\frac{[A^-(aq)]}{[HA(aq)]}\right) = +\log\left(\frac{[HA(aq)]}{[A^-(aq)]}\right)$$

Again it is possible to make the assumption that in a mixture of a weak acid and its salt, the weak acid is only slightly ionised and the salt is fully ionised. This means that it is often accurate enough to assume that all the anions come from the salt present, and all the un-ionised molecules come from the acid. Hence:

$$pH = pK_a + \log\left(\frac{[salt]}{[acid]}\right)$$

This form of the equilibrium law cannot be used to calculate the pH of a solution of a weak acid on its own. However, it can help to account for the behaviour of buffer solutions (Section 12.4), and to explain the properties of acid–base indicators (Section 12.6).

Note

If you want to use the logarithmic form of the equilibrium law, make sure that you can derive it for yourself. Also check that you understand the assumptions made in deriving this form of the law so that you know just when it applies.

Figure 12.23▲
The flowers of this variety of hydrangea respond to soil pH. In acid soils they produce blue flowers; elsewhere the flowers are pink.

12.6 Indicators

Acid–base indicators change colour when the pH changes. They signal the end-point of a titration. No single indicator is right for all titrations and the equilibrium law can help chemists to choose the indicator which will give accurate results.

The indicator chosen for a titration must change colour completely in the pH range of the near vertical part of the pH curve (see Figures 12.18, 12.19 and 12.21). This is essential if the visible end-point is to correspond to the equivalence point when exactly equal amounts of acid and base are mixed. Table 12.2 gives some data for four common indicators. Note that each indicator changes colour over a range of pH values, which differs from one indicator to the next.

Indicator	pK_a	Colour change HIn/In⁻	pH range over which the colour change occurs
methyl orange	3.6	red/yellow	3.2–4.2
methyl red	5.0	yellow/red	4.2–6.3
bromothymol blue	7.1	yellow/blue	6.0–7.6
phenolphthalein	9.4	colourless/red	8.2–10.0

Table 12.2▲

Figure 12.24▲
The colours of screened methyl orange indicator at pH 6 (left), pH 4 (middle) and pH 2 (right). This indicator includes a green dye to make the colour change easier to see.

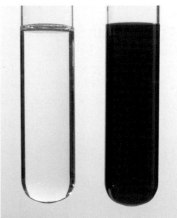

Figure 12.25▲
The colours of phenolphthalein indicator at pH 7 (left) and pH 11 (right).

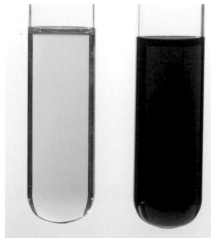

Figure 12.26▲
The colours of bromothymol blue indicator at pH 5 (left) and pH 8 (right).

Test yourself

36 Using le Chatelier's principle, explain qualitatively why methyl red is yellow at pH 3 but red at pH 7.

37 a) Why is methyl orange an unsuitable indicator for the titration illustrated by Figure 12.19?
   b) Why is phenolphthalein an unsuitable indicator for the titration illustrated by Figure 12.20?
   c) Identify the indicators that can be used to detect the end-points of the titrations illustrated by Figures 12.18, 12.19 and 12.21.
   d) Explain why it is not possible to use an indicator to give a sharp and accurate end-point for the titration illustrated by Figure 12.22.

Indicators are themselves weak acids or bases which change colour when they lose or gain hydrogen ions. When added to a solution, an indicator gains or loses protons, depending on the pH of the solution. It is conventional to represent a weak acid indicator as HIn, where 'In' is a shorthand for the all of the rest of molecule other than the ionisable hydrogen atom. In water:

$$HIn(aq) \rightleftharpoons H^+(aq) + In^-(aq)$$

un-ionised   indicator after
indicator   losing a proton
colour 1   colour 2

Note that an analyst adds only a drop or two of indicator during a titration. This means that there is so little indicator that it cannot affect the pH of the mixture. The pH is determined by the nature of the titration (as shown in Figures 12.18, 12.19 and 12.21). The position of the equilibrium for the ionisation of the indicator shifts once way or the other as dictated by the pH of the solution in the titration flask.

The pH range over which an indicator changes colour is determined by its acid strength. Typically the range is given roughly by $pK_a \pm 1$. The logarithmic form of the equilibrium law derived at the end of Section 12.5 shows why this is so. For an indicator, it takes the form:

$$pH = pK_a + \log\left[\frac{[In^-(aq)]}{[HIn(aq)]}\right]$$

When $pH = pK_a$, $[HIn(aq)] = [In^-(aq)]$ and the two different colours of the indicator are present in equal amounts. The indicator is midway through its colour change range.

Add a few drops of acid and the pH falls. If the two colours of the indicator are equally intense, it turns out that our eyes see the characteristic acid colour of the indicator clearly when $[HIn] = 10 \times [In^-(aq)]$.

At this point, $pH = pK_a + \log 0.1 = pK_a - 1$, since $\log 0.1 = -1$.

Add a few drops of alkali and the pH rises. Similarly our eyes see the characteristic alkaline colour of the indicator clearly when $[In^-(aq)] = 10 \times [HIn(aq)]$.

At this point, $pH = pK_a + \log 10 = pK_a + 1$, since $\log 10 = +1$.

Note

The theory of acid–base indicators and the theory of buffer solutions is essentially the same. The difference is that a large amount of buffer mixture is added to control the pH of a solution, whereas the drop or two of an indicator in a titration flask is too little to affect the pH. An indicator follows the pH changes dictated by the mixture of acid and alkali during the titration.

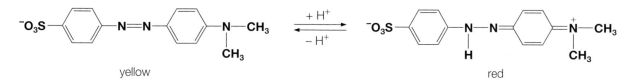

yellow   red

Figure 12.27 ▲
The structures of methyl orange in acid and alkaline solutions. In acid solution, the added hydrogen ion (proton) localises two electrons to form a covalent bond. In alkaline solution, the removal of the hydrogen ion allows the two electrons to join the other delocalised electrons. The change in the number of delocalised electrons causes a shift in the peak of the wavelengths of light absorbed – so the colour changes and the molecule acts as an indicator.

Test yourself

38 Suggest an explanation for the fact that the indicators shown in Table 12.2 do not all change colour over a pH range of 2 units.

Figure 12.28▲
Limestone etched by rainwater made acidic by dissolved carbon dioxide. Bloody cranesbill is a plant that can only flourish when growing in soil where the minerals, such as limestone, neutralise acids and keep the soil water alkaline.

12.7 Neutralisation reactions

Chemists use the term 'neutralisation' to describe any reaction in which an acid reacts with a base to form a salt – even when the pH is not exactly 7 on mixing equivalent amounts of the acid and the alkali.

The pH of salts

Mixing equal amounts (in moles) of hydrochloric acid with sodium hydroxide produces a neutral solution of sodium chloride. Strong acids, such as hydrochloric acid, and strong bases, such as sodium hydroxide, are fully ionised in solution – as is the salt formed in the reaction, sodium chloride. Writing ionic equations for reactions such as this shows that neutralisation is essentially a reaction between aqueous hydrogen ions and hydroxide ions. (This similarity is also supported by the values for enthalpies of neutralisation – see the next part in this section.)

$$H^+(aq) + OH^-(aq) \rightleftharpoons H_2O(l)$$

The surprise is that 'neutralisation' reactions do not always produce neutral solutions. 'Neutralising' a weak acid such as ethanoic acid with an equal amount, in moles, of a strong base, such as sodium hydroxide, produces a solution of sodium ethanoate that is alkaline.

'Neutralising' a weak base such as ammonia with an equal amount of the strong acid hydrochloric acid produces a solution of ammonium chloride that is acidic.

Where a salt has either a 'parent' acid or a 'parent' base which is weak, it dissolves to give a solution which is not neutral. The strong 'parent' in the partnership 'wins':

● weak acid + strong base – the salt formed is alkaline in solution
● strong acid + weak base – the salt formed is acidic in solution.

Data

Test yourself

39 Predict, with the help of a table of K_a or pK_a values, whether the salt formed on mixing equivalent amounts of these acids and alkalis gives a solution with pH of 7, pH above 7 or pH below 7:
a) nitric acid and potassium hydroxide
b) chloric(I) acid and sodium hydroxide
c) hydrobromic acid and ammonia
d) propanoic acid and sodium hydroxide.

Enthalpy change of neutralisation

Strong acids and bases
The 'enthalpy change of neutralisation' is the enthalpy change for a reaction when an acid neutralises an alkali. For example:

$$HCl(aq) + NaOH(aq) \rightarrow NaCl(aq) + H_2O(l) \quad \Delta H^\ominus_{neutralisation} = -57.5 \, kJ \, mol^{-1}$$

The standard enthalpy of neutralisation for dilute solutions of a strong acid with a strong base is always close to $57.5 \, kJ \, mol^{-1}$. The reason is that these acids and alkalis are fully ionised. So in every instance the reaction is the same:

$$H^+(aq) + OH^-(aq) \rightarrow H_2O(l) \quad \Delta H^\ominus = -57.5 \, kJ \, mol^{-1}$$

Approximate values of enthalpies of neutralisation can be measured by mixing solutions of acids and alkalis in a calorimeter.

Worked example

$50\,cm^3$ of $1.0\,mol\,dm^{-3}$ dilute nitric acid was mixed with $50\,cm^3$ of $1.0\,mol\,dm^{-3}$ dilute potassium hydroxide solution in an expanded polystyrene cup. The temperature rise was $6.7\,°C$. Calculate the enthalpy change of neutralisation for the reaction.

Notes on the method
Note that the total volume of solution on mixing is $100\,cm^3$.

Assume that the density and specific heat capacity of the solutions is the same as for pure water.

The specific heat capacity of water is $4.18\,J\,g^{-1}\,K^{-1}$.

The density of water is $1\,g\,cm^{-3}$ so the mass of $100\,cm^3$ is $100\,g$.

A change of $6.7\,°C$ is the same as a temperature change of $6.7\,K$ on the Kelvin scale.

The energy from the exothermic reaction is trapped in the system by the expanded polystyrene, so it heats up the mixture.

Answer
The energy change $= 4.18\,J\,g^{-1}\,K^{-1} \times 100\,g \times 6.7\,K = 2800\,J$

Amount of acid neutralised $= \dfrac{50}{1000}\,dm^3 \times 1.0\,mol\,dm^{-3} = 0.05\,mol$

$$HNO_3(aq) + KOH(aq) \rightarrow KNO_3(aq) + H_2O(l)$$

$$\Delta H_{neutralisation} = \frac{-2800\,J}{0.05\,mol} = -56\,000\,J\,mol^{-1} = -56.0\,kJ\,mol^{-1}$$

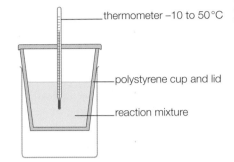

Figure 12.29 ▲
Apparatus for measuring the enthalpy change of the neutralisation of an acid by a base.

Weak acids and bases
The standard enthalpy changes for neutralisation reactions involving weak acids and weak bases are less negative than those for neutralisation reactions between strong acids and strong bases. For example, the standard enthalpy change for the neutralisation of ethanoic acid by sodium hydroxide is $-56.1\,kJ\,mol^{-1}$.

This is partly because the weak acids and weak bases are not fully ionised at the start, so bonds have to be broken and the neutralisations cannot be described simply as reactions between readily available aqueous hydrogen ions and aqueous hydroxide ions. Another reason is that the solutions are not neutral at the equivalence point.

Test yourself

40 Account for the discrepancy between the value calculated in the worked example from experimental results and the expected value of about $-57.5\,kJ\,mol^{-1}$.

41 Suggest an explanation for the difference in the values of $\Delta H^{\ominus}_{neutralisation}$ for HCl/NaOH and $CH_3COOH/NaOH$.

42 Here are three pairs of acids and bases that can react to form salts: HBr/NaOH, HCl/NH_3, CH_3COOH/NH_3.
Here are three values for standard enthalpy changes of neutralisation:
$-50.4\,kJ\,mol^{-1}$, $-53.4\,kJ\,mol^{-1}$, $-57.6\,kJ\,mol^{-1}$.
Write the equations for the three neutralisation reactions, and match each with its corresponding value of $\Delta H^{\ominus}_{neutralisation}$.

REVIEW QUESTIONS

1 a) Write an equation for the reaction which occurs when weak acid HX is added to water. **(1)**

b) Write an expression for the acid dissociation constant of the weak acid. **(1)**

c) The ionisation of HX in aqueous solution is endothermic. Predict the effect, if any, of:

   i) an increase in temperature on the value of its acid dissociation constant **(1)**

   ii) an increase in temperature on the pH of an aqueous solution of the weak acid **(1)**

   iii) a decrease in concentration of the acid on the value of its acid dissociation constant. **(1)**

2 a) Describe and explain the use of buffer solutions with the help of examples. **(6)**

b) i) What is the pH of a buffer solution in which the concentration of ethanoic acid is $0.080 \, \text{mol dm}^{-3}$ and the concentration of sodium ethanoate is $0.040 \, \text{mol dm}^{-3}$. K_a for ethanoic acid is $1.7 \times 10^{-5} \, \text{mol dm}^{-3}$. **(2)**

   ii) Calculate the new pH value if 0.020 mol NaOH is dissolved in $1 \, \text{dm}^3$ of the buffer solution in part a). **(2)**

   iii) Calculate the pH of a solution of 0.020 mol NaOH in $1 \, \text{dm}^3$ of water. **(2)**

   iv) Comment on the effectiveness of the buffer solution **(1)**

3 a) Give examples to explain the difference between a strong acid and a weak acid. **(4)**

b) At 298 K, what is the pH of:

   i) $0.01 \, \text{mol dm}^{-3} \, HNO_3(aq)$ **(1)**

   ii) $0.01 \, \text{mol dm}^{-3} \, KOH(aq)$? **(2)**

c) Butanoic acid, C_3H_7COOH, has an acid dissociation constant, K_a, of $1.5 \times 10^{-5} \, \text{mol dm}^{-3}$ at 298 K.

   i) Calculate the pH of a $0.020 \, \text{mol dm}^{-3}$ solution of butanoic acid at this temperature. **(2)**

   ii) Draw a sketch graph to show the pH changes when $0.020 \, \text{mol dm}^{-3}$ NaOH(aq) is added to $25 \, \text{cm}^3$ of $0.020 \, \text{mol dm}^{-3}$ butanoic acid. **(4)**

   iii) Choose, from the table below, the indicator that would be most suitable for detecting the end-point of a titration between butanoic acid and sodium hydroxide. Give your reasons. **(2)**

Indicator	Colour change acid/alkaline	pH range over which colour change occurs
thymol blue	red/yellow	1.2–2.8
congo red	violet/red	3.0–5.0
thymolphthalein	colourless/blue	8.3–10.6

4 A solution containing $0.050 \, \text{mol dm}^{-3}$ chloric(I) acid (HClO) and $0.050 \, \text{mol dm}^{-3}$ sodium chlorate(I) has a pH of 7.43 at 298 K.

a) i) Write an equation for the ionisation of chloric(I) acid. **(1)**

   ii) Write an expression for the acid dissociation constant of chloric(I) acid. **(1)**

b) Work out the values of K_a and pK_a for chloric(I) acid showing your working. **(5)**

13 Lattice enthalpy and Born–Haber cycles

Some compounds are stable and remain unchanged even when heated to high temperatures. Other compounds decompose very readily forming their elements or other compounds at relatively low temperatures. By measuring the enthalpy changes of the various stages which occur when metals react with non-metals, it is possible to compare the stability of different ionic compounds. The enthalpy (energy) cycles which chemists draw up to link the relevant changes and investigate the stability of ionic compounds are called Born–Haber cycles.

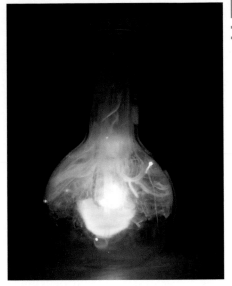

Figure 13.1 ▲
Hot sodium reacting with chlorine.

13.1 Ionic bonding and structures

Compounds of metals with non-metals, such as sodium chloride and magnesium oxide, are composed of ions. When compounds form between metals and non-metals, the metal atoms lose electrons and form positive ions (cations). At the same time, the non-metal atoms gain electrons and form negative ions (anions). For example, when sodium reacts with chlorine (Figure 13.1), each sodium atom loses its one outer electron forming a sodium ion, Na^+. Chlorine atoms gain these electrons and form chloride ions, Cl^- (Figure 13.2).

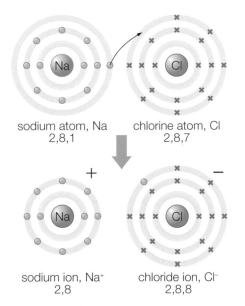

sodium atom, Na
2,8,1

chlorine atom, Cl
2,8,7

+

−

sodium ion, Na⁺
2,8

chloride ion, Cl⁻
2,8,8

Figure 13.2 ◄
The formation of ions in sodium chloride when sodium reacts with chlorine.

From your studies in AS Chemistry, you should know that diagrams like that in Figure 13.2, in which the electrons of one element are shown as dots and those of the other element are shown as crosses, are called dot-and-cross diagrams. These diagrams provide a useful balance sheet for keeping track of the electrons when ionic compounds form.

Very often it is sufficient to show simply the outer shell electrons in dot-and-cross diagrams and two of these simplified diagrams are shown in Figure 13.3.

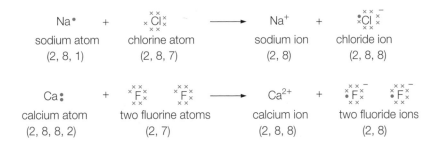

| Na• | + | × Cl × | ⟶ | Na⁺ | + | •Cl × |
| sodium atom (2, 8, 1) | | chlorine atom (2, 8, 7) | | sodium ion (2, 8) | | chloride ion (2, 8, 8) |

| Ca: | + | ×F× ×F× | ⟶ | Ca²⁺ | + | •F× •F× |
| calcium atom (2, 8, 8, 2) | | two fluorine atoms (2, 7) | | calcium ion (2, 8, 8) | | two fluoride ions (2, 8) |

Figure 13.3 ◄
Dot-and-cross diagrams for the formation of sodium chloride and calcium fluoride showing only the electrons in the outer shells of the reactant atoms and product ions.

When metals react with non-metals, the ions produced form ionic crystals. These ionic crystals are giant lattices containing billions of positive and negative ions packed together in a regular pattern. Strong ionic bonds hold the ions firmly together in ionic lattices like that shown in Figure 13.4.

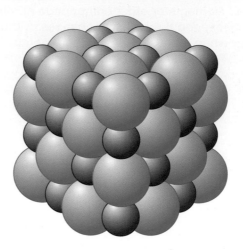

Figure 13.4 ▲
A 3D model of the structure of sodium chloride. The red balls represent Na⁺ ions; the larger green balls represent Cl⁻ ions.

Many other compounds have the same lattice structure as sodium chloride including the chlorides, bromides and iodides of lithium, sodium and potassium, and the oxides and sulfides of magnesium, calcium and strontium.

Test yourself

1 Draw dot-and-cross diagrams, similar to those in Figure 13.3, for:
  a) potassium oxide
  b) magnesium sulfide.
2 Why do metals form positive ions, whereas non-metals form negative ions?
3 Why do you think the melting point of magnesium oxide (2852 °C) is so much higher than that of sodium fluoride (993 °C)?

13.2 Enthalpy changes and ionic bonding

When sodium reacts with chlorine, a very exothermic reaction occurs and energy is given out to the surroundings. When the product, sodium chloride, cools down to room temperature, it is clear that the system has less energy than it had before the reaction took place. Figure 13.5 shows an enthalpy profile (level) diagram for the reaction that occurs.

Figure 13.5▶
An enthalpy profile diagram for the formation of sodium chloride.

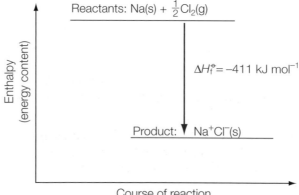

Reactants: $Na(s) + \frac{1}{2}Cl_2(g)$

$\Delta H_f^\ominus = -411$ kJ mol⁻¹

Product: $Na^+Cl^-(s)$

Enthalpy (energy content)

Course of reaction

The enthalpy change shown in Figure 13.5 relates to the formation of 1 mole of sodium chloride from its elements sodium and chlorine. If the measurements have been made at 25 °C (298 K) and 1 atmosphere pressure (10^5 Pa), the result is described as the standard enthalpy change of formation of sodium chloride. This can be written either as:

$$Na(s) + \tfrac{1}{2}Cl_2(g) \rightarrow Na^+Cl^-(s) \qquad \Delta H_f^\ominus = -411\,kJ\,mol^{-1}$$

or as: $\quad \Delta H_f^\ominus [NaCl(s)] = -411\,kJ\,mol^{-1}$

Standard enthalpy changes

In order to compare energy changes, such as enthalpy changes of formation, fairly and consistently, it is important to make thermochemical measurements under the same conditions. The conditions chosen for comparing enthalpy changes and other thermochemical measurements are called standard conditions. These standard conditions are:

- a temperature of 25 °C (298 K)
- a pressure of 1 atmosphere (1×10^5 Pa = 100 kPa)
- all reactants and products in their standard (stable) states at 25 °C and 1 atmosphere pressure
- all solutions at a concentration of 1 mol dm^{-3}.

The symbol for these *standard* enthalpy changes is $\Delta H^\ominus$, and $\Delta H_f^\ominus$ for standard enthalpy changes of formation.

From the standard conditions just described, you will appreciate how important it is to specify the states of the chemicals involved in any relevant process. Equations should always include state symbols, and in this respect the state for water in all standard enthalpy changes should relate to water liquid, $H_2O(l)$, not water vapour, $H_2O(g)$. In addition, the standard state for carbon is graphite, $C_{(graphite)}$, and not diamond, $C_{(diamond)}$, because graphite is energetically more stable than diamond at 25 °C and 1 atmosphere pressure.

13.3 A closer look at the enthalpy changes when ions form

Figure 13.2 shows the formation of sodium chloride from its elements, but it simplifies the process in many ways. As far as sodium is concerned, Figure 13.2 ignores the fact that:

- sodium starts as a giant lattice of atoms
- energy is required to separate the sodium atoms in the giant lattice. This process is called the enthalpy change of atomisation of sodium
- energy is also required to remove one electron from each sodium atom in order to form positive sodium ions, Na^+. This is the first ionisation energy of sodium.

As far as chlorine is concerned, Figure 13.2 ignores the fact that:

- chlorine consists of Cl_2 molecules
- energy is required to break the bonds between Cl atoms in the Cl_2 molecules and form separate Cl atoms. This process is the enthalpy change of atomisation of chlorine
- an energy change also occurs when one electron is added to each Cl atom forming chloride ions, Cl^-. This process is called the electron affinity of chlorine.

Finally, but equally importantly, Figure 13.2 ignores the fact that energy is given out when gaseous Na^+ and Cl^- ions come together forming a giant ionic lattice of sodium chloride, $Na^+Cl^-(s)$. This process is called the lattice enthalpy of sodium chloride.

Definition

The **standard enthalpy change of formation** of a compound, $\Delta H_f^\ominus$, is the enthalpy change when one mole of the compound forms from its elements under standard conditions with the elements and the compound in their standard (stable) states.

Notes

The superscript sign in $\Delta H^\ominus$ shows that the value quoted is for standard conditions. The symbol is pronounced 'delta H standard'.

The definition of standard enthalpy changes of formation means that $\Delta H_f^\ominus = 0\,kJ\,mol^{-1}$ for all elements because there is no change when an element forms from itself, and therefore no enthalpy change. In other words, the standard enthalpy change of formation of any element is zero.

The **standard enthalpy change of atomisation** of an element is the energy needed to produce one mole of gaseous atoms of the element under standard conditions. For sodium this is:

$$Na(s) \rightarrow Na(g) \quad \Delta H^{\ominus}_{at}[Na(s)] = +107 \text{ kJ mol}^{-1}$$

And for chlorine this is:

$$\tfrac{1}{2}Cl_2(g) \rightarrow Cl(g) \quad \Delta H^{\ominus}_{at}[\tfrac{1}{2}Cl_2(g)] = +122 \text{ kJ mol}^{-1}$$

The **first ionisation energy** of an element is the energy needed to remove one electron from each atom in one mole of gaseous atoms of the element under standard conditions. For sodium this is:

$$Na(g) \rightarrow Na^+(g) + e^- \quad \Delta H^{\ominus}_{i,1}[Na(g)] = +496 \text{ kJ mol}^{-1}$$

Successive ionisation energies for the same element measure the energy needed to remove a second, third, fourth electron and so on. For example, the third ionisation energy of sodium relates to the process:

$$Na^{2+}(g) \rightarrow Na^{3+}(g) + e^-$$

The **first electron affinity** of an element is the energy change when each atom in one mole of gaseous atoms gains one electron to form one mole of gaseous ions with a single negative charge.

The following two equations define the first and second electron affinities for oxygen:

$$O(g) + e^- \rightarrow O^-(g) \quad E^{\ominus}_{aff.1} = -141 \text{ kJ mol}^{-1}$$
$$O^-(g) + e^- \rightarrow O^{2-}(g) \quad E^{\ominus}_{aff.2} = +798 \text{ kJ mol}^{-1}$$

The gain of the first electron is exothermic, but adding a second electron to a negatively charged ion is endothermic.

Lattice enthalpies

The lattice enthalpy of a compound is usually defined as the standard enthalpy change when one mole of an ionic compound is formed from free gaseous ions. For sodium chloride, this is summarised by the equation:

$$Na^+(g) + Cl^-(g) \rightarrow Na^+Cl^-(s) \quad \Delta H^{\ominus}_{lattice}[NaCl(s)] = -787 \text{ kJ mol}^{-1}$$

This lattice enthalpy process is shown diagrammatically in Figure 13.6.

Figure 13.6▶
Lattice enthalpy is the energy that would be given out to the surroundings (red arrows) if one mole of a compound could be formed directly from free gaseous ions coming together (black arrows) and arranging themselves into a crystal lattice.

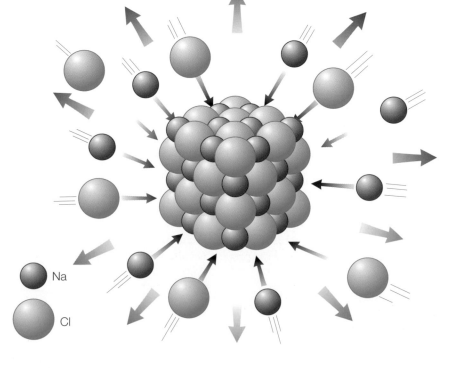

Definition

The **lattice enthalpy** of an ionic compound is the standard enthalpy change when one mole of the compound forms from free gaseous ions.

Some chemists use the term 'lattice energy' as an alternative to lattice enthalpy.

Lattice enthalpies are important because they can be used as a measure of the strength of ionic bonds in different ionic compounds.

The strengths of ionic bonds, measured as lattice enthalpies in $kJ\,mol^{-1}$, arise from the energy given out as billions upon billions of positive and negative ions come together to form a crystal lattice.

The force of attraction between the ions is stronger, and this results in a more exothermic lattice enthalpy, if:

- the charges on the ions are large
- the ionic radii are small, allowing the ions to get closer to each other.

It is important to distinguish between the lattice enthalpy of an ionic compound and its standard enthalpy change of formation. The lattice enthalpy relates to the formation of 1 mole of a compound from its free gaseous ions, whereas the standard enthalpy change of formation relates to the formation of 1 mole of the compound from its elements in their normal states under standard conditions.

During the early part of the twentieth century, scientists found ways of measuring enthalpy changes of formation and atomisation, ionisation energies and electron affinities of various elements. This led the German scientists Max Born (1882–1970) and Fritz Haber (1868–1934) to analyse the energy changes in the formation of different ionic compounds. Their work resulted in Born–Haber cycles which are thermochemical cycles for calculating lattice enthalpies and for investigating the stability and bonding in ionic compounds.

13.4 Born–Haber cycles

Born–Haber cycles are an application of Hess's law (Section 16.5 in *OCR Chemistry for AS*). They provide a model for the determination of lattice enthalpies which cannot be measured experimentally. They also enable chemists to test the ionic model of bonding in different substances.

 Tutorial

A Born–Haber cycle identifies all the enthalpy changes that contribute to the standard enthalpy change of formation of a compound. These changes, shown in Figure 13.7, involve:

- the energy (enthalpy changes) required to create free gaseous ions by atomising and then ionising the elements
- the energy given out (the lattice enthalpy) when the ions come together to form a crystal lattice.

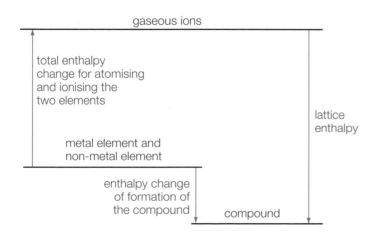

Figure 13.7 ▲
The overall structure of a Born–Haber cycle.

A Born–Haber cycle is usually set out like an enthalpy profile diagram, with enthalpy changes one after another. All the processes in the cycle can be measured experimentally except the lattice enthalpy. So, by using Hess's law it is possible to calculate the lattice enthalpy.

Figure 13.8 shows the Born–Haber cycle for sodium oxide, Na_2O.

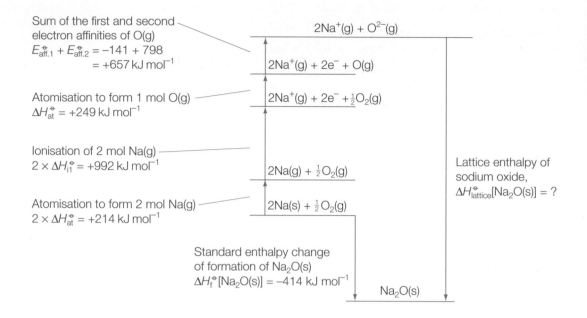

Sum of the first and second electron affinities of O(g)
$E_{aff.1}^{\ominus} + E_{aff.2}^{\ominus} = -141 + 798$
$= +657\,kJ\,mol^{-1}$

Atomisation to form 1 mol O(g)
$\Delta H_{at}^{\ominus} = +249\,kJ\,mol^{-1}$

Ionisation of 2 mol Na(g)
$2 \times \Delta H_{i1}^{\ominus} = +992\,kJ\,mol^{-1}$

Atomisation to form 2 mol Na(g)
$2 \times \Delta H_{at}^{\ominus} = +214\,kJ\,mol^{-1}$

$2Na^+(g) + O^{2-}(g)$

$2Na^+(g) + 2e^- + O(g)$

$2Na^+(g) + 2e^- + \frac{1}{2}O_2(g)$

$2Na(g) + \frac{1}{2}O_2(g)$

$2Na(s) + \frac{1}{2}O_2(g)$

Lattice enthalpy of sodium oxide,
$\Delta H_{lattice}^{\ominus}[Na_2O(s)] = ?$

Standard enthalpy change of formation of $Na_2O(s)$
$\Delta H_f^{\ominus}[Na_2O(s)] = -414\,kJ\,mol^{-1}$

$Na_2O(s)$

Figure 13.8 ▲
The Born–Haber cycle for sodium oxide.

Starting with the elements sodium and oxygen, the measured value for the standard enthalpy change of formation of sodium oxide has been written downwards on the cycle, showing that it is exothermic. Above that, the terms and values for the atomisation and then ionisation of sodium are written upwards as endothermic processes.

Notice also that the amount of sodium required is 2 mol because there are 2 moles of sodium in 1 mole of sodium oxide.

These terms and values for sodium are followed by those required for the conversion of half a mole of oxygen molecules, $\frac{1}{2}O_2(g)$, to one mole of oxide ions, $O^{2-}(g)$. This involves the atomisation of oxygen followed by its first and second electron affinities. From the experimentally determined values, which we now have in the cycle, it is possible to calculate the lattice enthalpy.

Worked example

Calculate the lattice enthalpy of sodium oxide, $\Delta H_{lattice}^{\ominus}[Na_2O(s)]$ using the data in Figure 13.8.

Notes on the method
Apply Hess's law to the cycle in Figure 13.8 remembering that an exothermic change in one direction becomes an endothermic change with the opposite sign in the reverse direction.

Answer
$$\Delta H_{lattice}^{\ominus}[Na_2O(s)] = (-657 - 249 - 992 - 214 - 414)\,kJ\,mol^{-1}$$
$$= -2526\,kJ\,mol^{-1}$$

Note

Lattice enthalpies, as usually defined, are negative. This means that the descriptions 'larger' and 'smaller' can be ambiguous in comparing lattice enthalpies. For this reason, it is better to describe one lattice enthalpy as being more exothermic or less exothermic than another.

Test yourself

DL
www
Tutorial

12 Why are lattice enthalpies:
  a) always negative
  b) impossible to measure directly?
13 Explain why a Born–Haber cycle is an application of Hess's law.
14 Look carefully at Figure 13.9, which is a Born–Haber cycle for magnesium chloride.

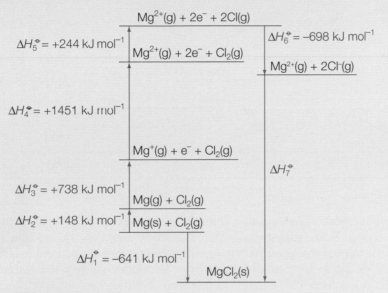

$Mg^{2+}(g) + 2e^- + 2Cl(g)$

$\Delta H_5^\ominus = +244 \text{ kJ mol}^{-1}$

$Mg^{2+}(g) + 2e^- + Cl_2(g)$

$\Delta H_6^\ominus = -698 \text{ kJ mol}^{-1}$

$Mg^{2+}(g) + 2Cl^-(g)$

$\Delta H_4^\ominus = +1451 \text{ kJ mol}^{-1}$

$Mg^+(g) + e^- + Cl_2(g)$

$\Delta H_7^\ominus$

$\Delta H_3^\ominus = +738 \text{ kJ mol}^{-1}$

$Mg(g) + Cl_2(g)$

$\Delta H_2^\ominus = +148 \text{ kJ mol}^{-1}$

$Mg(s) + Cl_2(g)$

$\Delta H_1^\ominus = -641 \text{ kJ mol}^{-1}$

$MgCl_2(s)$

Figure 13.9 ▲
A Born–Haber cycle for magnesium chloride.

a) Identify the enthalpy changes $\Delta H_1^\ominus$, $\Delta H_2^\ominus$, $\Delta H_3^\ominus$, $\Delta H_4^\ominus$, $\Delta H_5^\ominus$, $\Delta H_6^\ominus$ and $\Delta H_7^\ominus$.
b) Calculate the lattice enthalpy of magnesium chloride.

13.5 Testing the ionic model – ionic or covalent?

One way in which scientists can test their theories and models is by comparing the predictions from their theoretical models with the values obtained by experiment. Born–Haber cycles are very helpful in this respect because they enable chemists to test the ionic model and check whether the bonding in a compound is truly ionic. The experimental lattice enthalpy obtained from a Born–Haber cycle can be compared with the theoretical value calculated by using the laws of electrostatics and assuming that the only bonding in the crystal is ionic.

Using the laws of electrostatics, it is possible to calculate a theoretical value for the lattice enthalpy of an ionic compound by summing up the effects of all the attractions and repulsions between the ions in the crystal lattice (Figure 13.10).

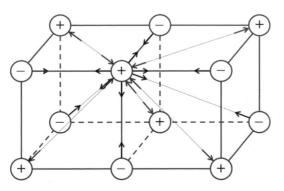

Note

Electrostatic forces operate between the ions in a crystal. Oppositely charged ions attract each other, and ions with like charges repel each other. The size of the electrostatic force, F, between two charges is given by the equation:

$$F \propto \frac{Q_1 \times Q_2}{d^2}$$

● the larger the charges, Q_1 and Q_2, the stronger the force
● the greater the distance, d, between the charges, the smaller the force – this has a big effect because it is the square of the distance that matters.

Figure 13.10 ◄
Some of the many attractions (red) and repulsions (blue) which must be taken into account in calculating a theoretical value for the lattice enthalpy of an ionic crystal.

Table 13.1 shows the experimentally determined lattice enthalpies and the theoretical lattice enthalpies for some ionic compounds.

Compound	Experimental lattice enthalpy from a Born–Haber cycle /kJ mol⁻¹	Theoretical lattice enthalpy calculated assuming that the only bonding is ionic / kJ mol⁻¹
NaCl	−780	−770
NaBr	−742	−735
NaI	−705	−687
KCl	−711	−702
KBr	−679	−674
KI	−651	−636
AgCl	−905	−833
MgI$_2$	−2327	−1944

Table 13.1 ▲

Pure ionic bonding arises solely from the electrostatic forces between the ions in a crystal. Notice that there is close agreement between the experimental and theoretical values of the lattice enthalpies for sodium and potassium halides in Table 13.1. In all these halides, the difference between the two values is less than 3%. This shows that ionic bonding can account almost entirely for the bonding in sodium and potassium halides.

But look at the experimental and theoretical lattice enthalpies of silver chloride and magnesium iodide in Table 13.1. In these two compounds, the experimental values are much larger than the theoretical values, which assume that the only bonding is ionic. The bonding is clearly stronger than that predicted by a pure ionic model. This suggests that there is some covalent bonding as well as ionic bonding in these substances.

Polarisation of ions

In ionic compounds, positive metal ions will attract the outermost electrons of negative ions, pulling these electrons into the spaces between the ions. This distortion of the electron clouds around anions by positively charged cations is an example of polarisation. As a result of polarisation, there is a significant degree of covalent bonding in some ionic compounds.

This makes the size of the lattice enthalpy greater numerically than that expected from the purely ionic model, because the calculation does not allow for the extra attraction resulting from the distortion of the anions. The values in Table 13.1 show clearly that both silver chloride and magnesium iodide, although mainly ionic, have a significant degree of covalent bonding.

Figure 13.11 shows three examples of ionic bonding with increasing degrees of electron sharing as a positive cation polarises the neighbouring negative ion. In general, results show that:

- the polarising power of a cation increases as its charge increases and as its radius decreases
- the polarisability of an anion increases as its radius increases.

As the negative anion gets larger, its outermost electrons are further from the attraction of its positive nucleus. Consequently, these outermost electrons are more readily attracted to a neighbouring positive ion and the anion is therefore more polarisable.

Definition

Polarisation is the distortion of the electron cloud in a molecule or ion by a nearby positive charge.

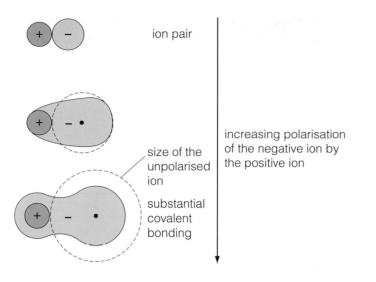

ion pair

increasing polarisation
of the negative ion by
the positive ion

size of the
unpolarised
ion

substantial
covalent
bonding

Figure 13.11▲
Ionic bonding with increasing amounts of electron sharing as a positive cation
polarises neighbouring negative anions. (Dotted circles show the size of
unpolarised ions.)

This means that iodide ions are more polarisable than bromide ions, bromide
ions are more polarisable than chloride ions and fluoride ions are very difficult
to polarise. In fact, fluorine, with its small, singly charged fluoride ion, forms
compounds which are more ionic than any other non-metal.

Test yourself

15 Look at Table 13.2, which lists the ionic radii of some ions.

Ion	Li^+	Na^+	K^+	Mg^{2+}	Al^{3+}
Ionic radius/nm	0.074	0.102	0.138	0.072	0.053
Ion	N^{3-}	O^{2-}	F^-		
Ionic radius/nm	0.171	0.140	0.133		

Table 13.2▲

Use the data in Table 13.2 to explain why:
a) the ionic radii decrease from N^{3-} through O^{2-} to F^-
b) the polarising power of Mg^{2+} is greater than that of Li^+
c) the polarising power of Li^+ is greater than that of K^+
d) the polarising power of Al^{3+} is greater than that of Na^+
e) the polarisability of N^{3-} is greater than that of F^-.

16 The lattice enthalpy of LiF is $-1031\,kJ\,mol^{-1}$ and that of LiI is $-759\,kJ\,mol^{-1}$.
a) Why is the lattice enthalpy of LiI less exothermic than the lattice enthalpy
    of LiF?
b) Which compound would you expect to have the closer agreement between
    the Born–Haber experimental value of its lattice enthalpy and its theoretical
    value based on the ionic model?
c) Explain your answer to part b).

17 Here are four values for lattice enthalpy in $kJ\,mol^{-1}$: -3791, -3299, -3054 and
    -2725.
    The four ionic compounds to which these values relate are BaO, MgO, BaS
    and MgS.
    Match the formulae with the values and justify your choices.

The stability of ionic compounds

Almost all the compounds of metals with non-metals are regarded as ionic, and these compounds have standard enthalpy changes of formation which are exothermic. This means that the compounds are at a lower energy level and therefore more stable than their elements.

If you look at the Born–Haber cycles in Figures 13.8 and 13.9, you will see that an ionic compound will have an exothermic standard enthalpy of formation if its negative lattice enthalpy outweighs the total energy needed to produce gaseous ions from the elements.

Using a Born–Haber cycle with a theoretically calculated value for the lattice enthalpy, it is possible to estimate the standard enthalpy change of formation for compounds which do not normally exist. For example, consider the Born–Haber cycle for the hypothetical compound MgCl in Figure 13.12.

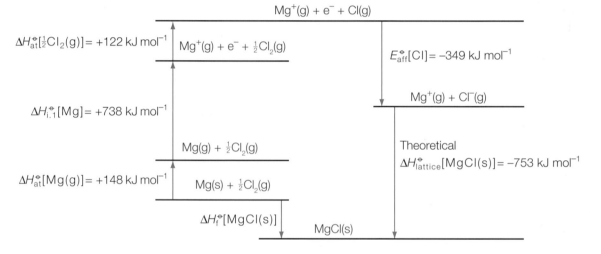

$Mg^+(g) + e^- + Cl(g)$

$\Delta H_{at}^{\ominus}[\frac{1}{2}Cl_2(g)] = +122\ kJ\ mol^{-1}$

$Mg^+(g) + e^- + \frac{1}{2}Cl_2(g)$

$E_{aff}^{\ominus}[Cl] = -349\ kJ\ mol^{-1}$

$Mg^+(g) + Cl^-(g)$

$\Delta H_{i.1}^{\ominus}[Mg] = +738\ kJ\ mol^{-1}$

Theoretical
$\Delta H_{lattice}^{\ominus}[MgCl(s)] = -753\ kJ\ mol^{-1}$

$Mg(g) + \frac{1}{2}Cl_2(g)$

$\Delta H_{at}^{\ominus}[Mg(g)] = +148\ kJ\ mol^{-1}$

$Mg(s) + \frac{1}{2}Cl_2(g)$

$\Delta H_f^{\ominus}[MgCl(s)]$

$MgCl(s)$

1 Use Figure 13.12 to calculate a value for the standard enthalpy change of formation of MgCl(s).

2 What does your answer to question **1** suggest about the stability of MgCl(s)?

3 Using the Hess cycle in Figure 13.13, calculate the standard enthalpy change for the reaction

$$2MgCl(s) \rightarrow MgCl_2(s) + Mg(s)$$

knowing that $\Delta H_f^{\ominus}[MgCl_2(s)] = -641\ kJ\ mol^{-1}$.

Figure 13.12 ▲
A Born–Haber cycle for the hypothetical compound MgCl.

Figure 13.13 ◄
A Hess cycle for the reaction
$2MgCl(s) \rightarrow MgCl_2(s) + Mg(s)$.

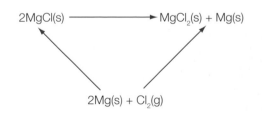

$2MgCl(s) \longrightarrow MgCl_2(s) + Mg(s)$

$2Mg(s) + Cl_2(g)$

> **4** What does your result for question **3** tell you about the stability of MgCl(s)?
>
> **5** The Born–Haber cycle for the hypothetical compound MgCl₃ suggests that $\Delta H_f^{\ominus}[MgCl_3(s)] = +3950\,kJ\,mol^{-1}$.
>
>   **a)** What does the value of $\Delta H_f^{\ominus}[MgCl_3(s)]$ tell you about the stability of MgCl₃(s)?
>
>   **b)** Suggest why the value of $\Delta H_f^{\ominus}[MgCl_3(s)]$ is so endothermic.
>
> **6** The estimated lattice enthalpy of MgCl₃(s) is $-5440\,kJ\,mol^{-1}$.
>
>   **a)** Write an equation to summarise the lattice enthalpy of MgCl₃.
>
>   **b)** Why is the lattice enthalpy of MgCl₃ more exothermic than that of MgCl₂(s)?

13.6 Enthalpy changes during dissolving

Why do ionic crystals dissolve in water, even though ions in the lattice are strongly attracted to each other? What, in general, are the factors which determine the extent to which an ionic salt dissolves in water?

Chemists look for answers to questions of this kind by analysing the energy changes which take place as crystals dissolve.

Figure 13.14◀
The concentration of sodium chloride in the Dead Sea in Israel is so high that salt crystallises out in some places.

An ionic compound such as sodium chloride does not dissolve in non-polar solvents like hexane, but it will dissolve in a polar solvent like water. When one mole of sodium chloride dissolves in water to produce a solution of concentration $1\,mol\,dm^{-3}$ under standard conditions, there is an enthalpy change of $+3.8\,kJ\,mol^{-1}$. This enthalpy change is described as the standard enthalpy change of solution, $\Delta H_{solution}^{\ominus}$, of sodium chloride. The process can be summarised by the equation:

$$NaCl(s) + aq \rightarrow Na^+(aq) + Cl^-(aq) \quad \Delta H_{solution}^{\ominus} = +3.8\,kJ\,mol^{-1}$$

or simply as $\Delta H_{solution}^{\ominus}[NaCl(s)] = +3.8\,kJ\,mol^{-1}$.

In the equation above, '+ aq' is short for the addition of water.

Enthalpy changes of solution are often measured and tabulated for 1 mole of a compound dissolving in different amounts of water under standard conditions.

For example, if 1 mole of sodium chloride is dissolved in 100 moles of water under standard conditions, the enthalpy change is represented by the equation:

$$NaCl(s) + 100H_2O(l) \rightarrow NaCl(aq,\,100\,H_2O) \quad \Delta H_{soln} = +4.1\,kJ\,mol^{-1}$$

Sodium chloride dissolves readily in water despite the fact that the process is slightly endothermic. This is another example which shows that the sign of ΔH is not a reliable guide to whether or not a process will happen. This is particularly the case when the magnitude of ΔH is small.

It is not immediately obvious why the charged ions in a crystal, such as sodium chloride, separate and go into solution in water. Where does the energy come from to overcome the attractive forces between oppositely charged ions?

When sodium chloride dissolves in water, the overall process can be pictured in two stages and these are shown in Figure 13.15.

Figure 13.15▶
The Born–Haber cycle for sodium chloride dissolving in water.

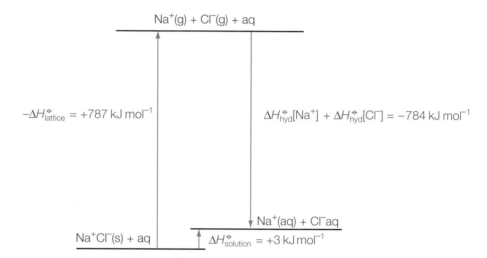

It is now possible to see from Figure 13.15 why sodium chloride dissolves so readily in water. The explanation is that the Na^+ and Cl^- ions are so strongly hydrated by polar water molecules that the exothermic enthalpy changes of hydration nearly balance the energy required to separate the ions (the reverse lattice enthalpy).

The enthalpy change of solution is the difference between the energy needed to separate the ions from the crystal lattice (the negative lattice enthalpy) and the energy given out as the ions are hydrated (the sum of the hydration enthalpies).

Figure 13.16 shows the structure of hydrated sodium and chloride ions. In water molecules, there is a $\delta+$ charge in the region between the hydrogen atoms and a $\delta-$ charge on the oxygen atoms. This means that the polar water molecules are attracted to both positive cations and negative anions. The bond between the ions and the water molecules is an electrostatic attraction. With cations, the electrostatic attraction involves the positive charge on the cations and the $\delta-$ charges on the oxygen atoms of the water molecules. In contrast, with anions, the attraction involves the negative charge on the anions and the $\delta+$ charge on the hydrogen atoms in the water molecules.

- First of all, Na^+ and Cl^- ions must be separated from the solid NaCl crystals to form well-spaced ions in the gaseous state, $Na^+(g)$ and $Cl^-(g)$. This is the reverse of the lattice enthalpy and is labelled $-\Delta H^\ominus_{lattice} = +787\,kJ\,mol^{-1}$ in Figure 13.15.
- In the second stage, gaseous $Na^+(g)$ and $Cl^-(g)$ ions are hydrated by polar water molecules forming a solution of sodium chloride, $Na^+(aq) + Cl^-(aq)$. Under standard conditions, this process is the sum of the standard enthalpy changes of hydration of $Na^+(g)$ and $Cl^-(g)$. This is written as $\Delta H^\ominus_{hyd}[Na^+] + \Delta H^\ominus_{hyd}[Cl^-] = -784\,kJ\,mol^{-1}$ in Figure 13.15.

Definitions

The **standard enthalpy change of solution**, $\Delta H^\ominus_{solution}$, is the enthalpy change when one mole of a compound dissolves to form a solution containing $1\,mol\,dm^{-3}$ under standard conditions.

Enthalpy changes of solution are often calculated and quoted for one mole of a compound dissolving in different amounts of water.

The **standard enthalpy change of hydration** is the enthalpy change when one mole of gaseous ions is hydrated under standard conditions to form a solution in which the concentration of ions is $1\,mol\,dm^{-3}$. For example, for sodium ions:

$Na^+(g) + aq \rightarrow Na^+(aq)$
$$\Delta H^\ominus_{hyd} = -444\,kJ\,mol^{-1}$$

Enthalpy changes of hydration are sometimes just called hydration enthalpies or hydration energies.

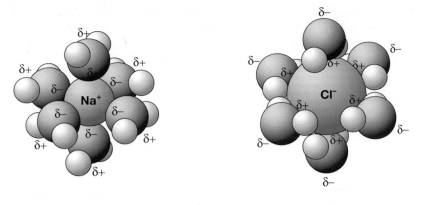

Figure 13.16◄
Sodium and chloride ions are hydrated when sodium chloride dissolves in water. Polar water molecules are attracted to both cations and anions.

Data

Test yourself

18 Look at the data sheet on the Dynamic Learning Student website headed 'Enthalpy changes of hydration'.
  a) How is the enthalpy change of hydration affected by increasing ionic charge?
  b) List an appropriate series of ions and their enthalpy changes of hydration to illustrate your conclusion in part a).
19 Look at Table 13.2 showing the radii of some ions, and the data sheet headed 'Enthalpy changes of hydration'.
  a) How is the enthalpy change of hydration affected by increasing ionic radius?
  b) List an appropriate series of ions, their radii and their enthalpy changes of hydration to illustrate your conclusion in part a).

The effect of ionic charge on enthalpy change of hydration and lattice enthalpy

Enthalpy changes of hydration and lattice enthalpies both involve electrostatic attractions between opposite charges. Because of these attractions, both processes are exothermic.

Furthermore, both processes become more exothermic as the charges on the ions increase because the charge density of an ion increases and therefore its attraction for any opposite charge increases.

This is illustrated very well by the enthalpy changes of hydration for Na^+ and Mg^{2+} and the lattice enthalpies of NaF and MgO in Table 13.3.

Enthalpy change of hydration /kJ mol⁻¹		Lattice enthalpy /kJ mol⁻¹	
Na^+	−444	NaF	−918
Mg^{2+}	−2003	MgO	−3791
Li^+	−559	LiF	−1031
K^+	−361	KF	−817

Table 13.3◄
Comparing enthalpy changes of hydration and lattice enthalpies.

The effect of ionic radius on enthalpy change of hydration and lattice enthalpy

As the radius of an ion increases, its charge density decreases. This results in a weaker attraction for oppositely charged ions and for the δ+ or δ− charges on polar molecules such as water. So, an increase in ionic radius leads to less exothermic values for enthalpy changes of hydration and lattice enthalpies. This point is neatly illustrated by the enthalpy changes of hydration for Li^+ and K^+ and the lattice enthalpies of LiF and KF in Table 13.3.

Trends in solubility

It is difficult to use enthalpy cycles, like that in Figure 13.15, to account for trends in the solubilities of ionic compounds for three reasons.

First, the enthalpy change of solution is generally a small difference between two large enthalpy changes, neither of which can be measured directly. So, even small errors in estimating trends in the values of lattice enthalpies and hydration enthalpies can lead to large percentage errors in the predicted enthalpy changes of solution.

Second, both lattice enthalpies and hydration enthalpies are affected in the same way, as we have seen, by changes in the size of ions and their charges. This tends to reduce the likelihood of any clear trends in enthalpy changes of solution.

Finally, it is clear from the small endothermic value for sodium chloride that the sign and magnitude of the enthalpy change of solution is not a reliable guide as to whether or not a solid will dissolve. Other factors must be taken into account – these are considered in Topic 14.

Test yourself

20 a) Use the equation

$$\text{energy change} = \mathbf{m}/\text{g} \times \mathbf{c}/\text{J g}^{-1}\,\text{K}^{-1} \times \mathbf{\Delta T}/\text{K}$$

to calculate the temperature change when 1 mole of sodium chloride is used to make 1 dm^3 of a solution containing 1.0 mol dm^{-3} of solute. ($\Delta H^{\ominus}_{\text{soln}}$ [NaCl(s)] = +3.8 kJ mol^{-1})
(Assume that the density and specific heat capacity of the solution are the same as those of water.)

b) Explain how the temperature of the solution will change.

21 a) Use the data sheets on the Dynamic Learning Student website headed 'Lattice enthalpies of some ionic compounds' and 'Enthalpy changes of hydration' to calculate the enthalpies of solution of lithium fluoride and lithium iodide.

b) Account for the relative values of the lattice enthalpies and hydration enthalpies of the two compounds in terms of ionic radii.

c) To what extent, if any, can your answers to part **a)** explain the differences in the solubilities of the two compounds?
(Solubilities: LiF = 5 × 10^{-5} mol in 100 g water; LiI = 1.21 mol in 100 g water)

22 Why do you think the lattice enthalpy of magnesium oxide ($\Delta H^{\ominus}_{\text{lattice}}$ [MgO (s)] = −3791 kJ mol^{-1}) is roughly four times more exothermic than that of sodium fluoride ($\Delta H^{\ominus}_{\text{lattice}}$ [NaF(s)] = −918 kJ mol^{-1})?

23 Suggest a reason why the nitrates of Group 1 elements are all soluble in water, but the sulfates of most Group 2 elements are insoluble.

DL
www
Data 1

DL
www
Data 2

REVIEW QUESTIONS

DL
www
Extension questions

1 a) Define the term first electron affinity. (3)

b) The equation below represents the change occurring during the second electron affinity of nitrogen:

$$N^-(g) + e^- \rightarrow N^{2-}(g)$$

i) Explain why the second electron affinity for all elements is endothermic. (2)

ii) Write equations for the first and third electron affinities of nitrogen. (2)

c) In magnesium iodide, MgI_2, the iodide ions are polarised, but in sodium iodide they are not polarised.

i) What is meant by the phrase 'polarisation of an ion'? (2)

ii) State two factors that help to explain the polarisation of iodide ions in magnesium iodide. (2)

2 The following data can be used in a Born–Haber cycle for copper(II) iodide, CuI_2.

Enthalpy change of atomisation of iodine
$\Delta H^{\ominus}_{at} [\frac{1}{2} I_2(s)] = +107 \text{ kJ mol}^{-1}$

Enthalpy change of atomisation of copper,
$\Delta H^{\ominus}_{at} [Cu(s)] = +338 \text{ kJ mol}^{-1}$

First ionisation energy of copper,
$\Delta H^{\ominus}_{i.1} [Cu(g)] = +746 \text{ kJ mol}^{-1}$

Second ionisation energy of copper,
$\Delta H^{\ominus}_{i.2} [Cu(g)] = +1958 \text{ kJ mol}^{-1}$

Electron affinity of iodine,
$\Delta H^{\ominus}_{aff.1} [I(g)] = -295 \text{ kJ mol}^{-1}$

Lattice enthalpy of copper(II) iodide,
$CuI_2(s)$, $\Delta H^{\ominus}_{lattice} [CuI_2(s)] = -963 \text{ kJ mol}^{-1}$

a) The following diagram shows an outline of the Born–Haber cycle for copper(II) iodide:

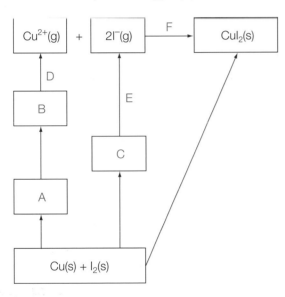

i) Write the formulae and state symbols of the species that should appear in boxes A, B and C. **(3)**

ii) Name the enthalpy changes D, E and F. **(3)**

b) Define the term lattice enthalpy. **(2)**

c) Use the diagram and the data supplied to calculate the enthalpy change of formation of copper(II) iodide. Give a sign and units in your answer. **(3)**

d) When the lattice enthalpy of copper(II) iodide is calculated from ionic radii and charges, the result is about 14% smaller than the one obtained from the Born–Haber cycle.

   i) What does this suggest about the nature of the bonding in copper(II) iodide? **(1)**

   ii) Draw a diagram to show how the smaller copper ion influences the larger iodide ion. **(1)**

3 When calcium chloride dissolves in water, the process can be represented by the equation:

$$Ca^{2+}(Cl^-)_2(s) + aq \rightarrow Ca^{2+}(aq) + 2Cl^-(aq)$$

The enthalpy change for this process is called the enthalpy change of solution. Its value can be calculated from a Born–Haber cycle using the following data:

lattice enthalpy of calcium chloride $= -2258 \text{ kJ mol}^{-1}$

enthalpy change of hydration of $Ca^{2+}(g) = -1657 \text{ kJ mol}^{-1}$

enthalpy change of hydration of $Cl^-(g) = -340 \text{ kJ mol}^{-1}$

a) Draw and label the Born–Haber cycle linking the enthalpy change of solution of calcium chloride with the enthalpy changes in the data above. **(4)**

b) Use your Born–Haber cycle to calculate the enthalpy change of solution of calcium chloride. **(3)**

c) What factors will affect the size of the enthalpy change of hydration of $Ca^{2+}(g)$ compared with that of $Li^+(g)$? **(2)**

d) Why are the hydration enthalpies of both anions and cations negative? **(2)**

4 The lattice enthalpy of rubidium iodide, RbI, can be determined indirectly using a Born–Haber cycle.

a) Use the data in the table below to construct a Born–Haber cycle for rubidium iodide. **(6)**

Enthalpy change	Energy/kJ mol^{-1}
Formation of rubidium iodide	−334
Atomisation of rubidium	+81
Atomisation of iodine	+107
First ionisation energy of rubidium	+403
First electron affinity of iodine	−295

b) Determine a value for the lattice enthalpy of rubidium iodide. **(2)**

c) Explain why the lattice enthalpy of lithium iodide, LiI, is more exothermic than that of rubidium iodide. **(2)**

d) Theoretical values for the lattice enthalpies of LiI and RbI can be calculated by assuming that the compounds are purely ionic. When this is done, the experimentally determined value of the lattice enthalpy of lithium iodide is greater than the calculated value by 21 kJ mol^{-1}, whereas the experimental value for rubidium iodide is greater than the calculated value by only 11 kJ mol^{-1}. Explain the difference in these values. **(4)**

14 Enthalpy and entropy

Chemists have devised a range of ways of predicting the direction and extent of chemical changes. They use equilibrium constants (Topics 11 and 12) and electrode potentials (Topic 15) to explain why some reactions go while others do not. How are these quantities related, and is there a more fundamental concept which links them together? The answer is yes – and the unifying concept is entropy.

Figure 14.1 ▲
Energy can drive change against its natural direction. Photosynthesis effectively reverses the changes of respiration. Leaves on plants harness energy from the Sun to convert carbon dioxide and water into carbohydrates.

Figure 14.2 ▶
A cheetah hunting its prey in Kenya. The cheetah gets its energy from respiration taking advantage of the natural direction of change. Carbohydrates react with oxygen in muscle cells forming carbon dioxide and water and giving out energy.

14.1 Entropy changes

Spontaneous changes

A spontaneous reaction is a reaction which tends to 'go' without being driven by any external agency. Spontaneous reactions are the chemical equivalent of water flowing downhill. Any reaction that naturally tends to happen is spontaneous in this sense, even if it is very slow – just as water has a tendency to flow down a valley even when held up behind a dam. The chemical equivalent of a dam is a high activation energy for a reaction.

Figure 14.3▲
Theory shows that the change of diamond to graphite is spontaneous. Graphite is more stable than diamond. Fortunately for owners of valuable jewellery, the change is very, very slow.

Figure 14.4▲
Metals such as magnesium, iron and aluminium react spontaneously with oxygen. They are ingredients of fireworks – they burn when heated by the spontaneous reactions between sulfur, carbon and potassium nitrate in gunpowder.

In practice, chemists also use the word 'spontaneous' in its everyday sense to describe reactions which not only tend to go but also go quickly on mixing the reactants at room temperature. Here is a typical example:

'The hydrides of silicon catch fire spontaneously in air, unlike methane which has an ignition temperature of about 500 °C.'

The reaction of methane with oxygen is also spontaneous in the thermodynamic sense, even at room temperature. However the activation energy for the reaction is so high that nothing happens until the gas is heated in air with a flame.

The possible ambiguity in the use of the word 'spontaneous' means that chemists often prefer an alternative term. They describe a reaction as *feasible* if it tends to go naturally.

> **Definition**
>
> A **feasible** (or **spontaneous**) **reaction** is one which naturally tends to happen, even if it is very slow because the activation energy is high.

Test yourself

1 Classify these changes as feasible/fast, feasible/slow or not feasible:
   a) ice melting at 5 °C
   b) ammonia gas condensing to a liquid at room temperature
   c) diamond reacting with oxygen at room temperature
   d) water splitting up into hydrogen and oxygen at room temperature
   e) sodium reacting with water at room temperature.

Enthalpy changes and feasible reactions

Most reactions that are feasible are also exothermic. They have a negative standard enthalpy change of reaction. This is such a common pattern that chemists often use the sign of ΔH to decide whether or not a reaction is likely to go.

However, some endothermic processes are feasible too. This shows the limitations of using the enthalpy change to decide the likely direction of change. One example is the reaction of citric acid with sodium hydrogencarbonate – the mixture fizzes vigorously while getting colder and colder. ΔH for this reaction is positive.

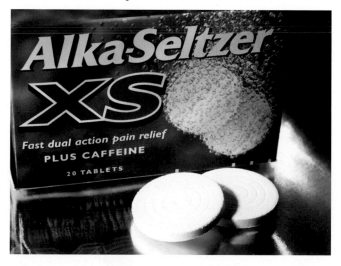

Figure 14.5▲
Alka-Seltzer tablets contain citric acid and sodium hydrogencarbonate. They fizz when added to water. The reaction of the acid and the hydrogencarbonate is a spontaneous endothermic reaction.

A more colourful example is the reaction of sulfur dichloride oxide with the dark red crystals of cobalt(II) chloride. The reaction looks violent and a large quantity of fuming hydrogen chloride gas bubbles out of the mixture while a thermometer dipping into the chemicals shows that the temperature falls sharply.

Entropy

Entropy, S, is a thermochemical quantity which makes it possible to decide whether or not a reaction is feasible – change happens in the direction which leads to a total increase in entropy. When considering chemical reactions, it is essential to calculate the total entropy change in two parts – the entropy change of the system and the entropy change of the surroundings:

$$\Delta S_{total} = \Delta S_{system} + \Delta S_{surroundings}$$

The entropy of a system measures the number of ways, W, of arranging the molecules involved and sharing out the energy between the molecules.

The relationship between S and W was derived by Ludwig Boltzmann (1844–1906), the Austrian physicist who was the first person to explain the laws of thermodynamics in terms of the behaviour of atoms and molecules in motion:

$$S = k \ln W$$

where S is the entropy of the system, k the Boltzmann constant and $\ln W$ the natural logarithm of the number of ways of arranging the particles and energy in the system.

Chemists sometimes describe entropy as a measure of disorder or randomness. These descriptions have to be interpreted with care because the disorder refers not only to the arrangement of the particles in space but, much more significantly, to the numbers of ways of distributing the energy of the system across all the available energy levels.

Standard molar entropies

Nothing seems to be happening in a closed flask of a gas kept at a constant temperature. However, kinetic theory tells us that the molecules are in rapid motion colliding with each other and with the walls of the container. The gas stays the same while the molecules are constantly rearranged and the energy redistributed. The 'number of ways', W, is large for a gas. Gases generally have higher entropies than comparable liquids, which have higher entropies than similar solids.

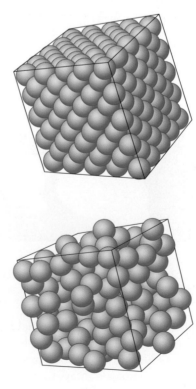

Figure 14.6▶
The structure of a solid. Solids have relatively low values for standard molar entropies. In diamond, the carbon atoms are held firmly in place by strong, highly directional covalent bonds – the standard molar entropy of diamond is low. Lead has a higher value for its standard molar entropy because metallic bonds are not directional – the heavier, larger atoms can vibrate more freely and share out their energy in more ways than can carbon atoms in diamond.

Figure 14.7▶
The structure of a liquid. In general, liquids have higher standard molar entropies than comparable solids because the atoms or molecules are free to move. There are many more ways of distributing the particles and energy – there is more disorder. The standard molar entropy of mercury is higher than that of lead. Molecules with more atoms have higher standard molar entropies because they can vibrate, rotate and arrange themselves in yet more ways.

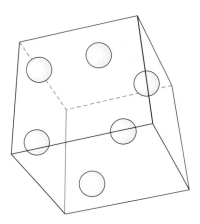

Figure 14.8▲
The atoms of a noble gas. Gases have even higher standard molar entropies than comparable liquids because the atoms or molecules are not only free to move but also widely spaced. There are even more ways of distributing the particles and energy – the disorder is even greater. The standard molar entropy of argon is higher than that of mercury. As with liquids, molecules with more atoms have even higher standard molar entropies because they can vibrate, rotate and arrange themselves in more ways.

Solids	$S^\ominus$/J mol^{-1} K^{-1}	Liquids	$S^\ominus$/J mol^{-1} K^{-1}	Gases	$S^\ominus$/J mol^{-1} K^{-1}
carbon (diamond)	2.4	mercury	76.0	argon	155
magnesium oxide	26.9	water	69.9	ammonia	192
copper	33.2	ethanol	160	carbon dioxide	214
lead	64.8	benzene	173	propane	270

Table 14.1▲
Standard molar entropies for selected solids, liquids and gases.

Test yourself

2 Refer to Table 14.1. Why is the value of the standard molar entropy of:
  a) mercury higher than the value for copper
  b) ammonia higher than the value for water
  c) propane higher than the value for argon?
3 Which substance in each of the following pairs is expected to have the higher standard molar entropy at 298 K?
  a) Br_2(l), Br_2(g)
  b) H_2O(s), H_2O(l)
  c) HF(g), NH_3(g)
  d) CH_4(g), C_2H_6(g)
  e) NaCl(s), NaCl(aq)
  f) ethene, poly(ethene)
  g) pentene gas, cyclopentane gas.

> **Definition**
>
> **Standard molar entropy, $S^\ominus$**, is the entropy per mole of a substance under standard conditions. Chemists use values for standard molar entropies to calculate entropy changes, and hence to predict the direction and extent of chemical change.
>
> The units for standard molar entropy are joules per mole per kelvin (J mol^{-1} K^{-1}). Note that the units are joules and not kilojoules.

The entropy change of the system

Tables of standard molar entropies make it possible to calculate the entropy change of a system of chemicals during a reaction.

$$S^\ominus_{system} = \text{the sum of the standard} - \text{the sum of the standard}$$
molar entropies   molar entropies
of the products   of the reactants

Worked example

Calculate the entropy change of the system, $S_{\text{system}}^{\ominus}$, in the synthesis of ammonia from nitrogen and hydrogen. Comment on the value.

www
Data

Notes on the method
Write the balanced equation for the reaction.
Look up the standard molar entropies in the data table, taking careful note of the units.

Answer
The balanced equation is:
$$N_2(g) + 3H_2(g) \rightarrow 2NH_3(g)$$

Sum of the standard molar entropies of the products = $2 \times S^{\ominus}[NH_3(g)]$
$$= 2 \times 192.4\,\text{J}\,\text{mol}^{-1}\,\text{K}^{-1} = 384.8\,\text{J}\,\text{mol}^{-1}\,\text{K}^{-1}$$

Sum of the standard molar entropies of the reactants
$$= S^{\ominus}[N_2(g)] + 3S^{\ominus}[H_2(g)]$$
$$= 191.6\,\text{J}\,\text{mol}^{-1}\,\text{K}^{-1} + (3 \times 130.6\,\text{J}\,\text{mol}^{-1}\,\text{K}^{-1}) = 583.4\,\text{J}\,\text{mol}^{-1}\,\text{K}^{-1}$$
$$\Delta S_{\text{system}}^{\ominus} = 384.8\,\text{J}\,\text{mol}^{-1}\,\text{K}^{-1} - 583.4\,\text{J}\,\text{mol}^{-1}\,\text{K}^{-1}$$
$$= -198.6\,\text{J}\,\text{mol}^{-1}\,\text{K}^{-1}$$

This shows that the entropy of the system decreases when nitrogen and hydrogen combine to form ammonia. This is not surprising since the change halves the number of molecules, so the amount of gas decreases.

www
Tutorial

Test yourself

4 Without doing any calculations, predict whether the entropy of the system increases or decreases as a result of these changes:
   a) $KCl(s) + aq \rightarrow KCl(aq)$
   b) $H_2O(l) \rightarrow H_2O(g)$
   c) $Mg(s) + Cl_2(g) \rightarrow MgCl_2(s)$
   d) $N_2O_4(g) \rightarrow 2NO_2(g)$
   e) $NaHCO_3(s) + HCl(aq) \rightarrow NaCl(aq) + H_2O(l) + CO_2(g)$
5 Use values from the data sheet to calculate the entropy change of the system for the catalytic reaction of ammonia with oxygen to form nitric oxide, NO, and steam. Comment on the value.

The entropy change of the surroundings

It is not enough to consider just the entropy of the system. What matters is the *total* entropy change, which is the sum of the entropy changes of the system and the entropy change in the surroundings.

$$\Delta S_{\text{total}}^{\ominus} = \Delta S_{\text{system}}^{\ominus} + \Delta S_{\text{surroundings}}^{\ominus}$$

It turns out that the entropy change of the surroundings during a chemical reaction is determined by the size of the enthalpy change, ΔH, and the temperature, T. The relationship is:

$$\Delta S_{\text{surroundings}} = \frac{-\Delta H}{T}$$

The minus sign is included because the entropy change is larger as more energy is transferred to the surroundings. For an exothermic reaction, which transfers energy to the surroundings, ΔH is negative, so $-\Delta H$ is positive.

What this relationship shows is that the more energy transferred to the surroundings by an exothermic process, the larger the increase in the entropy of the surroundings. It also shows that, for a given quantity of energy, the increase in entropy is greater when the surroundings are cool than when they are hot. Adding energy to molecules in a cool system has a proportionately greater effect on the number of ways of distributing matter and energy than adding the same quantity of energy to a system that is already very hot.

Bearing in mind that a reaction is only feasible if the total entropy change, ΔS_{total}, is positive:

● Most exothermic reactions tend to go because at about room temperature the value of $-\Delta H/T$ is much larger and more positive than ΔS_{system}, which means that ΔS_{total} is positive.
● An endothermic reaction can be feasible so long as the increase in the entropy of the system is greater than the decrease in the entropy of the surroundings.
● A reaction which does not tend to go at room temperature may become feasible as the temperature rises because $\Delta S_{\text{surroundings}}$ decreases in magnitude as T increases.

Figure 14.9▲
The thermite reaction is highly exothermic – it gives out a great deal of energy to its surroundings. The entropy change in the surroundings is large and positive.

14.2 Free energy

A chemical change is feasible if the total entropy change is positive. There is no doubt about this. The problem is that using entropy to decide on the direction change involves three steps – first, working out the entropy change of the system, then working out the entropy change of the surroundings, and then putting the two together to calculate the total entropy change. This can be laborious and chemists are grateful to the American physicist Willard Gibbs who discovered an easier way of unifying all that chemists know about predicting the extent and direction of change.

Free energy and entropy

Willard Gibbs (1839–1903) was the first to define the thermochemical quantity 'free energy'. The symbol for a free energy change is ΔG. If ΔG is negative then the reaction is feasible and tends to go.

The advantage of $\Delta G^{\ominus}$ values for chemists is that tables of standard free energies of formation can be used to calculate the standard free energy change for any reaction. The calculations follow exactly the same steps as the calculations to calculate standard enthalpy changes for reactions from standard enthalpies of formation.

The quantity 'free energy' is closely related to the idea of entropy and can be thought of as the 'total entropy change' in disguise. Willard Gibbs defined free energy as:

$$\Delta G^{\ominus} = -T\Delta S^{\ominus}_{total}$$

Given that:

$$\Delta S^{\ominus}_{total} = \Delta S^{\ominus}_{system} + \Delta S^{\ominus}_{surroundings}$$

and that for a change at constant temperature and pressure:

$$\Delta S^{\ominus}_{surroundings} = \frac{-\Delta H^{\ominus}}{T}$$

It follows that:

$$\Delta S^{\ominus}_{total} = \Delta S^{\ominus}_{system} + \left(\frac{-\Delta H^{\ominus}}{T}\right)$$

Hence, $-T\Delta S^{\ominus}_{total} = -T\Delta S^{\ominus}_{system} + \Delta H^{\ominus}$

From Gibb's definition this becomes $\Delta G^{\ominus} = \Delta H^{\ominus} - T\Delta S^{\ominus}_{system}$

The great advantage of this equation is that all the terms refer to the system, and so it is no longer necessary to calculate changes in the surroundings. Given that this is the case, the equation is usually written as below, with the understanding that the entropy change is $\Delta S^{\ominus}_{system}$:

$$\Delta G^{\ominus} = \Delta H^{\ominus} - T\Delta S^{\ominus}$$

Table 14.2 summarises the implications of this important relationship.

Enthalpy change	Entropy change of the system	Is the reaction feasible?
exothermic (ΔH –ve)	increase (ΔS +ve)	yes, ΔG is –ve
exothermic (ΔH –ve)	decrease (ΔS –ve)	yes, if the number value of ΔH is greater than the magnitude of $T\Delta S$
endothermic (ΔH +ve)	increase (ΔS +ve)	yes, if the magnitude of $T\Delta S$ is greater than the number value of ΔH
endothermic (ΔH +ve)	decrease (ΔS –ve)	no, ΔG is +ve

Table 14.2 ▲

The possibilities listed in Table 14.2 show why chemists sometimes say that the feasibility of a reaction depends on the balance between the enthalpy change and the entropy change for the process.

Table 14.2 also shows that a change that is not feasible at a lower temperature may become feasible if the temperature increases. Generally the values of $\Delta H^\ominus$ and $\Delta S^\ominus$ do not change markedly with temperature, so it is possible to estimate the temperature at which a reaction which is not feasible at room temperature becomes feasible at a higher temperature.

Full data is not available for all reactions so it is not always possible to calculate the free energy change. At relatively low temperatures, the $T\Delta S^\ominus$ term is often relatively small compared to the enthalpy change so that $\Delta G^\ominus \approx \Delta H^\ominus$.

This means that chemists can often use the sign of $\Delta H^\ominus$ as a guide to feasibility. This can be misleading if the magnitude of the entropy change of the reaction system is large. Also, the approximation becomes less justified at higher temperatures when T is bigger and so the magnitude of $T\Delta S^\ominus$ is bigger.

www
Tutorial

www
Data

Test yourself

6 Can an exothermic reaction which is not feasible at room temperature become feasible at a higher temperature if the entropy change of the reaction is negative?

7 a) Calculate $\Delta S^\ominus$ and $\Delta H^\ominus$ for the synthesis of methanol from carbon monoxide and hydrogen, taking the information you need from the data sheets on the Dynamic Learning Student website.

   b) Work out the temperature at which the synthesis ceases to be feasible.

8 Consider the reaction of magnesium with oxygen:
   $2Mg(s) + O_2(g) \rightarrow 2MgO(s)$ $\Delta H^\ominus = -602\,kJ\,mol^{-1}$; $\Delta S^\ominus = -217\,J\,mol^{-1}\,K^{-1}$
   a) Why does the entropy of the system decrease?
   b) Show why the reaction of magnesium with oxygen is feasible at 298 K despite the decrease in the entropy.

9 Consider the reduction of iron(III) oxide by carbon:
   $2Fe_2O_3(s) + 3C(s) \rightarrow 4Fe(s) + 3CO_2(g)$ $\Delta H^\ominus = +468\,kJ\,mol^{-1}$;
   $\Delta S^\ominus = +558\,J\,mol^{-1}\,K^{-1}$
   a) Why does the entropy of the system increase for this reaction?
   b) Show that the reaction is not feasible at room temperature (298 K).
   c) Assuming that $\Delta H^\ominus$ and $\Delta S^\ominus$ do not vary with temperature, estimate the temperature at which the decomposition becomes feasible.

How far and in which direction?

Gibbs's concept of free energy makes it possible to unify all the means that chemists use to predict the extent and direction of change.

For many reactions, such as acid–base reactions, the easiest guide to the direction and extent of change is the equilibrium constant, K_c. It is possible to show that the standard free energy change is related to the value of the equilibrium constant:

$$\Delta G^\ominus \propto -\log K_c$$

For redox reactions, standard electrode potentials offer an alternative way of deciding whether or not reactions tend to go (see Topic 15). The free energy change for a redox reaction and a corresponding cell e.m.f. are closely related:

$$\Delta G^\ominus \propto -E^\ominus_{cell}$$

So, if the cell e.m.f is positive the redox reaction in the cell will tend to go. What this shows is that $\Delta G^\ominus$, $E^\ominus_{cell}$ and K_c values can all answer the same questions for a reaction:

- will the reaction go?
- how far will it go?

In practice, chemists use the quantity which is most convenient to measure. Knowing the value of one of the three quantities it is possible to calculate the other two.

However, it is always important to bear in mind that even if a reaction is feasible it may be very slow.

Stable or inert?

The study of energetics (thermochemistry) and rates of reaction (kinetics) helps to explain why some chemicals are stable while others react rapidly.

Compounds are *stable* if they have no tendency to decompose into their elements or change into other compounds. For example, magnesium oxide has no tendency to split up into magnesium and oxygen. However, a compound which is stable at room temperature and pressure may become more or less stable as conditions change.

Chemists often use standard enthalpy change as an indicator of stability. Strictly they should use standard free energy, $\Delta G_f^{\ominus}$, values – but in many cases $\Delta G_f^{\ominus} \approx \Delta H_f^{\ominus}$.

A chemical is *inert* if it has no tendency to react even when the reaction is feasible. The lighter noble gases helium and neon live up to the original name for Group 8 elements – they are inert towards all other reagents.

Figure 14.10▲
Roofer fitting copper to a roof in Boston, USA. Copper in air and water – stable or inert?

Figure 14.11◄
Coils of aluminium at a processing plant. Aluminium in air – stable or inert?

Nitrogen is a relatively unreactive gas which can be used to create an 'inert' atmosphere free of oxygen (which is much more reactive). However, nitrogen is not inert in all circumstances. It reacts with hydrogen in the Haber process to form ammonia, and with oxygen at high temperatures to form nitrogen oxides.

A compound such as the gas N_2O, for example, is thermodynamically unstable but it continues to exist at room temperature because it is kinetically inert ($\Delta H_f^{\ominus} = +82 \text{ kJ mol}^{-1}$ and $\Delta G_f^{\ominus} = +104 \text{ kJ mol}^{-1}$). The free energy change for the decomposition reaction is negative, so the compound tends to decompose into its elements, but the rate is very slow under normal conditions.

Examples of kinetic inertness are:

- a mixture of hydrogen and oxygen at room temperature
- a solution of hydrogen peroxide in the absence of a catalyst
- aluminium metal in dilute hydrochloric acid.

'Kinetic stability' is a term sometimes used for 'kinetic inertness'. However, it helps to make a sharp distinction between two quite different types of explanation. For clarity, chemists refer to:

- systems with no tendency to react as 'stable'
- systems which should react but do not do so for a rate (kinetic) reason, as 'inert'.

$\Delta G^{\ominus}$ ($\approx \Delta H^{\ominus}$)	Activation energy	Change observed	
positive	high	no reaction	reactants stable relative to products
negative	high	no reaction	reactants unstable relative to products but kinetically inert
positive	low	no reaction	reactants stable relative to products
negative	low	fast reaction	reactants unstable relative to products

Table 14.3 ▲

Test yourself

10 Suggest examples of reactions to illustrate each of the four possibilities in Table 14.3.
11 Draw a reaction profile to show the energy changes from reactants to products for reactants which are thermodynamically unstable relative to the products, but kinetically inert.

Sometimes there is no tendency for a reaction to go because the reactants are stable. This is so if the free energy change for the reaction is positive. Sometimes there is no reaction even though thermochemistry suggests that it should go. The free energy change is negative, so the change is feasible, but a high activation energy means that the rate of reaction is very, very slow.

Activity

The thermal stability of Group 2 carbonates

The decomposition of Group 2 metal carbonates is used on a large scale to make oxides such as magnesium and calcium oxides.

The carbonates of Group 2 metals do not decompose at room temperature. They do decompose on heating:

$MgCO_3(s) \rightarrow MgO(s) + CO_2(g)$
$\Delta H^{\ominus} = +117 \, kJ \, mol^{-1}$; $\Delta S^{\ominus} = +175 \, J \, mol^{-1} \, K^{-1}$

$BaCO_3(s) \rightarrow BaO(s) + CO_2(g)$
$\Delta H^{\ominus} = +268 \, kJ \, mol^{-1}$; $\Delta S^{\ominus} = +172 \, J \, mol^{-1} \, K^{-1}$

1 Why does the entropy increase when a Group 2 carbonate decomposes?

2 a) Calculate the free energy change for the room temperature (298 K) decomposition of:

i) magnesium carbonate

ii) barium carbonate.

b) Are these two compounds stable or unstable relative to decomposition into their oxide and carbon dioxide at room temperature?

Figure 14.12 ▲
Crystals of dolomite (foreground) and magnesite (background) from Brazil. Dolomite is a calcium–magnesium carbonate rock. Magnesite is pure magnesium carbonate. Large crystals of magnesite are rare.

3 Assuming that $\Delta H^\ominus$ and $\Delta S^\ominus$ for the reactions do not vary with temperature, estimate the temperatures at which the two decomposition reactions become feasible.

4 Down Group 2, do the metal carbonates become more stable or less stable relative to decomposition into the oxide and carbon dioxide?

Chemists seek to explain the trend in thermal stability of the Group 2 carbonates by analysing the energy changes.

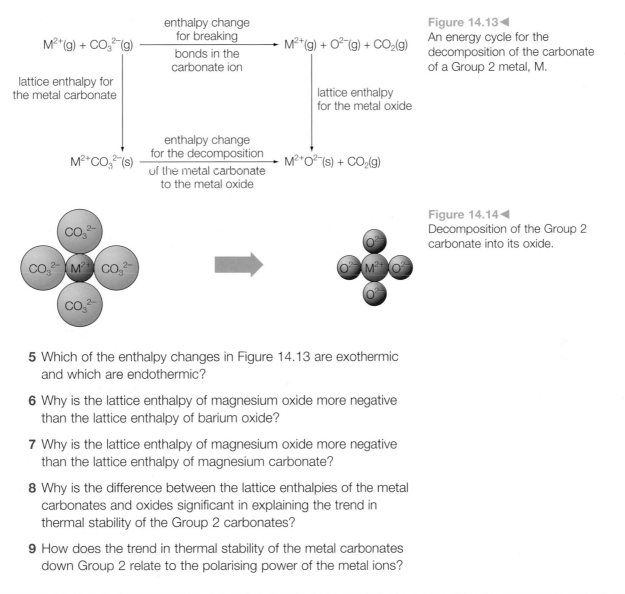

Figure 14.13◄
An energy cycle for the decomposition of the carbonate of a Group 2 metal, M.

Figure 14.14◄
Decomposition of the Group 2 carbonate into its oxide.

5 Which of the enthalpy changes in Figure 14.13 are exothermic and which are endothermic?

6 Why is the lattice enthalpy of magnesium oxide more negative than the lattice enthalpy of barium oxide?

7 Why is the lattice enthalpy of magnesium oxide more negative than the lattice enthalpy of magnesium carbonate?

8 Why is the difference between the lattice enthalpies of the metal carbonates and oxides significant in explaining the trend in thermal stability of the Group 2 carbonates?

9 How does the trend in thermal stability of the metal carbonates down Group 2 relate to the polarising power of the metal ions?

REVIEW QUESTIONS

DL
www
Extension questions

1 The graph below shows how the entropy of water changes from 0 K to 450 K.

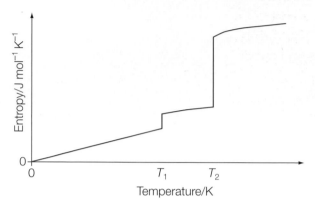

a) Explain why the molar entropy of water is zero at 0 K. **(2)**

b) Account for the entropy changes at temperatures T_1 and T_2. Explain why one is bigger than the other. **(3)**

c) i) Why does $\Delta G = 0\,kJ\,mol^{-1}$ for the change of water to steam at 373 K and 1 atmosphere pressure? **(2)**

   ii) The enthalpy change of vaporisation of water is $41.1\,kJ\,mol^{-1}$ at 373 K. Calculate the value of ΔS for the conversion of water into steam at 373 K and 1 atmosphere pressure. **(3)**

2 Electrolysis is usually used to extract aluminium metal. In principle, it should be possible to extract the metal by heating its oxide with carbon. Use the data in the table to answer the questions.

	$Al_2O_3(s)$	$C(s)$	$Al(s)$	$CO(g)$
$\Delta H^{\ominus}_f$/kJ mol^{-1}	−1669	0	0	−111
$S^{\ominus}$/J mol^{-1} K^{-1}	50.9	5.7	28.3	198

a) Write the equation for the reduction of aluminium oxide by carbon, assuming that the carbon is converted to carbon monoxide. **(1)**

b) Calculate the standard enthalpy change for the reduction reaction. **(3)**

c) Calculate the standard entropy change for the reduction reaction. **(3)**

d) i) Calculate the standard free energy change for the reduction at 298 K. **(2)**

   ii) What does you answer to part **d) i)** tell you about the feasibility of the reaction at 298 K? **(1)**

e) Calculate the minimum temperature at which the reduction of aluminium oxide by carbon becomes feasible. **(2)**

f) Suggest a reason why the reaction between aluminium oxide and carbon does not happen to a significant extent until the temperature is about 1000 degrees higher than your answer to part **d)**. **(1)**

3 Carbon monoxide is one of the products when methane burns in a limited supply of air.

$$CH_4(g) + \tfrac{3}{2}O_2(g) \rightarrow CO(g) + 2H_2O(g)$$
$$\Delta H^{\ominus} = -519\,kJ\,mol^{-1}; \ \Delta S^{\ominus} = +82\,J\,mol^{-1}\,K^{-1}$$

a) Calculate $\Delta G^{\ominus}$ for the reaction. **(2)**

b) i) Plot a graph to show how ΔG for this reaction varies with temperature, using your answer to part **a)** and these values: **(2)**

Temperature/K	1500	3000	4000
ΔG/kJ mol^{-1}	−640	−765	−845

   ii) From the shape of the line on the graph, what can you conclude about the variation with temperature of ΔS for this reaction? **(2)**

c) i) Is the reaction of methane with oxygen to form carbon monoxide and steam feasible in the temperature range 200 K to 3000 K? **(2)**

   ii) Why does methane not burn in air at 298 K? **(2)**

d) Sooty carbon is another of the products when methane burns in a limited supply of air.

$$CH_4(g) + O_2(g) \rightarrow C(s) + 2H_2O(g)$$
$$\Delta S^{\ominus} = -8\,J\,mol^{-1}\,K^{-1}$$

How do you account for the difference in the values for $\Delta S^{\ominus}$ for the reaction producing carbon monoxide and the reaction that forms soot? **(4)**

15 Redox, electrode potentials and fuel cells

Redox reactions are very important in the natural environment, in living things and in modern technology. It should be no surprise that the Earth, with its oxygen-containing atmosphere, has an extensive range of redox chemistry.

Redox reactions involve electron transfer and chemists have developed the concept of electrode potentials in electrochemical cells in order to explain redox changes more fully. Some electrochemical cells have great practical and technological importance, while others, particularly fuel cells, are becoming a serious alternative to oil-based fuels for vehicles. Measurements of the electrode potentials of cells help us to assess the feasibility and likelihood of redox reactions.

15.1 Redox reactions

About one million million (10^{12}) moles of oxygen are removed from the atmosphere every year in the process of oxidising ions such as iron(II), Fe^{2+}, from weathered rocks, and molecules such as hydrogen sulfide, carbon monoxide and methane in volcanic gases.

Figure 15.1 ◄
Volcanoes release millions of tonnes of reducing gases into the atmosphere, where they react with oxygen. This photo shows Mount St Helens in British Columbia erupting in 1980.

Redox reactions are also involved in the metabolic pathways of respiration. These pathways produce adenosine triphosphate (ATP). ATP transfers the energy released during the oxidation of food into movement, growth and all the other reactions in living things which need a source of energy.

In addition, the voltages of chemical cells are obtained from the energy of redox reactions, and redox is also involved in manufacturing processes that use electrolysis to make products such as chlorine and aluminium.

Definitions of redox

Descriptions and theories of oxidation and reduction have developed over the years and, although there are now several definitions of redox, oxidation and reduction always occur together.

From your AS studies, you should recall that oxidation originally meant addition of oxygen, but the term now covers all reactions in which atoms, molecules or ions lose electrons. Chemists have further extended the definition of oxidation to cover reactions which do not appear to involve electron transfer by defining oxidation as a change in which the oxidation number of an element becomes more positive, or less negative.

Similarly, reduction originally meant removal of oxygen, but the term now covers all reactions in which atoms, molecules or ions gain electrons. Defining reduction as a change in which the oxidation number of an element becomes more negative, or less positive, further extends the definitions of reduction like that of oxidation.

Oxidation states and oxidation numbers

Most elements in the p block and d block of the periodic table form compounds in which their atoms have different oxidation states. Displaying the compounds of an element on an oxidation state diagram provides a 'map' of its chemistry and shows the different oxidation numbers that it can have. Figure 15.2 shows such a map for sulfur.

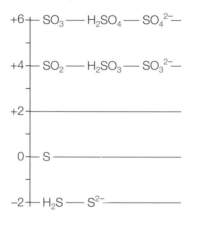

Figure 15.2▲
The oxidation numbers of sulfur in its different oxidation states.

There are strict rules for assigning oxidation numbers and these are shown below.

Oxidation number rules

1 The oxidation number of the atoms in uncombined elements is zero.

2 In simple ions, the oxidation number of the element is the charge on the ion.

3 In neutral molecules, the sum of the oxidation numbers of the constituent elements is zero.

4 In ions containing two or more elements, the charge on the ion is the sum of the oxidation numbers.

5 In any compound, the more electronegative element has a negative oxidation number and the less electronegative element has a positive oxidation number.

6 The oxidation number of hydrogen in all its compounds is +1, except in metal hydrides in which it is −1.

7 The oxidation number of oxygen in all its compounds is −2, except in peroxides in which it is −1 and OF_2 in which it is +2.

Definitions

Redox stands for **red**uction + **ox**idation.

Oxidation involves the loss of electrons, or an increase in oxidation number.

Reduction involves the gain of electrons, or a decrease in oxidation number.

Remember the mnemonic **OILRIG** – Oxidation Is Loss; Reduction Is Gain of electrons.

An **oxidation number** is a number assigned to an atom or ion to describe its relative state of oxidation or reduction.

Half-reactions and half-equations

Half-reactions are reactions which relate to one half (either the oxidation half or the reduction half) of a redox reaction. Of course, no half-reaction can take place without another half-reaction to complete both the oxidation and reduction halves of a redox reaction.

Half-reactions can be summarised by half-equations – these are ionic equations used to describe either the gain or the loss of electrons during a redox reaction. Half-equations help to show what is happening during a redox reaction. In a similar fashion to half-reactions, two half-equations can combine to give the full equation for a redox reaction.

For example, zinc metal can reduce Cu^{2+} ions in copper(II) sulfate solution forming copper metal and Zn^{2+} ions in zinc sulfate solution. This can be shown as two half-equations:

- electron loss (oxidation); $\quad Zn(s) \rightarrow Zn^{2+}(aq) + 2e^-$
- electron gain (reduction); $\quad Cu^{2+}(aq) + 2e^- \rightarrow Cu(s)$

Balancing the number of electrons lost by Zn with the number gained by $Cu^{2+}(aq)$, we can add the two half-equations to get the full equation:

$$Zn(s) + Cu^{2+}(aq) \rightarrow Zn^{2+}(aq) + Cu(s)$$

Test yourself

1 Describe, in terms of gain or loss of electrons, the redox reactions in these examples:
   a) the changes at the electrodes during the manufacture of aluminium from molten (liquid) aluminium oxide
   b) the reaction of iron with chlorine to form iron(III) chloride.
2 Explain why the oxidation number of oxygen is:
   a) +2 in OF_2
   b) −1 in peroxides such as Na_2O_2.
3 State the changes in oxidation number when concentrated sulfuric acid reacts with potassium bromide:

   $4KBr(s) + 2H_2SO_4(aq) \rightarrow K_2SO_4(aq) + K_2SO_3(aq) + Br_2(aq) + 2HBr(aq) + H_2O(l)$

4 What is the oxidation number of each element in:
   a) KIO_3
   b) NO_3^-
   c) H_2O_2
   d) SF_6
   e) NaH?
5 Which sulfur compounds in Figure 15.2 can:
   a) act as an oxidising agent or as a reducing agent depending on the conditions
   b) only act as an oxidising agent
   c) only act as a reducing agent?
6 Draw a chart similar to Figure 15.2 to show the main oxidation states of:
   a) nitrogen
   b) chlorine.
7 Are the named elements oxidised or reduced in the following conversions:
   a) magnesium to magnesium sulfate
   b) iodine to aluminium iodide
   c) hydrogen to lithium hydride
   d) iodine to iodine monochloride, ICl?

Activity

Redox reactions in the Space Shuttle

Unlike most vehicles on Earth, spacecraft must carry oxidising agents as well as fuels. The mixtures of fuels plus oxidising agents are called propellants.

In order to launch the Space Shuttle from ground level into the Earth's upper atmosphere, a solid propellant mixture of powdered aluminium and ammonium chlorate(VII), NH_4ClO_4 is used. The reaction involved is:

$$3Al(s) + 3NH_4ClO_4(s) \rightarrow Al_2O_3(s) + AlCl_3(s) + 3NO(g) + 6H_2O(g)$$

1 What is:

  a) the fuel;

  b) the oxidising agent in the solid propellant?

2 What are the oxidation numbers of each element in NH_4ClO_4?

3 **a)** Which elements are oxidised in the reaction?

  b) State the change in oxidation numbers of these elements.

4 Which element is reduced in the reaction, and what is the change in its oxidation number?

5 What actually propels the Space Shuttle?

Figure 15.3 ▲
The Space Shuttle *Endeavour* takes off on its journey to the International Space Station.

Propulsion of the Shuttle from the upper atmosphere into orbit is achieved using a mixture of liquid hydrogen and liquid oxygen. Once the hydrogen and oxygen are ignited, they continue to vaporise and burn continuously producing a clean water-vapour exhaust.

6 Write an equation for the combustion of liquid hydrogen and oxygen during the second stage.

Once in orbit, a propulsion system is needed for manoeuvrability – one in which the fuel and oxidising agent ignite spontaneously on mixing and which can be readily started and stopped.

In this stage, the fuel is liquid methylhydrazine (CH_3NHNH_2) with liquid dinitrogen tetroxide (N_2O_4) as the oxidiser. The reaction produces water vapour, carbon dioxide and nitrogen.

7 Write a balanced equation for the reaction between CH_3NHNH_2 and N_2O_4 in this stage.

8 Explain why CH_3NHNH_2 acts as the reducing agent and why N_2O_4 acts as the oxidising agent during the reaction.

15.2 Oxidising agents and reducing agents

Oxidising agents (oxidants) are chemical reagents that can oxidise other substances. They do this either by taking electrons away from these substances or by increasing their oxidation number. Common oxidising agents include oxygen, chlorine, bromine, hydrogen peroxide, the manganate(VII) ion in potassium manganate(VII) and the dichromate(VI) ion in potassium or sodium dichromate(VI).

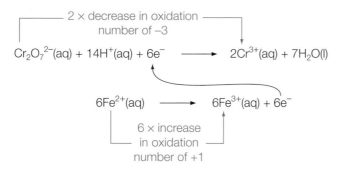

Figure 15.4▲
Dichromate(VI) ions act as oxidising agents by taking electrons from iron(II) ions in acid solution. An oxidising agent is itself reduced when it reacts.

Some reagents change colour when they are oxidised and this makes them useful for detecting oxidising agents. For example, a colourless solution of iodide ions is oxidised to iodine, which turns the solution to a yellow–brown colour:

$$2I^-(aq) \rightarrow I_2(aq) + 2e^-$$

electrons taken by the oxidising agent.

This can be a very sensitive test if starch is also present because starch forms an intense blue–black colour with iodine. Moistened starch–iodide paper can detect oxidising gases such as chlorine and bromine vapour.

   Reducing agents (reductants) are chemical reagents that can reduce other substances. They do this either by giving electrons to these substances or by reducing their oxidation number. Common reducing agents include metals such as zinc and iron (often with acid), sulfite ions (SO_3^{2-}), iron(II) ions and iodide ions.

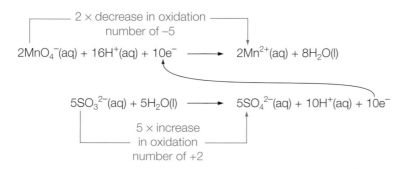

Figure 15.5▲
Sulfite ions act as reducing agents by giving electrons to manganate(VII) ions. A reducing agent is itself oxidised when it reacts

Some reagents change colour when they are reduced and this makes them useful for detecting reducing agents (Figures 15.6 and 15.7).

Figure 15.6▲
A test for reducing agents.
The test – add a solution of purple potassium manganate(VII) acidified with dilute sulfuric acid to the reducing agent.
The result – the purple solution turns colourless as purple MnO_4^- ions are reduced to very pale pink Mn^{2+} ions.

Figure 15.7▲
Another test for reducing agents.
The test – add orange dichromate(VI) solution acidified with dilute sulfuric acid to the reducing agent.
The result – the orange solution turns green as orange $Cr_2O_7^{2-}$ ions are reduced to green Cr^{3+} ions.

15.3 Constructing redox equations

The easiest way to write a balanced equation for a redox reaction is to combine the relevant half-equations. Just write the half-equations for the reactants involved and then balance the number of electrons given up by the reducing agent with those taken by the oxidising agent.

Worked example

Construct a balanced equation for the redox reaction between acidified potassium manganate(VII) and hydrogen peroxide.

Answer
Step 1: Write the relevant half-equations:

$$MnO_4^- + 8H^+ + 5e^- \rightarrow Mn^{2+} + 4H_2O$$
$$H_2O_2 \rightarrow O_2 + 2H^+ + 2e^-$$

(Note that the oxygen in oxoanions, such as MnO_4^- and $Cr_2O_7^{2-}$, usually gets converted to water by H^+ ions in the acid solution, while the Mn and Cr in the oxoanions are converted to stable simple ions.)

Step 2: Balance the number of electrons given up by the reducing agent with those taken by the oxidising agent. In this case, we need to multiply one half-equation by 5 and the other by 2 so that 10 electrons are given up and then taken:

$$2MnO_4^- + 16H^+ + 10e^- \rightarrow 2Mn^{2+} + 8H_2O$$
$$5H_2O_2 \rightarrow 5O_2 + 10H^+ + 10e^-$$

Step 3: Add the two half-equations to get the full equation. When you do this the electrons cancel and, in this particular case, some of the H^+ ions can be cancelled as well.

$$2MnO_4^- + 6H^+ + 5H_2O_2 \rightarrow 2Mn^{2+} + 8H_2O + 5O_2$$

Oxidation numbers can also help in the construction of redox equations. In fact, oxidation numbers can be used even when you don't know the relevant half-equations, provided that you do know the formulae of the atoms, ions and molecules involved in the reaction. We can illustrate this in the following worked example.

Worked example

Construct a balanced equation for the oxidation of iron(II) ions by hydrogen peroxide in acid solution.

Notes on the method
The key to this method is to set the decrease in oxidation number of the element reduced equal to the increase in oxidation number of the element oxidised.

Answer
Step 1: Write the formulae of the atoms, ions and molecules involved in the reaction.

$$H_2O_2 + H^+ + Fe^{2+} \rightarrow H_2O + Fe^{3+}$$

Step 2: Identify the elements which change in oxidation number and the extent of change.

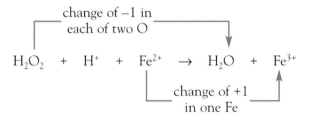

Step 3: Balance the equation so that the overall decrease in oxidation number of one element equals the overall increase in oxidation number of the other.

In this example, the overall decrease in oxygen is $2 \times -1 = -2$. So, this must be balanced by two Fe^{2+} ions each increasing their oxidation number by $+1$ ($2 \times +1 = +2$):

$$H_2O_2 + H^+ + 2Fe^{2+} \rightarrow H_2O + 2Fe^{3+}$$

Step 4: Balance for oxygen and hydrogen, if necessary.

In this case, the two oxygen atoms of the H_2O_2 molecule form two molecules of water and this requires two H^+ ions to balance hydrogen on both sides of the equation:

$$H_2O_2 + 2H^+ + 2Fe^{2+} \rightarrow 2H_2O + 2Fe^{3+}$$

Step 5: Finally, check that the overall charges on each side of the equation balance and then add state symbols.

The net charge on the left is 6+, which is the same as that on the right. After adding state symbols, the final equation is:

$$H_2O_2(aq) + 2H^+(aq) + 2Fe^{2+}(aq) \rightarrow 2H_2O(l) + 2Fe^{3+}(aq)$$

Test yourself

8 Write half-equations to show the following reactants acting as oxidising agents:
 a) $Fe^{3+}(aq)$
 b) $Br_2(aq)$
 c) $H_2O_2(aq)$ in acid solution.
9 Write half-equations to show the following reactants acting as reducing agents:
 a) $Zn(s)$
 b) $I^-(aq)$
 c) $Fe^{2+}(aq)$.
10 Explain why moist starch–iodide paper can be used as a very sensitive test for chlorine.
11 a) Write the half-equations involved in the reaction between hydrogen peroxide and iron(II) sulfate in acid solution.
 b) Write a full redox equation for the reaction involved.
 c) Describe the change you would see in the solution when the reaction occurs.
 d) How many moles of iron(II) sulfate react with 1 mole of H_2O_2?
12 a) Write the half-equations involved when dichromate(VI) ions in acid solution react with sulfite ions, SO_3^{2-}, to form chromium(III) ions and sulfate ions, SO_4^{2-}.
 b) Write a full, balanced redox equation for the reaction.
 c) Describe the change you would see in the solution when the reaction occurs.
 d) How many moles of sulfite react with one mole of dichromate(VI)?

Test yourself

13 Write balanced equations for each of the following redox reactions:
 a) manganese(IV) oxide with hydrochloric acid to form manganese(II) ions and chlorine
 b) copper metal with nitrate ions, NO_3^-, in nitric acid to form copper(II) ions and nitrogen dioxide gas, NO_2.

15.4 Electrode potentials

Redox reactions involve the transfer of electrons from a reducing agent to an oxidising agent. The electron transfer can be shown by writing half-equations. So, for example, when zinc is added to copper(II) sulfate solution, Zn atoms give up electrons forming Zn^{2+} ions. At the same time, the electrons are transferred to Cu^{2+} ions, which form Cu atoms.

The two half-equations for the reaction are:

$$Zn(s) \rightarrow Zn^{2+}(aq) + 2e^-$$

↙ electron transfer

$$Cu^{2+}(aq) + 2e^- \rightarrow Cu(s)$$

The overall balanced equation is:

$$Zn(s) + Cu^{2+}(aq) \rightarrow Zn^{2+}(aq) + Cu(s)$$

Electrochemical cells

Instead of mixing two reagents, it is possible to carry out a redox reaction in an electrochemical cell so that the electron transfer takes place along a wire connecting the two electrodes. This harnesses the energy from the redox reaction to produce an electrical potential difference (voltage).

One of the first useable electrochemical cells was based on the reaction of zinc metal with aqueous copper(II) ions (Figure 15.8). In this cell, zinc is oxidised to zinc ions as copper(II) ions are reduced to copper metal:

$$Zn(s) \rightarrow Zn^{2+}(aq) + 2e^-$$

$$Cu^{2+}(aq) + 2e^- \rightarrow Cu(s)$$

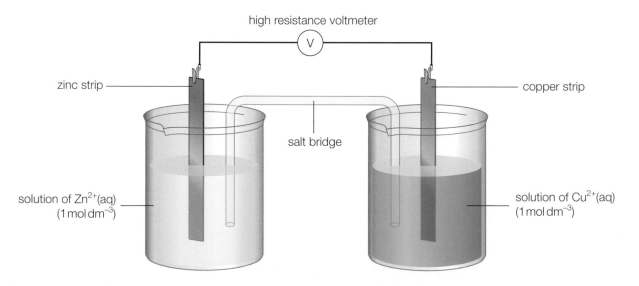

Figure 15.8 ▲
An electrochemical cell based on the reaction of zinc metal with aqueous copper(II) ions. Electrons flow from the negative zinc electrode to the positive copper electrode through the external circuit.

In electrochemical cells, the two half-reactions happen in separate half-cells. The electrons flow from one cell to the other through a wire connecting the electrodes. A salt bridge connecting the two solutions completes the electrical circuit. The salt bridge makes an electrical connection between the two halves of the cell by allowing ions to flow while preventing the two solutions from mixing.

At its simplest, a salt bridge consists of a strip of filter paper soaked in potassium nitrate solution and folded over each of the two beakers. All potassium salts and all nitrates are soluble, so the potassium nitrate in the salt bridge does not form precipitates with any of the ions in the half-cells. In more permanent cells, a salt bridge may consist of a porous solid such as sintered glass.

Chemists measure the tendency for the current to flow in the external circuit by using a high-resistance voltmeter to measure the maximum cell voltage when no current is flowing.

In Figure 15.8, electrons flow out of the zinc electrode (negative) through the external circuit to the copper electrode (positive). The maximum voltage of the cell, usually called the cell potential or the electromotive force (e.m.f.), is 1.10 V under standard conditions.

Standard conditions

In order to compare the voltages (cell potentials) developed by different electrochemical cells, scientists carry out the measurements under standard conditions. These standard conditions for electrochemical measurements are the same as those for thermochemical measurements that we met during the AS course. They are:

- temperature 298 K (25 °C)
- gases at a pressure of 1 atmosphere (1.013×10^5 Pa $\approx$ 100 kPa)
- solutions at a concentration of 1.0 mol dm^{-3}.

Chemists have also developed a convenient shorthand, called a cell diagram, for describing cells. The cell diagram for the cell in Figure 15.8 is shown in Figure 15.9 with an explanation below each entry. Under standard conditions the symbol for a cell potential is $E^{\ominus}_{cell}$ and this is called the standard cell potential.

Zn(s)	Zn^{2+}(aq)	salt bridge	Cu^{2+}(aq)	Cu(s)	$E^{\ominus}_{cell}$ = +1.10 V
metal electrode on the left	materials in contact with left electrode	salt bridge	materials in contact with right electrode	metal electrode on the right	The cell potential (e.m.f.) The sign of E is the charge on the right electrode

Figure 15.9 ▲
A cell diagram for the cell composed of the Zn(s)│Zn^{2+}(aq) and Cu(s)│Cu^{2+}(aq) half-cells.

If the cell potential is positive, the reaction in the cell tends to go according to the cell diagram reading from left to right. As a current flows in the external circuit connecting the two electrodes in Figure 15.9, zinc atoms turn into zinc ions and go into solution, while copper ions turn into copper atoms and deposit on the copper electrode as shown in Figure 15.10.

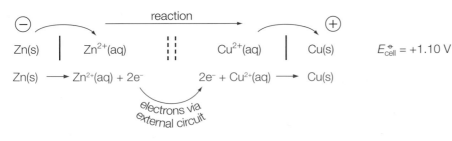

Figure 15.10 ▲
The direction of change in an electrochemical cell.

Test yourself

15 Consider a cell based on the redox reaction below, which tends to go in the direction shown:

Cu(s) + 2Ag$^+$(aq)
$\rightarrow$ Cu^{2+}(aq) + 2Ag(s)

The voltage between the electrodes is 0.46 V.
a) Write the half-equations for the electrode processes when the cell supplies a current.
b) Write the conventional cell diagram for the cell, including the value for E_{cell}.

Standard electrode potentials

The study of many cells has shown that a half-electrode, such as the $Cu^{2+}(aq)|Cu(s)$ electrode, makes the same contribution to the cell potential in *any* cell, so long as the measurements are made under the same conditions. But there is no way of measuring the potential (voltage) of an isolated, single electrode because it has only one terminal.

Chemists have solved this problem by selecting a standard electrode system as a reference electrode against which they can compare all other electrode systems. The chosen reference electrode is the standard hydrogen electrode. By convention the electrode potential of the standard hydrogen electrode is zero. This is represented as $Pt[H_2(g)]|2H^+(aq)$ ¦ $E^\ominus = 0.00\,V$.

The standard electrode potential for any half-cell is measured relative to a standard hydrogen electrode under standard conditions, as shown in Figure 15.11. A standard hydrogen electrode sets up an equilibrium between hydrogen ions in solution ($1\,mol\,dm^{-3}$) and hydrogen gas (1 atm. pressure) at $298\,K$ on the surface of a platinum electrode coated with platinum black.

Note

It is only in a standard hydrogen electrode that the platinum metal is covered with finely divided platinum black. This helps to maintain an equilibrium between hydrogen gas and hydrogen ions, and ensures a reversible reaction between them.

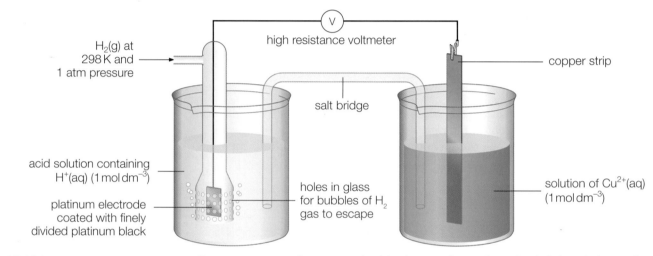

Figure 15.11 ▲
The overall potential of this cell under standard conditions is, by definition, the standard electrode potential of the $Cu^{2+}(aq)|Cu(s)$ electrode.

Definition

The **standard electrode potential**, $E^\ominus$, of a standard half-cell is the potential (voltage) of that half-cell relative to a standard hydrogen electrode under standard conditions.

Standard electrode potentials are sometimes called standard redox potentials or standard reduction potentials.

By convention, when a standard hydrogen electrode is the left-hand electrode in an electrochemical cell, the overall cell potential is the electrode potential of the right-hand electrode.

So, the conventional cell diagram for the cell that defines the standard electrode potential of the $Cu^{2+}(aq)|Cu(s)$ electrode is:

$$Pt[H_2(g)]|2H^+(aq) \;¦¦\; Cu^{2+}(aq)|Cu(s) \quad E^\ominus = +0.34\,V$$

The electrode and its standard electrode potential are often represented more simply as:

$$\underset{\text{oxidised form}}{Cu^{2+}(aq)} \;\; + 2e^- \;\rightleftharpoons\; \underset{\text{reduced form}}{Cu(s)} \qquad E^\ominus = +0.34\,V$$

This also serves to emphasise that standard electrode potentials represent reduction processes.

A hydrogen electrode is difficult to set up and maintain, so it is much easier to use a secondary standard such as a silver/silver chloride electrode or a calomel electrode as a **reference electrode**. These electrodes are available commercially and are reliable to use. They have been calibrated against a standard hydrogen electrode. 'Calomel' is an old-fashioned name for mercury(I) chloride. The cell reaction and electrode potential for a calomel electrode relative to a hydrogen electrode are:

$$Hg_2Cl_2(s) + 2e^- \rightleftharpoons 2Hg(l) + 2Cl^-(aq) \qquad E^\ominus = +0.27\,V$$

For the reverse reaction, $E^\ominus$ has the opposite sign so:

$$2Hg(l) + 2Cl^-(aq) \rightleftharpoons Hg_2Cl_2(s) + 2e^- \qquad E^\ominus = -0.27\,V$$

Figure 15.11 shows how to measure the standard electrode potential of a metal or a non-metal in contact with its ions in aqueous solution.

It is also possible to measure the standard electrode potentials of electrode systems in which both the oxidised and reduced forms are ions in solution, such as ions of the same element in different oxidation states. In these cases, the electrode in the system is platinum (Figure 15.12).

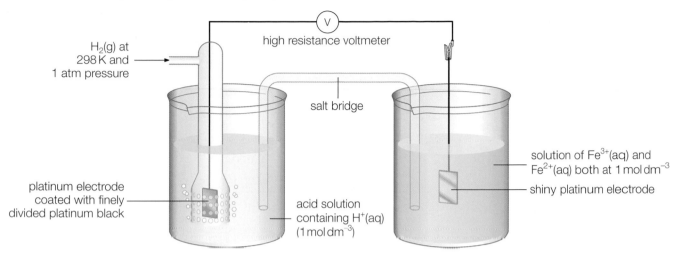

The cell diagram for the cell in Figure 15.12 is:

$Pt[H_2(g)]\,|\,2H^+(aq)\,\vdots\vdots\,Fe^{3+}(aq),\ Fe^{2+}(aq)\,|\,Pt$ $E^{\ominus} = +0.77\,V$

Figure 15.12▲
The diagram of a cell for measuring the standard electrode potential of the redox reaction $Fe^{3+}(aq) + e^- \rightleftharpoons Fe^{2+}(aq)$.

Test yourself

16 Suggest why a hydrogen electrode is difficult to set up and maintain.
17 Why do you think that platinum is used as the electrode for systems in which both the oxidised and reduced forms are ions in solution, such as $Fe^{3+}(aq)$ and $Fe^{2+}(aq)$?
18 What are the half-equations and standard electrode potentials of the right-hand electrode in each of the following cells?
    a) $Pt[H_2(g)]\,|\,2H^+(aq)\,\vdots\vdots\,Sn^{2+}(aq)\,|\,Sn(s)$ $E^{\ominus} = -0.14\,V$
    b) $Pt[H_2(g)]\,|\,2H^+(aq)\,\vdots\vdots\,Br_2(aq),\ 2Br^-(aq)\,|\,Pt$ $E^{\ominus} = +1.07\,V$
    c) $Pt\,|\,[2Hg(l) + 2Cl^-(aq)],Hg_2Cl_2(s)\,\vdots\vdots\,Cr^{3+}(aq)\,|\,Cr(s)$ $E^{\ominus} = -1.01\,V$
19 The standard electrode potential for the $Cu^{2+}(aq)\,|\,Cu(s)$ electrode is +0.34 V. For the cell: $Cu(s)\,|\,Cu^{2+}(aq)\,\vdots\vdots\,Pb^{2+}(aq)\,|\,Pb(s)$ $E^{\ominus}_{cell} = -0.47\,V$.
    What is the standard electrode potential for the $Pb^{2+}(aq)\,|\,Pb(s)$ electrode?
20 a) What is the standard cell potential when a standard calomel electrode is connected to a standard $Cu^{2+}(aq)\,|\,Cu(s)$ electrode?
    b) Write half-equations for the reactions at the electrodes.

15.5 Cell potentials and the direction of change

Chemists use standard electrode potentials to:

- calculate standard cell potentials and
- predict the feasibility (direction) of redox reactions.

The data sheet headed 'Standard electrode potentials' on the Dynamic Learning Student website lists redox half-reactions in order of their standard electrode (reduction) potentials from the most negative to the most positive.

The size and sign of a standard electrode potential tells you how likely it is that a half-reaction will occur. The more positive the standard electrode potential, the more likely it is that the half-reaction will occur.

So, the half-reaction $H_2O_2(aq) + 2H^+(aq) + 2e^- \rightarrow 2H_2O(l)$ with a standard electrode potential of +1.77 volts near the bottom of the table is much more likely to happen than the half-reaction $Li^+(aq) + e^- \rightarrow Li(s)$ with a standard electrode potential of −3.03 volts at the top of the list. Indeed, this

www
Data

Redox, electrode potentials and fuel cells

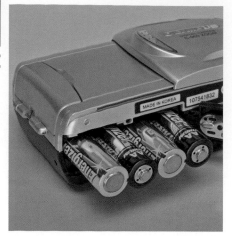

Figure 15.13▲
The four lithium batteries in this camera have a total cell potential (e.m.f.) of about 6 volts.

Figure 15.14▲
Crystals of copper metal have deposited on a strip of zinc placed in copper(II) sulfate solution.

last half-reaction will be much more likely to occur in the opposite direction when it would contribute a voltage of +3.03 volts to any electrochemical cell.

$$Li(s) \rightarrow Li^+(aq) + e^- \qquad E^\ominus = +3.03\,V$$

Using a table of standard electrode potentials, it is possible to calculate standard cell potentials by combining the standard electrode potentials of the two half-cells that make up the full cell.

Look again at Figure 15.9 and the value of the cell potential, $E^\ominus_{cell}$. The value of +1.10 V arises from the sum of the $E^\ominus$ values for two half-reactions:

$$Cu^{2+}(aq) + 2e^- \rightarrow Cu(s) \qquad E^\ominus = +0.34\,V$$

and the reverse of:

$$Zn^{2+}(aq) + 2e^- \rightarrow Zn(s) \qquad E^\ominus = -0.76\,V$$

So, we have:

$$Cu^{2+}(aq) + 2e^- \rightarrow Cu(s) \qquad E^\ominus = +0.34\,V$$
$$Zn(s) \rightarrow Zn^{2+}(aq) + 2e^- \qquad E^\ominus = +0.76\,V$$

Overall: $Zn(s) + Cu^{2+}(aq) \rightarrow Zn^{2+}(aq) + Cu(s) \qquad E^\ominus_{cell} = +1.10\,V$

From this discussion, you will see that:

$$E^\ominus_{cell} = - E^\ominus_{(left\text{-}hand\ electrode)} + E^\ominus_{(right\text{-}hand\ electrode)}$$

A positive value of $E^\ominus_{cell}$ indicates that the changes shown in the overall equation are likely to occur. In this case, zinc atoms will go into solution as zinc ions at the zinc electrode. Electrons will flow through the external circuit from the zinc terminal to the copper terminal as an electric current, where copper ions will take these electrons and form copper atoms.

The more positive the value of $E^\ominus_{cell}$, the more likely are the changes at the electrodes. On the other hand, negative values for $E^\ominus_{cell}$ indicate that the changes summarised in the overall equation will not happen.

In fact, if the reactants are available the changes shown in an overall equation with a negative cell potential will occur in the reverse direction, for which the cell potential would be positive.

By setting up a cell as in Figure 15.8, it is possible to separate the two halves of the redox reaction involving zinc and copper(II) ions. But the same changes will also occur if zinc is added directly to a solution containing copper ions. Zinc will go into solution as zinc ions, giving up electrons to copper(II) ions which then form a deposit of copper (Figure 15.14).

So, a positive value for a cell potential suggests that the half-reactions which could take place at the electrodes are feasible (likely to occur) if the reactants are mixed together in a test tube. In fact, the more positive the cell potential, the more feasible the reaction is on direct mixing of the reactants.

Worked example

Draw the cell diagram for a cell based on the two half-equations below. Work out the cell potential and write the overall equation for the reaction which is likely to occur (the spontaneous reaction).

$$Fe^{3+}(aq) + e^- \rightleftharpoons Fe^{2+}(aq) \qquad E^\ominus = +0.77\,V$$

$$Cu^{2+}(aq) + 2e^- \rightleftharpoons Cu(s) \qquad E^\ominus = +0.34\,V$$

Notes on the method
Write the cell diagram with the more positive electrode on the right. Then use the equation:

$$E^\ominus_{cell} = E^\ominus_{(right\text{-}hand\ electrode)} - E^\ominus_{(left\text{-}hand\ electrode)}$$

to calculate the cell potential.

Answer

The $Fe^{3+}(aq)$, $Fe^{2+}(aq)$ electrode is the more positive so it should be on the right-hand side of the cell diagram. Both the oxidised and reduced forms are in solution, so a shiny platinum electrode is needed. This is represented as $Fe^{3+}(aq)$, $Fe^{2+}(aq) | Pt(s)$.

The left-hand electrode is $Cu^{2+}(aq) | Cu(s)$ so the copper metal can also be the conducting electrode. The cell diagram is therefore:

$$Cu(s) | Cu^{2+}(aq) \vdots Fe^{3+}(aq), Fe^{2+}(aq) | Pt(s)$$

and the e.m.f. of the cell is given by:

$$E^{\ominus}_{cell} = +0.77V - (+0.34)V = +0.43\ V$$

Balancing the two half-equations in the direction of the cell diagram gives the overall equation:

$$Cu(s) + 2Fe^{3+}(aq) \rightarrow Cu^{2+}(aq) + 2Fe^{2+}(aq) \quad E^{\ominus}_{cell} = +0.43\ V$$

Tutorial

Test yourself

21 Draw the cell diagram for a cell based on each of the following pairs of half-equations. For each example look up the standard electrode potentials, work out the cell potential and write the overall equation for the reaction which tends to happen (the spontaneous reaction):
   a) $V^{3+}(aq) + e^- \rightleftharpoons V^{2+}(aq)$; $Zn^{2+}(aq) + 2e^- \rightleftharpoons Zn(s)$
   b) $Br_2(aq) + 2e^- \rightleftharpoons 2Br^-(aq)$; $I_2(aq) + 2e^- \rightleftharpoons 2I^-(aq)$
   c) $Cl_2(aq) + 2e^- \rightleftharpoons 2Cl^-(aq)$; $PbO_2(s) + 4H^+(aq) + 2e^- \rightleftharpoons Pb^{2+}(aq) + 2H_2O(l)$
22 Using the standard electrode potential data on the Dynamic Learning Student website, arrange the following sets of metals in order of decreasing strength as reducing agents:
   a) Ca, K, Li, Mg, Na
   b) Cu, Fe, Pb, Sn, Zn.
23 Using the standard electrode potential data on the Dynamic Learning Student website, arrange the following sets of molecules/ions in order of decreasing strength as oxidising agents in acid solution:
   a) $Cr_2O_7^{2-}$, Fe^{3+}, H_2O_2, MnO_4^-
   b) Br_2, Cl_2, ClO^-, H_2O_2, O_2

Data

The electrochemical series

A list of electrode systems set out in order of their electrode potentials (in the table on the Dynamic Learning Student website and in Table 15.1) is a useful guide to the behaviour of oxidising and reducing agents. It is an electrochemical series.

The metal ion | metal electrodes with highly negative electrode potentials involve half-reactions for Group 1 metal ions and metals (Table 15.1). Lithium is the most reactive of these metals when it reacts as a reducing agent forming metal ions. Consequently, the reverse reaction of Li^+ ions forming Li metal is the least likely, and this results in the most negative standard electrode potential.

The metal ion | metal electrodes with positive electrode potentials involve half-reactions of d-block metal ions and metals such as copper and silver. These metals are relatively unreactive as reducing agents and they do not react with dilute acids to form hydrogen gas. However, their ions are readily reduced to the metal and this results in positive standard electrode potentials.

So, as you might expect, the order of metal ion | metal systems in Table 15.1 corresponds closely to the reactivity series for metals and the reactions shown by ion | metal ion displacement reactions.

The electrode potentials of the half-equations involving halogen molecules and halide ions are positive. The $F_2(aq) | 2F^-(aq)$ system is the most positive,

Data

Metal ion | metal electrode	Standard electrode potential, $E^{\ominus}/V$
$Li^+(aq) \| Li(s)$	−3.03
$K^+(aq) \| K(s)$	−2.92
$Na^+(aq) \| Na(s)$	−2.71
$Al^{3+}(aq) \| Al(s)$	−1.66
$Zn^{2+}(aq) \| Zn(s)$	−0.76
$Fe^{2+}(aq) \| Fe(s)$	−0.44
$Pb^{2+}(aq) \| Pb(s)$	−0.13
$Cu^{2+}(aq) \| Cu(s)$	+0.34
$Ag^+(aq) \| Ag(s)$	+0.80

Table 15.1 ▲
The standard electrode potentials of some common metals.

showing that fluorine is the most reactive of the halogens as an oxidising agent. The next most reactive halogen is chlorine, then bromine and finally iodine is the least reactive. This corresponds to the order of reactivity of the halogens and the results of their displacement reactions.

The limitations of predictions from $E^{\ominus}$ data

In some cases, the predictions from standard electrode potentials may not be borne out in practice.

Although an overall positive value of $E^{\ominus}$ for a redox reaction suggests that the reaction should take place, in practice the reaction may be too slow. The important point to appreciate is that $E^{\ominus}$ values relate to the relative stabilities of reactants and products.

Therefore, a positive value for $E^{\ominus}$ indicates that the products are more stable than the reactants and the reaction is energetically feasible. But $E^{\ominus}$ values do not give any indication about the rates of reactions or their kinetic feasibility.

For example, $E^{\ominus}$ values predict that $Cu^{2+}(aq)$ should oxidise $H_2(g)$ to H^+ ions:

$$Cu^{2+}(aq) + H_2(g) \rightarrow Cu(s) + 2H^+(aq) \quad E^{\ominus} = +0.34\,V$$

However, nothing happens when hydrogen is bubbled into copper(II) sulfate solution because the activation energy is so high and the reaction rate is effectively zero.

A second important point about $E^{\ominus}$ values is that they relate only to standard conditions. Changes in concentration, temperature and pressure affect electrode potentials. In particular, all electrode (reduction) potentials become more positive if the concentration of reactant ions is increased and less positive if their concentration is reduced. This means that some reactions that are not possible under standard conditions occur under non-standard conditions, and vice versa.

For example, under standard conditions MnO_2 will not oxidise $1.0\,mol\,dm^{-3}$ $HCl(aq)$ to Cl_2:

$$MnO_2(s) + 4H^+(aq) + 2e^- \rightarrow Mn^{2+}(aq) + 2H_2O(l) \quad E^{\ominus} = +1.23\,V$$
$$2Cl^-(aq) \rightarrow Cl_2(g) + 2e^- \quad E^{\ominus} = -1.36\,V$$

And the overall equation is:

$$MnO_2(s) + 4H^+(aq) + 2Cl^-(aq) \rightarrow Mn^{2+}(aq) + 2H_2O(l) + Cl_2(g) \quad E^{\ominus} = -0.13\,V$$

But if MnO_2 is heated with *concentrated* HCl, the electrode potentials of both half-equations become more positive, the overall $E^{\ominus}$ becomes positive and chlorine is produced.

So, our predictions from cell potentials about the feasibility (probability) of redox reactions may not occur in practice if the kinetics of the reactions are so slow, or if the concentration of reactants or the temperatures differ from standard conditions.

Tutorial

Data

15.6 Modern storage cells

From alarm clocks to wrist watches, from radios to calculators – most of us rely on the electrical power of cells and batteries.

Electrochemical cells are a useful and economic way of storing and, when convenient, using the energy from chemical reactions. Because of this they are sometimes called storage cells. However, the impractical cells discussed in the last two sections have been replaced by more convenient, portable cells for everyday use.

Activity

The dry cell

Probably the commonest, cheapest and most convenient cell in use today is the modern dry cell shown in Figure 15.15. This is an adaptation of a cell developed by the French chemist, Georges Leclanché in the nineteenth century. It is sometimes called the Leclanché dry cell. The dry cell is used in a wide range of small electrical appliances such as radios, torches and alarm clocks.

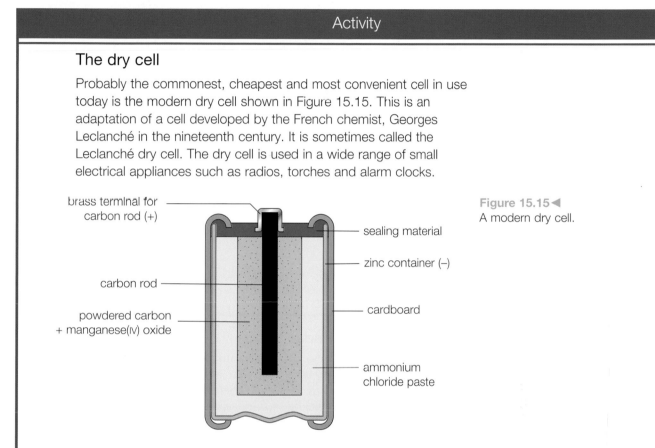

brass terminal for carbon rod (+)
sealing material
zinc container (−)
carbon rod
powdered carbon + manganese(IV) oxide
cardboard
ammonium chloride paste

Figure 15.15 ◄
A modern dry cell.

The cell diagram for a dry cell is:

$$Zn(s) \mid Zn^{2+}(aq) \vdots\vdots NH_4^+(aq), [2NH_3(g) + H_2(g)] \mid C_{(graphite)} \qquad E = 1.5\,V$$

The negative terminal in the cell is zinc. The positive terminal is a carbon (graphite) rod where ammonium ions are converted to ammonia and hydrogen when the cell delivers a current.

A single dry cell can produce a potential difference of 1.5 V, although batteries of these cells giving 100 V or more have been used.

In recent years, a modified form of the dry cell, known as the alkaline cell, is becoming more common. You can study the alkaline cell in Review question **2** at the end of this topic.

1 Why is the dry cell more convenient than the cells described in Sections 15.4 and 15.5?

2 Why is ammonium chloride used as a paste rather than as a dry solid?

3 Write a half-equation for the reaction at:

   a) the zinc terminal

   b) the carbon (graphite) terminal.

4 Assuming that the electrode potential for the $Zn^{2+}(aq)\,|\,Zn(s)$ half-cell is $-0.76\,V$, calculate the electrode potential of the other half-cell in a dry cell.

5 The surface area of the positive terminal is increased by surrounding the carbon rod with a mixture of powdered graphite and manganese(IV) oxide. The purpose of the manganese(IV) oxide is to oxidise hydrogen produced at the electrode to water. This prevents bubbles of hydrogen from coating the carbon terminal and reducing its efficiency.

   a) Why do you think it is important to increase the surface area of the carbon terminal?

   b) Write an equation for the reaction of manganese(IV) oxide with hydrogen to produce water.

   c) Why does ammonia not cause the same problems as hydrogen in reducing the efficiency of the carbon terminal?

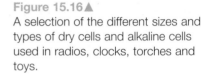

Figure 15.16▲
A selection of the different sizes and types of dry cells and alkaline cells used in radios, clocks, torches and toys.

Figure 15.17▲
Most battery-operated wheelchairs are powered by lead–acid cells.

Rechargeable (secondary) cells

Dry cells and alkaline cells cannot, of course, provide continuous supplies of electrical energy indefinitely. Nor is there any way of recharging these cells so that they can be used again. However, there are cells which can be recharged and used again. These are called secondary cells, in contrast to primary cells like dry cells and alkaline cells, which cannot be recharged. When a secondary cell is recharged, an electric current passes through it in the opposite direction to that which the cell produces. Recharging is an example of electrolysis as chemical reactions occur to reform the chemicals which make up the electrodes.

Lead–acid cells (car batteries)

Almost all car batteries are composed of six lead–acid cells in series giving a total battery potential of 12 volts. These batteries are only used to provide electricity for lights and windscreen wipers and a spark to ignite the fuel when a vehicle is started. Most milk floats and battery-operated wheelchairs are actually powered by lead–acid cells.

In recent years, the increasing cost of fossil fuels has made the electrically powered car a more viable alternative. Unfortunately, attempts to develop and market a vehicle of this type using lead–acid cells have not been successful. The main reasons for this are:

● the high cost of lead–acid batteries
● the low power/weight ratio of lead–acid batteries
● the limited mileage before recharging is necessary.

The negative terminal in a lead–acid cell is lead. This gives up electrons forming lead(II) ions when the cell is working normally (discharging):

$$Pb(s) \rightarrow Pb^{2+}(aq) + 2e^-$$

The positive terminal is lead coated with lead(IV) oxide. During discharge, the lead(IV) oxide reacts with H^+ ions in the sulfuric acid electrolyte and takes electrons:

$$PbO_2(s) + 4H^+(aq) + 2e^- \rightarrow Pb^{2+}(aq) + 2H_2O(l)$$

Notice that lead(II) ions, $Pb^{2+}(aq)$, are formed at both terminals during discharge. These react with sulfate ions, $SO_4^{2-}(aq)$, in the electrolyte forming insoluble lead(II) sulfate on both terminals:

$$Pb^{2+}(aq) + SO_4^{2-}(aq) \rightarrow PbSO_4(s)$$

The formation of insoluble lead(II) sulfate creates another potential problem for lead–acid cells. If the cells are discharged for long periods, the precipitate of lead(II) sulfate becomes coarser and thicker and the process cannot be reversed when the cells are recharged.

When a lead–acid cell is recharged, the current is reversed and the reactions at each terminal are reversed. This turns Pb^{2+} ions back to lead metal at one terminal and back to PbO_2 at the other, with sulfate ions going back into the electrolyte.

Test yourself

27 Why have attempts to develop family cars powered by lead–acid batteries been unsuccessful?

28 The milk float in Figure 15.18 is powered by lead–acid batteries. Why is this both possible and convenient?

29 a) Use the data sheet on the Dynamic Learning Student website listing 'Standard electrode potentials' to write down the value of $E^\ominus$ for a $Pb^{2+}(aq)\,|\,Pb(s)$ half-cell.

   b) What is the approximate cell potential for one lead–acid cell?

   c) What is the approximate electrode potential of the $[PbO_2(s) + 4H^+(aq)]$, $[Pb^{2+}(aq) + 2H_2O(l)]\,|\,Pb(s)$ half-cell in a lead–acid cell?

   d) Write a balanced equation for the overall reaction in a lead–acid cell when it is supplying current.

   e) Write the half-equations for the processes at the two terminals when the cell is being recharged.

DL
www
Data

Figure 15.18 ▲

Lithium cells

Modern mobile phones and laptop computers use lithium batteries. The advantages of electrodes based on lithium are that the metal has a low density, so cells based on lithium electrodes can be relatively light. Also, lithium is very reactive, which means that the electrode potential of a lithium half-cell is relatively high and each cell has a large e.m.f.

The difficulty to overcome is that lithium is so reactive that it readily combines with oxygen in the air forming a layer of non-conducting oxide on the surface of the metal. The metal also reacts rapidly with water. Research workers have solved these technical problems by developing electrodes with lithium atoms and ions inserted into the crystal lattices of other materials. In addition, the electrolyte is a polymeric material rather than an aqueous solution.

Figure 15.19▶
A schematic diagram of a lithium battery discharging. The electrode processes are reversible, so the battery can be recharged.

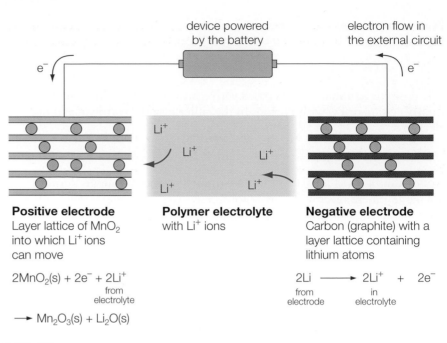

Positive electrode
Layer lattice of MnO_2 into which Li^+ ions can move

$2MnO_2(s) + 2e^- + 2Li^+$
from electrolyte
$\longrightarrow Mn_2O_3(s) + Li_2O(s)$

Polymer electrolyte
with Li^+ ions

Negative electrode
Carbon (graphite) with a layer lattice containing lithium atoms

$2Li \longrightarrow 2Li^+ + 2e^-$
from electrode   in electrolyte

15.7 Fuel cells

Fuel cells are electrochemical cells in which the chemical energy of a fuel is converted directly into electrical energy. Fuel cells differ from typical electrochemical cells, such as dry cells and lead–acid accumulators, in having a continuous supply of reactants from which to produce a steady electric current. Fuel cells use a variety of fuels including hydrogen, hydrocarbons (such as methane) and alcohols. Inside a fuel cell, energy from the redox reaction between a fuel and oxygen is used to create a potential difference (voltage).

The hydrogen–oxygen fuel cell

One of the most important fuel cells is the hydrogen–oxygen fuel cell. In the hydrogen–oxygen fuel cell, the negative electrode is porous graphite impregnated with nickel and the positive electrode is porous graphite impregnated with nickel and nickel(II) oxide.

The nickel and nickel oxide catalyse the breakdown of hydrogen and oxygen molecules into single atoms.

Figure 15.20▶
A hydrogen–oxygen fuel cell.

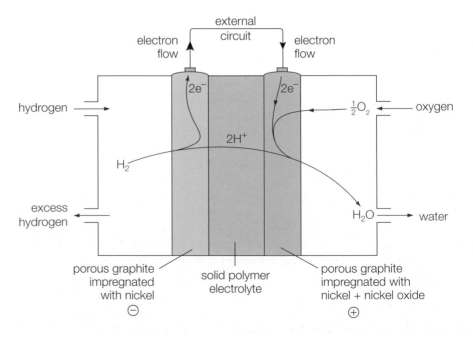

Hydrogen gas flows onto the negative electrode, where the H_2 molecules split into single H atoms on the nickel catalyst. The H atoms then lose electrons and form H^+ ions:

Negative electrode: $H_2 \rightarrow 2H \rightarrow 2H^+ + 2e^-$ Equation 1

The electrons flow into the external circuit as an electric current, while the hydrogen ions migrate through the electrolyte.

Oxygen flows onto the positive electrode where the nickel/nickel(II) oxide catalyses its splitting into single oxygen atoms, and then its combination with hydrogen ions from the electrolyte and electrons to form water:

Positive terminal: $O + 2H^+ + 2e^- \rightarrow H_2O$ Equation 2

The overall reaction in the hydrogen–oxygen fuel cell (obtained by adding Equations 1 and 2) is:

$H_2 + O \rightarrow H_2O$

This cell is no different in principle from more familiar electrochemical cells. The innovation is that new reactants (H_2 and O_2) are constantly fed into the cell and the product (H_2O) is drawn off. This continuous flow of materials allows the cell potential to remain constant at about 1.2 volts and the power output is uninterrupted.

The great advantage of all fuel cells is that they convert chemical energy into electricity directly and in doing so achieve a remarkable efficiency of about 70%. In comparison, modern power plants and petrol engines using fossil fuels have a conversion efficiency from chemical energy to electrical energy or kinetic energy of only about 45%.

15.8 Fuel cell vehicles (FCVs)

As calls for a cleaner environment become louder and reserves of fossil fuels become scarcer, the search for alternative fuels is on. One possible alternative to petrol is to run vehicles on hydrogen using fuel cells that are far more efficient than petrol engines. What is more, vehicles emitting water vapour as the only exhaust gas are an attractive green proposition.

The idea of a car powered by hydrogen is not new, but until recently it has not been feasible due to technological problems. These problems include the weight of fuel cells and the difficulty of carrying and containing sufficient hydrogen in a vehicle.

Figure 15.21 ◄

A technician assembling a fuel cell for testing. The fuel cell is constructed from lightweight polymeric materials.

In recent years, compact lightweight fuel cells have been developed, along with the technology to store large quantities of hydrogen much more conveniently and safely.

Three possible methods of storing hydrogen in fuel cell vehicles (FCVs) are being considered:

- as a liquid under pressure
- adsorbed on the surface of a solid
- absorbed within a solid material.

The efficiency of fuel cells is so much better than petrol engines that fuel cell vehicles of the future might well use hydrogen-rich fuels such as methanol, natural gas and petrol in place of hydrogen. Although fuel cells have been constructed which use methane and methanol directly, scientists are now working on the development of compact catalytic 'reformers' which will produce hydrogen from these fuels as on-board components of FCVs.

Limitations to the development of hydrogen FCVs

The development of lightweight hydrogen fuel cells made from polymeric materials and an appreciation that their efficiency could be five times that of petrol engines has led to renewed interest in the development of hydrogen-powered FCVs.

At present, the most serious limitations to the development of a hydrogen-powered FCV are:

- the safe storage and transport of hydrogen
- the hazards posed by highly pressurised liquid hydrogen
- the limited life cycle of solid 'adsorbers' and 'absorbers'
- the finite life and high cost of fuel cells requiring regular replacement and disposal.

Everyone knows that hydrogen is explosive, and explosions such as the Hindenburg disaster in 1937 only serve to emphasise the hazards in its storage and transport.

The method of storing liquid hydrogen for industrial uses in heavy, thick steel vessels at pressures above 100 atmospheres would never be suitable for moving vehicles.

Liquid hydrogen is useful in industry, but the energy used in liquefying it is a major fraction of what could be generated when it is oxidised in a fuel cell. Furthermore, liquid hydrogen would present a serious safety problem if it were used as a fuel for vehicles. Liquid hydrogen is extremely cold (boiling point −253 K) and it is highly volatile and extremely flammable.

Fortunately, chemists have discovered a much safer storage arrangement for hydrogen at normal temperatures. This involves the formation of metal hydrides.

Most metals react with hydrogen to form a hydride. In many cases, the reaction occurs simply by passing hydrogen over the hot metal. For example, with magnesium the equation is:

$$Mg(s) + H_2(g) \rightleftharpoons MgH_2(s)$$

Notice that the reaction is reversible. If the pressure is above a certain level, the reaction goes to the right and more metal hydride is formed. If the pressure is below that level, the metal hydride decomposes to the metal and hydrogen gas.

Figure 15.22 ▲
People have long memories over disasters. In 1937, the Hindenburg airship filled with hydrogen exploded when attempting to dock with its mooring mast.

The main reason why some metal hydrides can be used for the storage of hydrogen is that they can accommodate an extremely high density of hydrogen. In fact, it is possible to pack more hydrogen into a metal hydride than into the same volume of liquid hydrogen.

When hydrogen reacts with a metal to form its hydride, hydrogen molecules (H_2) are first adsorbed onto the surface of the metal. Some of the molecules dissociate into hydrogen atoms (H) and are absorbed deeper into the metal lattice as they react to form the metal hydride (Figure 15.23).

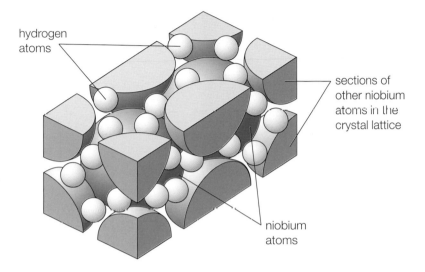

hydrogen atoms

sections of other niobium atoms in the crystal lattice

niobium atoms

Figure 15.23◄
Hydrogen atoms absorbed into the crystal lattice of the metal niobium.

If the pressure of hydrogen in contact with the metal is increased, even greater amounts of hydrogen can be absorbed into the spaces between metal atoms. In most metal hydrides, the number of hydrogen atoms in the lattice will be two to three times the number of metal atoms.

Although there is an increasing political and social desire to move to a greener, more environmentally friendly economy including the use of FCVs powered by hydrogen, there are still obstacles to be overcome. A 'hydrogen economy' may well contribute to our future energy needs, but the obstacles that will limit its development include:

- the public and political acceptance of hydrogen as a safe fuel
- the handling, storage, transport and maintenance of hydrogen systems in vehicles
- a realisation that FCVs powered by hydrogen are not totally 'green' – significant amounts of energy are needed to manufacture hydrogen and there are toxic chemicals used in the manufacture of fuel cells.

Test yourself

30 Hydrogen is said to have 'the highest density of energy per unit mass of any fuel'. What does this expression mean?
31 Why is liquid hydrogen unsuitable for use as a fuel in motor vehicles?
32 What is the difference between hydrogen *adsorbed* by a metal and hydrogen *absorbed* by a metal?
33 Explain briefly why some metal hydrides can accommodate a high packing-density of hydrogen.

Activity

A greener future for transport!

Figure 15.24 ◄
Technicians assembling the components of an FCV based on a modified Honda.

Read Section 15.8 again and then answer the following questions.

1 Why are compounds such as methanol, natural gas and petrol described as 'hydrogen-rich' fuels?

2 What are the major problems in developing FCVs powered by hydrogen and hydrogen-rich fuels?

3 What are the major advantages of FCVs over conventional petrol-engine and diesel-engine vehicles?

4 What is the main advantage of fuel cell vehicles powered by hydrogen rather than hydrogen-rich fuels?

5 Write equations for the oxidation of hydrogen and petrol in fuel cells, assuming that they are completely oxidised and that petrol is pure octane.

6 a) Use the data sheet on the Dynamic Learning Student website headed 'Average bond enthalpies and bond lengths' to find the average bond enthalpies for the different bonds in hydrogen, oxygen, octane, carbon dioxide and water.

Data

b) Make a table showing the bonds broken and the bonds formed during the complete combustion of hydrogen, and then calculate a value for the enthalpy change of combustion of hydrogen.

Figure 15.25 ▼
The limited edition Honda FCX Clarity was first made available for lease in Southern California in 2008.

c) Calculate the energy produced during the complete combustion of 1 gram of hydrogen.

7 Repeat the calculations in questions **6b)** and **c)** for petrol (octane) in place of hydrogen.

8 Bearing in mind that fuel cells are approximately 70% efficient and petrol engines are about 40% efficient, how many times more efficient is a fuel cell vehicle powered by hydrogen compared to a vehicle with a petrol engine per gram of fuel?

REVIEW QUESTIONS

1 Use the standard electrode potentials in the table below to answer the questions that follow.

A	$Fe^{3+}(aq) + e^- \rightarrow Fe^{2+}(aq)$	$E^\ominus = +0.77\,V$
B	$Cu^{2+}(aq) + 2e^- \rightarrow Cu(s)$	$E^\ominus = +0.34\,V$
C	$2H^+(aq) + 2e^- \rightarrow H_2(g)$	$E^\ominus = 0.00\,V$
D	$O_2(g) + 4H^+(aq) + 4e^- \rightarrow 2H_2O(l)$	$E^\ominus = +0.40\,V$

a) An electrochemical cell was arranged using systems A and B.

i) Write half-equations for the reactions which occur in each half-cell when a current flows. Say which half-equation involves oxidation and which involves reduction. **(2)**

ii) Calculate the change in oxidation number of the oxidised and reduced elements in each half-cell. **(2)**

iii) Determine the cell potential of the cell. **(1)**

b) Fuel cells using systems C and D are increasingly being used to generate electricity.

i) Construct an overall equation for the cell reaction and show your working. **(2)**

ii) From which half-cell do electrons flow into the external circuit? **(1)**

iii) State two advantages and two disadvantages of using fuel cells based on systems C and D to generate energy rather than using fossil fuels. **(4)**

2 A more efficient, and more expensive, form of the dry cell is the alkaline cell.

The reaction at the negative terminal is again the oxidation of zinc, but in contact with OH^- ions to form zinc oxide.

The positive terminal is manganese(IV) oxide which is reduced to manganese(III) oxide:

$$2MnO_2(s) + H_2O(l) + 2e^- \rightarrow Mn_2O_3(s) + 2OH^-\,(aq)$$

a) An alkaline cell is an example of a primary cell. What is meant by a 'primary' cell? **(1)**

b) How does a secondary cell differ from a primary cell? **(2)**

c) Write a half-equation for the reaction at the negative terminal when an alkaline cell is used. **(2)**

d) State the changes in oxidation number at each terminal. **(2)**

e) Why is an alkaline cell in continuous use more efficient than a dry cell? **(2)**

3 A student set up the electrochemical cell shown below.

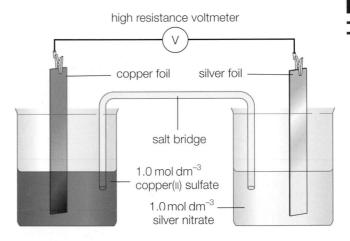

You are provided with the following standard electrode potentials:

$Cu^{2+}|Cu \quad E^\ominus = +0.34\,V$

$Ag^+|Ag \quad E^\ominus = +0.80\,V$

a) How could the student have made the salt bridge? **(1)**

b) Write a half-equation to show the reaction that occurred in:

i) the $Cu|Cu^{2+}$ half-cell. **(1)**

ii) the $Ag|Ag^+$ half-cell. **(1)**

c) Write an equation for the overall cell reaction. **(1)**

d) Calculate the standard cell potential for this cell. **(2)**

e) At which electrode does reduction occur? Explain your answer. **(2)**

f) The student found that the cell potential was less than the calculated value. Suggest two reasons for this. **(2)**

4 a) What are the principal differences between a hydrogen–oxygen fuel cell and a conventional electrochemical cell like the dry cell? **(3)**

b) Outline and explain two advantages that would be gained by generating electricity using fuel cells rather than in thermal power stations. **(4)**

c) What major advantage would hydrogen-powered fuel cells have over other fuel cells? **(2)**

d) Suggest three obstacles to the present development and production of hydrogen-powered fuel cell vehicles. **(3)**

16 Transition elements

The transition elements are vital to life and bring colour to our lives. They are also metals of great engineering and industrial importance. Chemically, these elements, which occupy the d-block of the periodic table, are more alike than might be expected. Across the ten elements from scandium to zinc in Period 4, the similarities are as striking as the differences. Chemists explain the characteristics of transition elements in terms of the electron configurations of their atoms.

Transition metal chemistry is colourful because of the range of oxidation states and complex ions. Transition metals matter because their properties are fundamental, not only to life but also to modern technology.

Figure 16.1▶

A stained glass window in Ely Cathedral. The commonest colorants in stained glass are the oxides of transition elements.

Tutorial

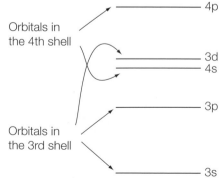

Figure 16.2▲

Relative energy levels of orbitals in the third and fourth shells.

16.1 Electron configurations

As the shells of electrons around the nuclei of atoms get further from the nucleus, they become closer in energy. So the difference in energy between the second and third shells is less than that between the first and second. When the fourth shell is reached, there is, in fact, an overlap between the orbitals of highest energy in the third shell (the 3d orbitals) and that of lowest energy in the fourth shell (the 4s orbital) (Figure 16.2).

The 3d sub-shell is on average closer to the nucleus than the 4s sub-shell, but at a higher energy level. So, once the 3s and 3p sub-shells are filled, the next electrons go into the 4s sub-shell because it occupies a lower energy level than the 3d sub-shell.

This means that potassium and calcium have the electron structure $[Ar]4s^1$ and $[Ar]4s^2$ respectively (Table 16.1).

Element	Symbol	Electron structure		
		spdf notation	Electrons-in-boxes notation	
			3d	4s
potassium	K	[Ar]4s^1	[Ar] ☐☐☐☐☐	↑
calcium	Ca	[Ar]4s^2	[Ar] ☐☐☐☐☐	↑↓
scandium	Sc	[Ar]3d^{1}4s^2	[Ar] ↑☐☐☐☐	↑↓
titanium	Ti	[Ar]3d^{2}4s^2	[Ar] ↑↑☐☐☐	↑↓
vanadium	V	[Ar]3d^{3}4s^2	[Ar] ↑↑↑☐☐	↑↓
chromium	Cr	[Ar]3d^{5}4s^1	[Ar] ↑↑↑↑↑	↑
manganese	Mn	[Ar]3d^{5}4s^2	[Ar] ↑↑↑↑↑	↑↓
iron	Fe	[Ar]3d^{6}4s^2	[Ar] ↑↓ ↑↑↑↑	↑↓
cobalt	Co	[Ar]3d^{7}4s^2	[Ar] ↑↓ ↑↓ ↑↑↑	↑↓
nickel	Ni	[Ar]3d^{8}4s^2	[Ar] ↑↓ ↑↓ ↑↓ ↑↑	↑↓
copper	Cu	[Ar]3d^{10}4s^1	[Ar] ↑↓ ↑↓ ↑↓ ↑↓ ↑↓	↑
zinc	Zn	[Ar]3d^{10}4s^2	[Ar] ↑↓ ↑↓ ↑↓ ↑↓ ↑↓	↑↓

Table 16.1 ◀
Electron configurations from potassium to zinc in Period 4 of the periodic table. ([Ar] represents the electron configuration of argon.)

Look carefully at Table 16.1. In Period 4, the d-block elements run from scandium ($1s^22s^22p^63s^23p^63d^14s^2$) to zinc ($1s^22s^22p^63s^23p^63d^{10}4s^2$). But, notice that the electron configurations of chromium and copper do not fit the general pattern. The explanation of these irregularities lies in the stability associated with half-filled and filled sub-shells. So, the electron structure of chromium, [Ar]3d^{5}4s^1, with half-filled sub-shells and an equal distribution of charge around the nucleus, is more stable than the electron structure [Ar]3d^{4}4s^2.

Similarly, the electron structure of copper, [Ar]3d^{10}4s^1, with a filled 3d sub-shell and a half-filled 4s sub-shell, is more stable than [Ar]3d^{9}4s^2.

Along the series of d-block elements from scandium to zinc, the number of protons in the nucleus increases by one from one element to the next. The added electrons go into an inner d sub-shell. The outer electrons are always in the 4s sub-shell, and this means that the changes in chemical properties across the series are much less marked than the big changes across a series of p-block elements such as aluminium to argon.

The chemistry of an element is determined to a large extent by its outer shell electrons because they are the first to get involved in reactions. All the d-block elements from Sc to Zn have their outer electrons in the 4s sub-shell, so they are similar in many ways.

Figure 16.3 ▼
Specimens of some d-block elements.

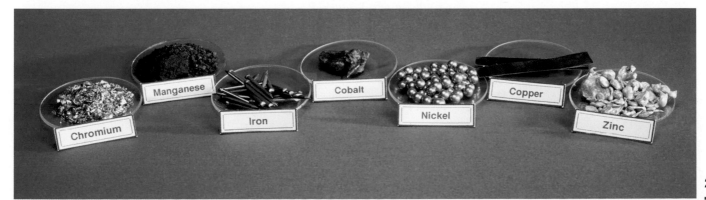

Ions of the transition metals

When transition metals form their ions, electrons are lost initially from the 4s sub-shell and not the 3d sub-shell. This may seem somewhat illogical because, prior to holding any electrons, the 4s level is more stable than the 3d level. But once the 3d sub-shell is occupied by electrons, being closer to the nucleus, these 3d electrons repel the 4s electrons to a higher energy level. The 4s electrons are, in fact, pushed to an energy level higher than those occupying the 3d sub-shell. So, when transition metals form ions they lose electrons from the 4s orbital before the 3d level. This further emphasises the fact that transition metals have similar chemical properties, which are dictated by the behaviour of the 4s electrons in their outer shells.

Test yourself

1 Write the full spdf electron configurations of:
  a) a scandium atom
  b) a scandium(III) ion
  c) a manganese atom
  d) a manganese(II) ion.
2 Look at the electron structures of iron and copper in Table 16.1.
  a) Write the electron structure of an iron(II) ion.
  b) Write the electron structure of an iron(III) ion.
  c) Which ion, Fe^{2+} or Fe^{3+}, would you expect to be the more stable? Explain your choice.
  d) Write the formula for the ion of copper that you would expect to be the most stable. Explain your choice.

16.2 Defining the transition elements

The simplest and neatest way to define the transition elements would be to say that they are the elements in the d-block of the periodic table. But, this simple definition leads to the inclusion of scandium and zinc as transition elements and ignores the fact that these two metals have some clear differences to the elements between them in the periodic table from titanium to copper. For example:

- scandium and zinc have only one oxidation state in their compounds (scandium +3, zinc +2), whereas the elements from titanium to copper have two or more
- the compounds of scandium and zinc are usually white, unlike those of transition metals which are generally coloured
- scandium and zinc, and their compounds, show little catalytic activity.

As scandium and zinc do not show the typical properties of transition elements, chemists looked for a more satisfactory definition. This definition had to exclude scandium and zinc, but include all the elements from titanium to copper. In order to achieve this, chemists describe transition elements as d-block elements that have at least one stable ion with an incomplete (partially filled) d sub-shell.

Definition

A **transition element** is a d-block element that has at least one stable ion with a partially filled d sub-shell.

Characteristics of the transition metals

Transition metals share a number of common properties.

- They are hard metals with useful mechanical properties, high melting points and high boiling points.
- They form compounds in more than one oxidation state.
- They form coloured compounds.
- They act as catalysts either as the elements or as their compounds.
- They form a variety of complex ions (Section 16.7).

Data

16.3 The transition elements as metals

Most of the transition elements have a close-packed structure in which each atom has 12 nearest neighbours. In addition, transition elements have relatively low atomic radii because an increasingly large nuclear charge is attracting electrons that are being added to an inner sub-shell. The dual effect of close packing and small atomic radii results in strong metallic bonding. So, transition metals have higher melting points, higher boiling points, higher densities and higher tensile strength than s-block metals such as calcium and p-block metals such as aluminium and lead. A plot of physical properties against atomic number often has two peaks or two troughs associated with a half-filled and then a filled d sub-shell.

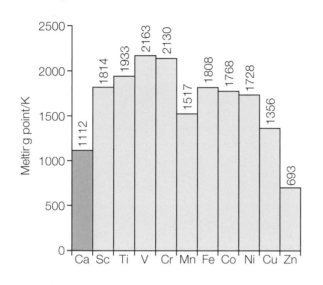

Figure 16.4▲
A plot of melting point against atomic number for the elements calcium to zinc in the periodic table.

Element	Standard electrode potential, $E^{\ominus}$ $M^{2+}(aq)\,|\,M(s)/V$
vanadium	−1.20
chromium	−0.91
manganese	−1.19
iron	−0.44
cobalt	−0.28
nickel	−0.25
copper	+0.34

Table 16.2▲
Standard electrode potentials of the transition metals from vanadium to copper.

The transition metals are much less reactive than the s-block metals. However, their electrode potentials, shown in Table 16.2, suggest that all of them, except copper, should react with dilute strong acids such as 1 mol dm^{-3} hydrochloric acid and sulfuric acid. In practice, many of these metals react very slowly with dilute acids because the metal is protected by a thin, unreactive layer of oxide. Chromium provides a very good example of this. Despite the predictions from its standard electrode potential, it is used as a protective, non-rusting metal owing to the presence of an unreactive, non-porous layer of chromium(III) oxide, Cr_2O_3.

Test yourself

3 Why can scandium and zinc be described as d-block elements, but not as transition metals?

4 Suggest a reason why zinc only forms compounds in the +2 oxidation state.

5 a) What is the general trend in standard electrode potentials of the $M^{2+}(aq)\,|\,M(s)$ systems for the transition metals in Table 16.2?

   b) What does this suggest about the reactivity of transition metals across Period 4 in the periodic table?

6 Explain why the atomic radius falls from 0.15 nm in titanium to 0.14 nm in vanadium and then 0.13 nm in chromium.

Activity

Studying the ionisation energies of transition metals

Earlier in this topic, we used the energy-level model to predict the electronic structures of d-block elements in Period 4 and their ions. These electronic structures can be fully substantiated by studying the ionisation energies of the elements concerned.

Look carefully at Figure 16.5 which shows graphs of the first, second and third ionisation energies of the elements from scandium to zinc.

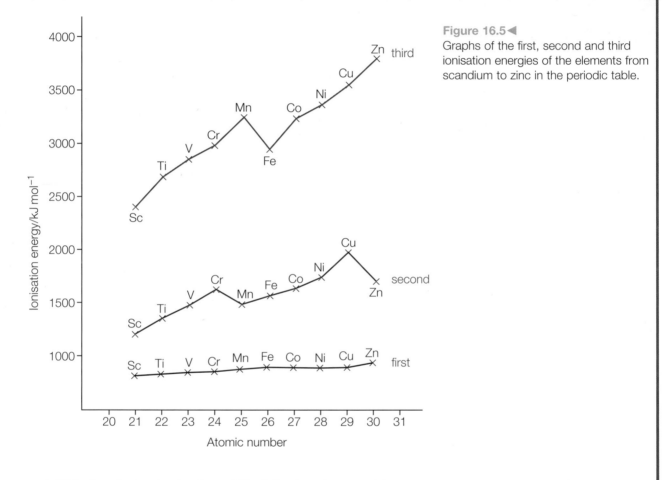

Figure 16.5◄
Graphs of the first, second and third ionisation energies of the elements from scandium to zinc in the periodic table.

1 Write the electronic structure of the following atoms and ions, using [Ar] for the electronic structure of argon:

a) Zn   **b)** Cu^+ **c)** Zn^+ **d)** Cr^+ **e)** Mn^+

2 Write an equation for:

a) the second ionisation energy of chromium

b) the third ionisation energy of iron.

3 Explain the general trend in ionisation energies as atomic number increases.

4 Why is the first ionisation energy of zinc significantly higher than that of any of the other elements?

16.4 Oxidation states

Most of the d-block elements in Period 4 show more than one oxidation state in their compounds. The main reason for this is that the transition metals from titanium to copper have electrons of similar energy in both the 3d and 4s levels. This means that each of these elements can form ions of roughly the same stability in aqueous solution or in crystalline solids by losing different numbers of electrons.

The formulae of the common oxides of the elements from scandium to zinc are shown in Figure 16.6 above the stable oxidation states of each element in its compounds. The main oxidation states of the elements are shown in bold blue print.

	Sc	Ti	V	Cr	Mn	Fe	Co	Ni	Cu	Zn
Common oxides	Sc_2O_3	Ti_2O_3 TiO_2	V_2O_3 V_2O_5	Cr_2O_3 CrO_3	MnO MnO_2 Mn_2O_7	FeO Fe_2O_3	CoO Co_2O_3	NiO	Cu_2O CuO	ZnO

	Sc	Ti	V	Cr	Mn	Fe	Co	Ni	Cu	Zn
					+7					
				+6	+6					
			+5							
		+4	+4		**+4**					
	+3	**+3**	**+3**	**+3**	+3	**+3**	+3			
		+2	+2	+2	**+2**	**+2**	**+2**	**+2**	**+2**	**+2**
									+1	

The elements at each end of the series, scandium and zinc, give rise to only one oxidation state. The elements near the middle of the series have the greatest range of oxidation states. Most of the elements form compounds in the +2 state corresponding to the use of both of the 4s electrons in bonding.

The +2 state is a main oxidation state for all the elements in the second half of the series, whereas +3 is a main oxidation state for all elements in the first part. Across the series, the +2 state becomes more stable relative to the +3 state.

From scandium to manganese, the highest oxidation state corresponds to the total number of electrons in the 3d and 4s energy levels. However, these higher oxidation states never exist as simple ions. Typically, they occur in compounds in which the metal is covalently bonded to an electronegative atom, particularly oxygen as in the dichromate(VI) ion, $Cr_2O_7^{2-}$ and the manganate(VII) ion, MnO_4^-.

One of the most attractive and effective demonstrations of the range of oxidation states in a transition element can be shown by shaking a solution of ammonium vanadate(V), NH_4VO_3, in dilute sulfuric acid with zinc (Figure 16.7). Before adding zinc, H^+ ions in the sulfuric acid react with VO_3^- ions to form dioxovanadium(V) ions and the solution is yellow:

$$VO_3^-(aq) + 2H^+(aq) \rightarrow VO_2^+(aq) + H_2O(l)$$

When the yellow solution, containing dioxovanadium(V) ions, is shaken with zinc, it is reduced first to blue oxovanadium(IV) ions, $VO^{2+}(aq)$, then to green vanadium(III) ions, $V^{3+}(aq)$, and finally to violet vanadium(II) ions, $V^{2+}(aq)$.

Figure 16.7▶
The oxidation states of vanadium showing the colours of its ions in the +5, +4, +3 and +2 oxidation states.

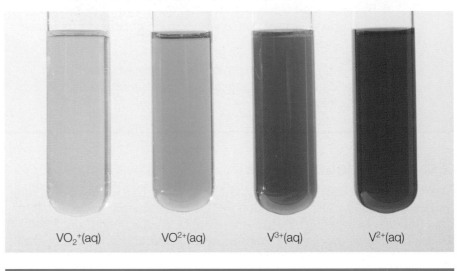

| $VO_2^+(aq)$ | $VO^{2+}(aq)$ | $V^{3+}(aq)$ | $V^{2+}(aq)$ |

Test yourself

7 Write down four generalisations about the oxidation states of transition metals based on Figure 16.6 and the text in Section 16.4.
8 Give examples of compounds, other than oxides, of:
   a) chromium in the +3 and +6 states
   b) manganese in the +2 and +7 states
   c) iron in the +2 and +3 states
   d) copper in the +1 and +2 states.
9 Explain why the oxidation state of vanadium in VO_2^+ ions is +5.
10 a) Write half-equations for:
      i) the reduction of dioxovanadium(V) ions, VO_2^+, to oxovanadium(IV) ions, VO^{2+}, in acid solution
      ii) the oxidation of zinc to zinc(II) ions.
   b) Use the data sheet headed 'Standard electrode potentials' on the Dynamic Learning Student website to show that zinc will reduce VO_2^+ ions to VO^{2+} ions in acid solution.
11 a) Why do you think that copper is the only transition metal to have +1 as a main oxidation state?
   b) Which other transition metal might you expect to form some compounds in the +1 state? Explain your answer.

www
Data

16.5 Coloured ions

In many cases, coloured compounds get their colour by absorbing some of the radiation in the visible region of the electromagnetic spectrum with wavelengths between 400 and 700 nm. When light strikes a substance, some of it is absorbed, some is transmitted (if the substance is transparent) and some is usually reflected.

If all the light is absorbed, the substance looks black. If all the light is reflected, the substance looks white. If very little light is absorbed and all the radiations in the visible region of the electromagnetic spectrum are transmitted equally, then the substance will be colourless like water.

However, many compounds, particularly those of transition metals, absorb radiations in only certain areas of the visible spectrum. This means that the substances take on the colour of the light that they transmit or reflect. For example, if a material absorbs all radiations in the green–blue–violet region of the spectrum, it will appear red–orange in white light (Figure 16.8).

Colour of compound	Wavelength absorbed/nm	Colour of light absorbed
greenish yellow	400–430	violet
yellow to orange	430–490	blue
red	490–510	blue-green
purple	510–530	green
violet	530–560	yellow-green
blue	560–590	yellow
greenish blue	590–610	orange
blue-green to green	610–700	red

Figure 16.8◄
A chart showing complementary colours in the left and right-hand columns. The colour of a compound is the complementary colour to the light it absorbs.

In coloured compounds, it is the electrons which absorb radiation and jump from their normal state to a higher excited state. According to the quantum theory, there is a fixed relationship between the size of the energy 'jump' and the wavelength of the radiation absorbed. In many compounds, the electron 'jumps' between one sub-level and the next are so large that the radiation absorbed is in the ultraviolet region of the spectrum. These compounds are therefore white or colourless because they are not absorbing any of the radiations in the visible region of the electromagnetic spectrum.

However, the colour of transition metal ions arises from the possibility of transitions between the orbitals within the 3d sub-shell.

In a free gaseous atom or ion, the five d orbitals are all at the same energy level even though they do not all have the same shape. But, when the ion of a d-block element is surrounded by other ions in a crystalline solid, or by molecules such as water in aqueous solutions, the differences in shape cause the five orbitals to split into two groups. Two of the 3d orbitals move to a slightly higher energy level than the other three. Because of this, ions such as $Cu^{2+}(aq)$ appear coloured because light of a particular frequency can be absorbed from visible light as electrons jump from a lower to a higher 3d orbital (Figure 16.9). If all the d orbitals are full, or empty, there is no possibility of electronic transitions between them.

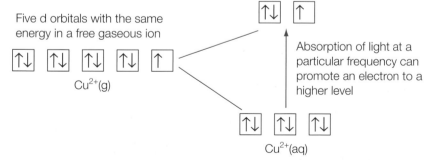

Five d orbitals with the same energy in a free gaseous ion

$Cu^{2+}(g)$

The d orbitals split into two groups with different energies in an aqueous ion

Absorption of light at a particular frequency can promote an electron to a higher level

$Cu^{2+}(aq)$

Figure 16.9◄
The energy difference between the d orbitals in an aqueous transition metal ion, like $Cu^{2+}(aq)$, allows electron transitions from a lower orbital to a higher orbital. The ion absorbs light with a particular frequency in the visible region of the electromagnetic spectrum.

In explaining the colour of transition metal ions, you should appreciate the limitations of our simple energy-level model of electronic structure. The need for more sophisticated explanations is clear, bearing in mind the existence of sub-shells and the different shapes of orbitals within d sub-shells.

Note

The **quantum theory** states that radiation is emitted or absorbed in tiny, discrete amounts called energy quanta. Quanta have energy $E = hv$, where h is Planck's constant and v is the frequency of the radiation.

Test yourself

12 a) By writing out their electron configurations, explain why Zn^{2+}, Cu^+ and Sc^{3+} ions are usually colourless in solution and white in solids.

b) What colours of light are absorbed most effectively by a Cu^{2+} ion?

16.6 Catalytic behaviour

Transition elements and their compounds play a crucial role as catalysts in industry. Table 16.3 lists some important examples of transition metals and their compounds as catalysts.

Transition element/compound used as catalyst	Reaction catalysed
vanadium(v) oxide, V_2O_5, or vanadate, VO_3^-	Contact process in the manufacture of sulfuric acid $2SO_2(g) + O_2(g) \rightarrow 2SO_3(g)$
iron or iron(III) oxide	Haber process to manufacture ammonia $N_2(g) + 3H_2(g) \rightarrow 2NH_3(g)$
nickel, platinum and palladium	manufacture of low fat spreads and margarine $RCH{=}CH_2(g) + H_2(g) \rightarrow RCH_2CH_3(g)$
platinum or platinum–rhodium alloys	conversion of NO and CO to CO_2 and N_2 in catalytic converters $2CO(g) + 2NO(g) \rightarrow 2CO_2(g) + N_2(g)$
platinum	reforming straight chain alkanes as cyclic alkanes and arenes $CH_3(CH_2)_5CH_3 \rightarrow \ CH_3{-}C_6H_5 \ + \ 4H_2$ $\qquad$ heptane $\qquad$ methylbenzene

Catalysts can be divided into two types – heterogeneous and homogeneous.

Heterogeneous catalysis

Heterogeneous catalysis involves a catalyst in a different state from the reactants it is catalysing. It is used in almost every large-scale manufacturing process such as the manufacture of ammonia in the Haber process (Table 16.3) in which nitrogen and hydrogen gas flow through a reactor containing lumps of iron or iron(III) oxide.

Platinum metal alloyed with other metals, such as rhodium, is used in catalytic converters. In a catalytic converter, such as that in Figure 16.10, a honeycombed ceramic structure is coated with a very thin layer of the expensive catalyst in order to increase its surface area in contact with the exhaust gases.

Figure 16.10▶
A catalytic converter is an example of a heterogeneous catalyst. Pollutant molecules of NO and CO in the exhaust gases become attached to the surface of the platinum alloy where they react to form N_2 and CO_2. In this computer graphic, oxygen and nitrogen atoms are shown conventionally as red and blue respectively, but carbon atoms are shown in green.

Impurities in reactants can 'poison' heterogeneous catalysts, particularly metals, causing them to become less effective. Carbon monoxide 'poisons' the iron catalyst used in the Haber process and lead compounds 'poison' catalytic converters, so lead-free petrol must be used.

Heterogeneous catalysts work by adsorbing reactants at active sites on their surface. Nickel acts as a catalyst for the addition of hydrogen to unsaturated compounds with carbon–carbon double bonds (Table 16.3). Hydrogen molecules are adsorbed on the catalyst surface where they are thought to split into single atoms. These highly reactive hydrogen atoms undergo addition with molecules of unsaturated compounds, like ethene, as the unsaturated compounds approach the catalyst surface (Figure 16.11).

> **Definition**
>
> A **heterogeneous catalyst** is one that is in a different state from the reactants. Generally, a heterogeneous catalyst is a solid while the reactants are gases or in solution.
> The advantage of heterogeneous catalysts is that they can be separated from the reaction products easily.

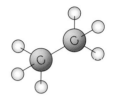

| Ethene approaches the catalyst surface where hydrogen gas is adsorbed as single atoms. | Ethene adds one hydrogen atom and the $CH_3CH_2\bullet$ radical is attached to the surface. | After adding a second hydrogen atom the hydrocarbon, now ethane, escapes from the surface. |

If a metal is to be a good catalyst for the addition of hydrogen, it must not adsorb the hydrogen so strongly that the hydrogen atoms become unreactive. This happens with tungsten. Equally, if adsorption is too weak, there will be insufficient adsorbed atoms for the reaction to occur at a useful rate, as is the case with silver. The strength of adsorption must have a suitable intermediate value as it does with nickel, platinum and palladium.

Figure 16.11▲
A possible mechanism for the hydrogenation of an alkene using a nickel catalyst. The reaction takes place on the surface of the catalyst, which adsorbs hydrogen molecules and then splits them into atoms.

Homogeneous catalysis

Homogeneous catalysis involves a catalyst in the same state as the reactants it is catalysing. This type of catalysis is most important in biological systems in which enzymes (proteins) catalyse the metabolic processes of all organisms. Very often transition metal ions act as co-enzymes in these processes, enhancing the catalytic activity of the associated enzyme. Cytochrome oxidase is an important enzyme which contains copper. This enzyme is involved when energy is released from the oxidation of food. In the absence of copper, cytochrome oxidase is totally ineffective and the animal or plant is unable to metabolise successfully.

Transition metal ions can also be effective as homogeneous catalysts themselves because they can gain and lose electrons, changing from one oxidation state to another. The oxidation of iodide ions by peroxodisulfate(VI) ions using iron(III) ions as a catalyst is a good example of this:

$$2I^-(aq) + S_2O_8^{2-}(aq) \rightarrow I_2(aq) + 2SO_4^{2-}(aq)$$

In the absence of Fe^{3+} ions the reaction is very slow, but the reaction is many times faster with Fe^{3+} ions in the mixture. A possible mechanism is that Fe^{3+} ions are reduced to Fe^{2+} as they oxidise iodide ions to iodine. Then the $S_2O_8^{2-}$ ions oxidise Fe^{2+} ions back to Fe^{3+}, ready to oxidise more of the iodide ions, and so on.

Transition elements

Sometimes one of the products of a reaction can act as a catalyst for the process. This is called autocatalysis. An autocatalytic reaction starts slowly, but then speeds up as the catalytic product is formed. Mn^{2+} ions act as autocatalysts in the oxidation of ethanedioate ions, $C_2O_4^{2-}$, by manganate(VII) ions in acid solution. This is also an example of homogeneous catalysis.

$$2MnO_4^- \text{ (aq)} + 16H^+\text{(aq)} + 5C_2O_4^{2-} \text{ (aq)} \rightarrow$$
$$2Mn^{2+}\text{(aq)} + 8H_2O\text{(l)} + 10CO_2\text{(g)}$$

Test yourself

13 What is the advantage of using a solid heterogeneous catalyst in:
  a) a continuous industrial process
  b) an industrial batch process.
14 a) Write half-equations to explain the mechanism by which iron(III) ions catalyse the reaction between iodide ions and peroxodisulfate ions.
  b) Do you think Fe^{2+} ions will also catalyse this reaction? Explain your answer.
15 a) Suggest two methods of speeding up the reaction between MnO_4^- (aq) and $C_2O_4^{2-}$ (aq) from the start of the reaction.
  b) What would you expect to see when a solution of potassium manganate(VII) is added to an acidified solution of potassium ethanedioate:
    i) at the start of the reaction
    ii) as the reaction gets underway?

16.7 Ligands and complex ions

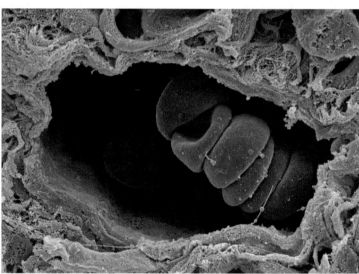

Figure 16.12▲
Red blood cells in a small artery. The blood cells are red because they contain haemoglobin, which is bright red when combined with oxygen. Haemoglobin is composed of complex ions with haem groups, globin molecules and Fe^{2+} ions.

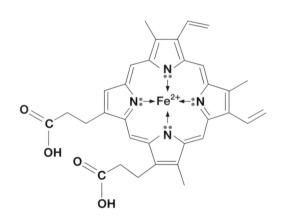

Figure 16.13▲
A haem group with its Fe^{2+} ion. Haem groups are ligands forming four dative covalent bonds to the central Fe^{2+} ion. Each Fe^{2+} ion also has two dative covalent bonds from a globin molecule.

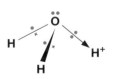

Figure 16.14▲
Dative covalent bonding in an aqueous H_3O^+ ion.

During the AS course, we found that H^+ ions in aqueous solution are strongly attached to water molecules by dative covalent bonds forming H_3O^+ ions. The structure of an H_3O^+ ion is shown in Figure 16.14.

In the same way as H^+, other cations can also exist in aqueous solution as hydrated ions. So, Mg^{2+}(aq), Cu^{2+}(aq) and Ag^+(aq) can be represented more precisely as $[Mg(H_2O)_6]^{2+}$(aq), $[Cu(H_2O)_6]^{2+}$(aq) and $[Ag(H_2O)_2]^+$(aq) in aqueous solution. But, notice that the larger size of these cations relative to H^+ enables them to associate with up to six water molecules.

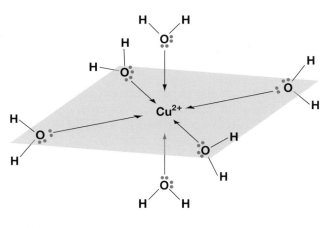

Figure 16.15▲
Dative covalent bonding in an aqueous Cu^{2+} ion.

Other polar molecules, besides water, can also form dative covalent bonds with metal ions. For example, in ammonia solution Cu^{2+} ions form $[Cu(NH_3)_4(H_2O)_2]^{2+}$ and Ag^+ ions form $[Ag(NH_3)_2]^+$.

In addition to polar molecules, anions can also associate with cations using dative covalent bonds, and when anhydrous copper(II) sulfate is added to concentrated hydrochloric acid the solution contains yellow $[CuCl_4]^{2-}$ ions. Ions such as $[Cu(H_2O)_6]^{2+}$, $[Cu(NH_3)_4(H_2O)_2]^{2+}$ and $[CuCl_4]^{2-}$, in which a metal ion is associated with a number of molecules or anions, are called complex ions, and the anions and molecules attached to the central metal ion are called ligands. Each ligand must contain at least one lone pair of electrons, which it uses to form a dative covalent bond with the metal ion. The number of ligands in a complex ion is typically two, four or six.

Chemists have an alternative name for dative covalent bonds which they often prefer to use when describing complex ions. The alternative name is 'co-ordinate bond', which gives rise to the terms 'co-ordination compound' and 'co-ordination number'. A co-ordination compound is one which contains a complex ion, and the co-ordination number of a complex ion is the number of co-ordinate bonds from the ligands to the central metal ion.

Co-ordination compounds contain complexes which may be cations, anions or neutral molecules. Examples of co-ordination compounds include:

● $K_3[Fe(CN)_6]$ containing the negatively charged complex ion $[Fe(CN)_6]^{3-}$

● $CuSO_4 \cdot 5H_2O$ containing the positively charged complex ion $[Cu(H_2O)_4]^{2+}$

● $Ni(CO)_4$ which is a neutral complex between nickel atoms and carbon monoxide molecules.

> **Definitions**
>
> A **complex ion** is an ion in which a number of molecules or anions are bound to a central metal cation by co-ordinate bonds.
>
> A **ligand** is a molecule or anion bound to the central metal ion in a complex ion by co-ordinate bonding.
>
> The **co-ordination number** of a metal ion in a complex is the number of co-ordinate bonds to the metal ion from the surrounding ligands.

Iron (II) sulfate
Chromium (III) sulfate
Cobalt chloride
Copper (II) sulfate
Nickel sulfate
Potassium hexacyanoferrate (III)

Figure 16.16◄
Crystals of six co-ordination compounds. From left to right these are $NiSO_4 \cdot 7H_2O$, $FeSO_4 \cdot 7H_2O$, $CoCl_2 \cdot 6H_2O$, $CuSO_4 \cdot 5H_2O$, $Cr_2(SO_4)_3 \cdot 18H_2O$ and $K_3[Fe(CN)_6]$.

There are two common visible signs that a reaction has occurred during the formation of a new complex ion:

- a colour change or
- an insoluble solid dissolving.

A familiar example of a colour change occurs when excess ammonia solution is added to copper(II) sulfate solution. Ammonia molecules displace water molecules from hydrated copper(II) ions forming $[Cu(NH_3)_4(H_2O)_2]^{2+}(aq)$ ions and the colour changes from pale blue to deep blue:

$$[Cu(H_2O)_6]^{2+}(aq) + 4NH_3(aq) \rightarrow [Cu(NH_3)_4(H_2O)_2]^{2+}(aq) + 4H_2O(l)$$

The test for chloride ions using aqueous silver nitrate followed by ammonia solution is an example of an insoluble solid dissolving as a complex ion forms. Adding silver nitrate to a solution containing chloride ions produces a white precipitate of silver chloride, AgCl. This precipitate dissolves on adding ammonia solution because silver ions form the complex ion $[Ag(NH_3)_2]^+(aq)$ with ammonia molecules:

$$AgCl(s) + 2NH_3(aq) \rightarrow [Ag(NH_3)_2]^+(aq) + Cl^-(aq)$$

16.8 Naming complex ions

There are four simple rules to follow when naming a complex ion.

1 Identify the number of ligands around the central cation using Greek prefixes mono-, di-, tri-, tetra-, penta-, hexa-, etc.
2 Name the ligand using names ending in '-o' for anions, e.g. chloro for Cl^-, fluoro- for F^-, cyano- for CN^-, hydroxo- for OH^-, along with aqua- for H_2O and ammine- for NH_3.
3 Name the central metal ion using the normal name of the metal for positive and neutral complex ions, and the old-fashioned Latinised name ending in '-ate' for negative complex ions, e.g. ferrate for iron, cuprate for copper, argentate for silver.
4 Finally, add the oxidation number of the central metal ion.

The examples in Table 16.4 illustrate how you should use the rules.

Table 16.4▶
Writing the systematic names of complex ions.

Formula of complex ion	1 Identify the number of ligands	2 Name the ligand	3 Name the central metal ion	4 Add the oxidation number of the central metal ion
$[Ag(NH_3)_2]^+$	di	ammine	silver	(I)
$[Cu(H_2O)_6]^{2+}$	hexa	aqua	copper	(II)
$[CuCl_4]^{2-}$	tetra	chloro	cuprate	(II)
$[Fe(CN)_6]^{3-}$	hexa	cyano	ferrate	(III)

Test yourself

16 What is the co-ordination number of:
   a) Fe^{2+} ions in haemoglobin   b) Cu^{2+} ions in $[Cu(H_2O)_6]^{2+}$
   c) Fe^{3+} ions in $[Fe(CN)_6]^{3-}$?
17 Write the systematic names of the following complex ions:
   a) $[Cu(NH_3)_4]^{2+}$ b) $[Zn(OH)_4]^{2-}$ c) $[AlH_4]^-$ d) $[Ni(H_2O)_6]^{2+}$
18 What is the oxidation state of the metal ion in the following complex ions?
   a) $[NiCl_4]^{2-}$ b) $[Ag(NH_3)_2]^+$ c) $[Fe(H_2O)_6]^{3+}$ d) $[Fe(CN)_6]^{4-}$
19 The fixer used to remove unexposed and undeveloped silver bromide from photographic film contains thiosulfate ions, $S_2O_3^{2-}$. Each silver ion forms a complex ion with two thiosulfate ions as the silver bromide dissolves. Write an equation for the formation of the complex.

Note

Notice that ammonia, NH_3, in complexes is described as 'ammine', whereas the $-NH_2$ group in organic compounds such as CH_3NH_2 is described as 'amine'.

16.9 The shapes of complex ions

The shapes of complex ions depend on the number of ligands around the central metal ion. There is no simple, definitive rule for predicting the shapes of complexes from their formulae, but:

- in complexes with a co-ordination number of six, the ligands usually occupy octahedral positions so that the six electron pairs around the central atom are repelled as far as possible.
- in complexes with a co-ordination number of four, the ligands usually occupy tetrahedral positions, although there are a few complexes with fourfold co-ordination, such as $[Pt(NH_3)_2Cl_2]$, with a square planar structure.
- in complexes with a co-ordination number of two, the ligands usually form a linear structure with the central metal ion.

These structures are all illustrated in Figure 16.17.

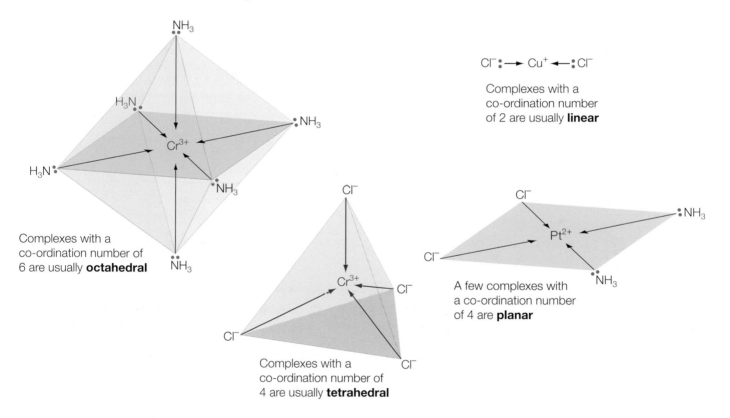

Figure 16.17 ▲
The shapes of complex ions.

Types of ligand

Most ligands use only one lone pair of electrons to form a co-ordinate bond with the central metal ion. These ligands are described as monodentate because they have only 'one tooth' to hold onto the central cation (*dens* is Latin for tooth). Examples of monodentate ligands include H_2O, NH_3, Cl^-, OH^- and CN^-.

Some ligands have more than one lone pair of electrons which can form co-ordinate bonds with the same metal ion. Bidentate ('two-toothed') ligands, for example, form two dative covalent bonds with metal ions in complexes. Bidentate ligands include 1,2-diaminoethane, $H_2NCH_2CH_2NH_2$, the ethanedioate ion, $C_2O_4^{2-}$, and amino acids.

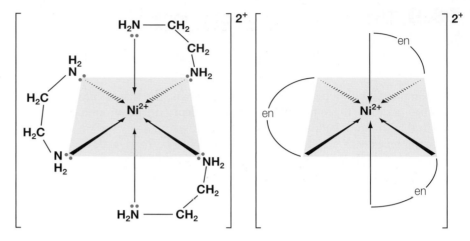

Figure 16.18▶
Representations of a complex formed by the bidentate ligand 1,2-diaminoethane with nickel(II) ions. Note the use of 'en' as an abbreviation for the ligand.

> **Note**
>
> **Edta** crystals consist of the disodium salt of **e**thane**d**iamine**t**etr**a**ethanoic **a**cid. Chemists sometimes use the abbreviation Na_2H_2Y for the salt, where Y represents the 4– ion.

The hexadentate ligand edta is particularly impressive because it can form six co-ordinate bonds with the central metal ion in complexes. The common abbreviation for this hexadentate ligand is edta. It binds so firmly with metal ions that it holds them in solution and makes them chemically inactive. Edta is added to commercially produced salad dressings to extend their shelf life. The ligand traps traces of metal ions which would otherwise catalyse the oxidation of vegetable oils. Edta is also an ingredient of bathroom cleaners to help remove scale by dissolving Ca^{2+} ions from the calcium carbonate left by hard water.

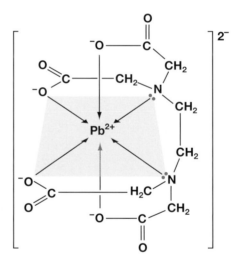

> **Note**
>
> Monodentate ligands may also be called unidentate ligands, and multidentate ligands are sometimes called polydentate ligands.

> **Definitions**
>
> **Multidentate ligands** are ligands which form more than one co-ordinate bond with the same metal ion.
>
> **Chelates** are complex ions involving multidentate ligands.

Figure 16.19▲
The complex ion formed by edta with a Pb^{2+} ion. The ligand can fold itself around metal ions, such as Pb^{2+}, so that four oxygen atoms and two nitrogen atoms form co-ordinate bonds to the metal ion. This is the ion formed when edta is used to treat lead poisoning. The edta forms such a stable complex with Pb^{2+} ions that it can be excreted through the kidneys.

Ligands like those in Figures 16.18 and 16.19, which form more than one co-ordinate bond with metal ions, are called multidentate ligands, and the complexes which these ligands form are called chelates (pronounced 'keelates'). The term 'chelate' comes from a Greek word for a crab's claw reflecting the claw-like way in which chelating ligands grip metal ions. Powerful chelating agents trap metal ions and effectively isolate them in solution.

Stereoisomerism in complex ions

As a result of the spatial positions of ligands around a central metal ion, four co-ordinated and six co-ordinated complexes can have stereoisomers. These stereoisomers have the same formula, but different spatial arrangements of their constituent atoms.

Two examples of *E/Z* isomerism (*cis/trans* isomerism) are shown in Figure 16.20.

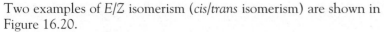

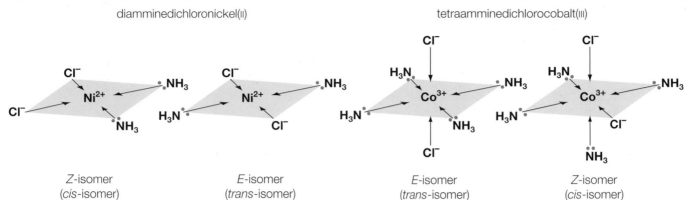

Z-isomer (*cis*-isomer)	*E*-isomer (*trans*-isomer)	*E*-isomer (*trans*-isomer)	*Z*-isomer (*cis*-isomer)

Figure 16.20▲
E/Z isomers of diamminedichloronickel(II) and tetraamminedichlorocobalt(III).

The chloride of tetraamminedichlorocobalt(III) is a particularly striking example of the stereoisomerism caused by complex ions in co-ordination compounds. In this compound, the two isomers have very different coloured crystals. The *E*-isomer forms green crystals, whereas those of the *Z*-isomer are violet.

Octahedral (six co-ordinated) complex ions can also form optical isomers because of their three-dimensional shape and an example of this is shown in Figure 16.21. In the complex $[Ni(H_2NCH_2CH_2NH_2)_3]^{2+}$, three 1,2-diaminoethane molecules each bind to the central Ni^{2+} ion in two places. The complex ion is asymmetric and the two stereoisomers are not superimposable.

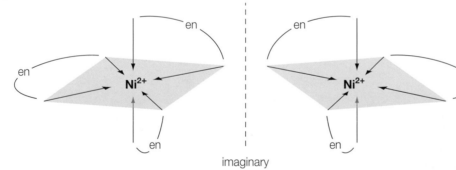

The ligand $H_2NCH_2CH_2NH_2$ is represented as — en —

Figure 16.21▲
Optical isomers of $[Ni(H_2NCH_2CH_2NH_2)_3]^{2+}$.

Test yourself

20 Predict the likely shape of the following complex ions:
   a) $[Ag(CN)_2]^-$; b) $[Fe(CN)_6]^{3-}$; c) $[NiCl_4]^{2-}$; d) $[CrCl_2(H_2O)_4]^+$
21 Explain how the amino acid glycine, (H_2NCH_2COOH), can act as a bidentate ligand.
22 a) Why is edta described as a hexadentate ligand?
   b) What is the overall shape of the edta complex in Figure 16.19?
23 a) Draw a diagram to represent the complex ion formed between a Cr^{3+} ion and three ethanedioate ions, $^-OOC-COO^-$
   b) What is the overall shape of this complex ion?
24 a) Predict an order of stability for the complex ions $[Ni(NH_3)_6]^{2+}$, $[Ni(en)_3]^{2+}$ and $[Ni(edta)]^{2-}$
   b) Explain your prediction.
25 Look at the painting and caption in Figure 16.22. Write the formula of:
   a) the hexacyanoferrate(II) ion
   b) iron(III) hexacyanoferrate(II).

Figure 16.22▲
The blue pigment in this painting by George Romney in 1763 is called Prussian blue. Its correct chemical name is iron(III) hexacyanoferrate(II).

Cis-platin

The neutral complex, $PtCl_2(NH_3)_2$, in which Cl^- ions and NH_3 molecules act as ligands, has two isomers. These isomers have different melting points and different chemical properties. One isomer, called *cis*-platin, is used in the treatment of certain cancers – the other isomer is ineffective against cancer.

Patients are given an intravenous injection of *cis*-platin which circulates all around the body including the cancerous area. *Cis*-platin diffuses relatively easily through the tumour cell membrane because it has no overall charge, like the cell membrane. Its action is shown in Figure 16.23.

Once inside the cell, *cis*-platin reacts by exchanging one of its chloride ions for a molecule of water forming $[Pt(NH_3)_2(Cl)(H_2O)]^+$ which is the 'active principle'. This positively charged ion then enters the cell nucleus where it readily bonds with two sites on the DNA. Binding involves co-ordinate bonding from the nitrogen or oxygen atoms in the bases of DNA to the platinum ion.

Figure 16.23 ◄
The action of *cis*-platin.

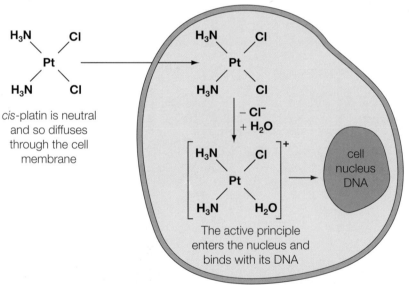

cis-platin is neutral and so diffuses through the cell membrane

The active principle enters the nucleus and binds with its DNA

The *cis*-platin binding changes the overall structure of the DNA helix, pulling it out of shape and shortening the helical turn.

The badly shaped DNA can no longer replicate and divide to form new cells, although the affected cells continue to grow. Eventually the cells die and, if enough of the cancerous cells absorb *cis*-platin, the tumour is destroyed.

Unfortunately, *cis*-platin is not a miracle cure without risks or drawbacks. It is toxic, resulting in unpleasant side-effects, and can cause kidney failure. However, clinical trials have led to the discovery of other platinum complexes which cause fewer problems and are already being used as anti-cancer drugs.

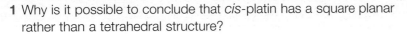

1 Why is it possible to conclude that *cis*-platin has a square planar rather than a tetrahedral structure?

2 What type of isomerism do *cis*-platin and its isomer show?

3 **a)** What is the oxidation number of platinum in *cis*-platin?

   b) Write the systematic name of *cis*-platin.

   c) Draw the structure of *cis*-platin.

4 Why does *cis*-platin diffuse easily through the membrane of cells?

5 What is meant by the term 'active principle' applied to $[Pt(NH_3)_2(Cl)(H_2O)]^+$?

6 When $[Pt(NH_3)_2(Cl)(H_2O)]^+$ has formed inside the cell, it cannot diffuse out through the cell membrane. Why is this?

7 Why is a cell with *cis*-platin binding to DNA unable to replicate?

8 Why is the binding to *cis*-platin from nitrogen and oxygen atoms rather than from carbon and hydrogen atoms in the bases of DNA?

9 Why is *cis*-platin more likely to affect cancerous cells than normal cells?

10 Why is any anti-cancer drug which acts like *cis*-platin likely to have undesirable side-effects?

16.10 Ligand substitution reactions

Complex ions often react by swapping one ligand for another. These ligand substitution reactions are usually reversible and the changes of ligand are often accompanied by colour changes. For example, when excess concentrated ammonia solution is added to pale blue copper(II) sulfate solution, ammonia molecules are substituted for water molecules around the central Cu^{2+} ion and the colour changes to a deep blue:

$$Cu(H_2O)_6^{2+}(aq) + 4NH_3(aq) \rightleftharpoons Cu(NH_3)_4(H_2O)_2^{2+}(aq) + 4H_2O(l)$$
      pale blue   deep blue

The NH_3 and H_2O ligands are both uncharged and similar in size. This allows substitution reactions between these ligands without there being a change in co-ordination number of the metal ion.

A similar ligand substitution reaction occurs when concentrated hydrochloric acid is added to copper(II) sulfate solution. This time, the colour changes from pale blue to yellow as Cl^- ions replace water molecules around the Cu^{2+} ion:

$$Cu(H_2O)_6^{2+}(aq) + 4Cl^-(aq) \rightleftharpoons CuCl_4^{2-}(aq) + 6H_2O(l)$$
      pale blue   yellow

In this case, the ligand exchange does involve a change in co-ordination number. Chloride ions are larger than water molecules, so fewer chloride ions can fit round the central Cu^{2+} ion.

Ligand substitution in oxygen transport by haemoglobin

Ligand substitution is important in the transport of oxygen by haemoglobin (Figures 16.12 and 16.13). The active part of haemoglobin is the Fe^{2+} ion. This forms co-ordinate bonds to four nitrogen atoms in the haem ligand and to two nitrogen atoms in the globin. One of the latter positions can be weakly and reversibly substituted by oxygen:

$$\text{haemoglobin(aq)} + O_2(g) \rightleftharpoons \text{haemoglobin–}O_2\text{(aq)}$$
$$\text{(oxyhaemoglobin)}$$

This property allows haemoglobin to transport oxygen from the lungs to all parts of the body, where the oxygen can be released for metabolic processes such as respiration.

Unfortunately, carbon monoxide can also act as a ligand with Fe^{2+} ions, and it binds more strongly than oxygen and irreversibly. Death is inevitable if most of the haemoglobin in someone's blood has combined with carbon monoxide.

Stability constants

In aqueous solution, the simple compounds of most transition metals contain complex ions with formulae such as $Cu(H_2O)_6^{2+}$, $Cr(H_2O)_6^{3+}$ and $Co(H_2O)_6^{2+}$.

When solutions containing other ligands, such as Cl^-, are added to aqueous solutions of these hydrated cations, the mixture comes to an equilibrium in which the water molecules of some complexes have been replaced by the added ligands. For example, the equilibrium which results when concentrated sodium chloride solution is added to aqueous copper(II) ions is:

$$Cu(H_2O)_6^{2+}(aq) + 4Cl^-(aq) \rightleftharpoons CuCl_4^{2-}(aq) + 6H_2O(l)$$

The equilibrium constant, K_c, for this reaction is given by:

$$K_c = \frac{[CuCl_4^{2-}(aq)]_{eq}}{[Cu(H_2O)_6^{2+}(aq)]_{eq}[Cl^-(aq)]_{eq}^4}$$

$[H_2O(l)]$ is constant and therefore it is not included in the equation for K_c.

Equilibrium constants like this for the formation of complex ions in aqueous solution are called stability constants and the symbol K_{stab} is normally used in place of K_c.

Stability constants enable chemists to compare the stabilities of complex ions of a cation with different ligands. The larger the stability constant, the more stable is the complex ion compared with that containing water.

Table 16.5 shows the stability constants of three complexes of the copper(II) ion. In order to avoid awkward powers of ten, the logarithms of the values of stability constants are often quoted.

From the values for the stability constants in Table 16.5, the relative stabilities of these three copper(II) complexes are:

$$Cu(edta)^{2-} > Cu(NH_3)_4(H_2O)_2^{2+} > CuCl_4^{2-}$$

Definitions

The **stability constant**, K_{stab}, of a complex ion is the equilibrium constant for the formation of the complex ion from its constituent ions in a solvent (usually water).

Table 16.5▶
The stability constants of three copper(II) complexes.

Ligand	Complex ion	K_{stab}	$\log K_{stab}$
Cl^-	$CuCl_4^{2-}$	4.0×10^5	5.6
NH_3	$Cu(NH_3)_4(H_2O)_2^{2+}$	1.3×10^{13}	13.1
edta	$Cu(edta)^{2-}$	6.3×10^{18}	18.8

Test yourself

26 Write equations for the ligand substitution reactions which occur when:
   a) hexaaquacobalt(II) ions react with ammonia molecules to form hexaamminecobalt(II) ions
   b) hexaamminecobalt(II) ions react with chloride ions to form tetrachlorocobaltate(II) ions
   c) hexaaquairon(II) ions react with cyanide ions to form hexacyanoferrate(II) ions.

27 Explain the following changes with the help of equations.
   a) Adding ammonia solution to a pale blue solution of hydrated copper(II) ions produces a pale blue precipitate of the hydrated hydroxide.
   b) On adding more ammonia solution, the precipitate dissolves to give a deep blue solution.

28 Write expressions for the stability constants K_{stab}, for the following ligand substitution reactions:
   a) $M^{2+}(aq) + 6X^-(aq) \rightleftharpoons MX_6^{4-}(aq)$
   b) $Co(H_2O)_6^{2+} + 4Cl^-(aq) \rightleftharpoons CoCl_4^{2-}(aq) + 6H_2O(l)$
   c) $Ag(H_2O)_2^+(aq) + 2NH_3(aq) \rightleftharpoons Ag(NH_3)_2^+(aq) + 2H_2O(l)$

29 A dilute solution of cobalt(II) chloride is pink because it contains hydrated cobalt(II) ions. The solution turns blue on adding concentrated hydrochloric acid with the formation of tetrachlorocobaltate(II) ions.
   a) Write an equation for the reaction which occurs when concentrated HCl is added to dilute cobalt chloride solution and indicate the colour of relevant species.
   b) Explain the chemical basis for the test illustrated in Figure 16.24.

Figure 16.24▲
Filter paper soaked in pink cobalt(II) chloride solution and dried in an oven until it is blue can be used to test for the presence of water.

16.11 Redox reactions and titrations

From Section 16.4 and Topic 15, you will know that transition elements can occur in different oxidation states and exhibit a wide range of redox behaviour. For example, chromium forms compounds in three oxidation states, +2, +3 and +6. In the +3 state, chromium exists as Cr^{3+} ions and these can be oxidised or reduced.

Under alkaline conditions, hydrogen peroxide oxidises green chromium(III) ions, $Cr^{3+}(aq)$, to yellow chromium(VI) in chromate ions, $CrO_4^{2-}(aq)$:

$$H_2O_2(aq) + 2e^- \rightarrow 2OH^-(aq)$$

$$Cr^{3+}(aq) + 8OH^-(aq) \rightarrow CrO_4^{2-}(aq) + 4H_2O(l) + 3e^-$$

In contrast to this, zinc reduces green $Cr^{3+}(aq)$ to blue–violet $Cr^{2+}(aq)$ ions:

$$Zn(s) \rightarrow Zn^{2+}(aq) + 2e^-$$

$$Cr^{3+}(aq) + e^- \rightarrow Cr^{2+}(aq)$$

Figure 16.25◄
Solutions containing ions in the three oxidation states of chromium. From left to right, these test tubes contain yellow CrO_4^{2-}, orange $Cr_2O_7^{2-}$, green Cr^{3+} and blue-violet Cr^{2+} ions in aqueous solution.

Both potassium dichromate(VI) and potassium manganate(VII) are powerful oxidising agents used as standard reagents in redox titrations.

In redox titrations, oxidising agents react with reducing agents. During the titration, you will usually measure the volume of a standard solution of an oxidising agent or a reducing agent that reacts exactly with a measured volume of the other reactant.

Measuring reducing agents – potassium manganate(VII) titrations

Potassium manganate(VII) is often chosen to measure reducing agents because it can be obtained as a pure, stable solid which reacts exactly as the following equation in acid solution:

$$MnO_4^-(aq) + 8H^+(aq) + 5e^- \rightarrow Mn^{2+}(aq) + 4H_2O(l)$$

In addition, no indicator is required in manganate(VII) titrations. On adding the potassium manganate(VII) solution from a burette, the MnO_4^- changes rapidly from purple to colourless because the Mn^{2+} ions produced are very pale pink. At the end-point, one drop of excess MnO_4^- is sufficient to produce a permanent red–purple colour.

Worked example

Two iron tablets (total mass 1.30 g) containing iron(II) sulfate were dissolved in dilute sulfuric acid and made up to 100 cm³ (Figure 16.26). 10 cm³ of this solution required 12.00 cm³ of a standard solution of 0.0050 mol dm⁻³ KMnO₄ to produce a faint red colour. What is the percentage of iron in the iron tablets? (Fe = 55.8)

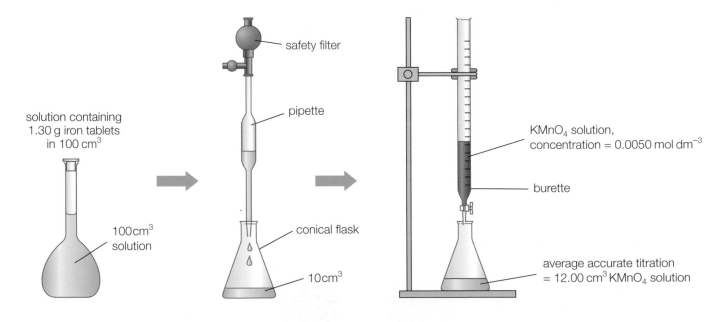

solution containing 1.30 g iron tablets in 100 cm³

100 cm³ solution

safety filter

pipette

conical flask

10 cm³

KMnO₄ solution, concentration = 0.0050 mol dm⁻³

burette

average accurate titration = 12.00 cm³ KMnO₄ solution

Figure 16.26 ▲ Finding the percentage of iron in iron tablets.

Notes on the method
1 Write the half-equations and work out the amounts in moles of Fe²⁺ and MnO₄⁻ which react.
2 Calculate the amount of MnO₄⁻ which reacts in the titration, and hence the amount of Fe²⁺ which reacts.
3 Work out the amount of Fe²⁺ in the whole solution, and hence in the tablets dissolved.
4 Calculate the percentage of iron in the tablets.

Answer

Step 1: The half-equations for the reaction are:

$$MnO_4^- + 8H^+ + 5e^- \rightarrow Mn^{2+} + 4H_2O$$

and $(Fe^{2+} \rightarrow Fe^{3+} + e^-) \times 5$

So 5 mol Fe^{2+} react with 1 mol MnO_4^-.

Step 2: Amount of MnO_4^- reacting $= \dfrac{12}{1000} \, dm^3 \times 0.0050 \, mol \, dm^{-3}$.

So the amount of Fe^{2+} reacting $= \dfrac{12}{1000} \times 0.0050 \times 5 \, mol$

Step 3: Amount of Fe^{2+} in 100 cm^3 of solution (2 tablets) $= \dfrac{12}{1000} \times 0.0050 \times 5 \times 10 \, mol$

$= \dfrac{3}{1000} \, mol$

Step 4: Mass of Fe^{2+} in two tablets $= \dfrac{3}{1000} \, mol \times 55.8 \, g \, mol^{-1}$

$= 0.1674 \, g$

So, % of iron in the tablets $= \dfrac{0.1674 \, g}{1.30 \, g} \times 100$

$= 12.9\%$

Measuring oxidising agents – iodine/thiosulfate titrations

The measurement of oxidising agents usually involves a combination of potassium iodide and sodium thiosulfate.

The oxidising agent to be estimated (e.g. iron(III) ions, copper(II) ions, chlorine or manganate(VII) ions in acid) is first added to excess potassium iodide. This produces iodine:

$$2Fe^{3+}(aq) + 2e^- \rightarrow 2Fe^{2+}(aq)$$

$$2I^-(aq) \rightarrow I_2(aq) + 2e^-$$

The iodine stays in solution in excess potassium iodide forming a yellow–brown solution.

The amount of iodine produced is then determined by titration with a standard solution of sodium thiosulfate, $Na_2S_2O_3(aq)$, which reduces the iodine back to colourless iodide ions:

$$I_2(aq) + 2e^- \rightarrow 2I^-(aq)$$

$$\underset{\text{thiosulfate}}{2S_2O_3^{2-}(aq)} \rightarrow \underset{\text{tetrathionate}}{S_4O_6^{2-}(aq)} + 2e^-$$

The greater the amount of oxidising agent added, the more iodine is formed and the more thiosulfate is needed to react with it. On adding thiosulfate from a burette, the colour of the iodine solution becomes paler. Near the end-point, the solution is a very pale yellow. Adding a small amount of soluble starch solution as an indicator at this point gives a sharp colour change from dark blue to colourless at the end-point.

The following activity illustrates the use of iodine/thiosulfate titrations in determining the concentration of supermarket bleaches, and then considers the accuracy, reliability and validity of the final results.

Supermarket bleaches

Figure 16.27 ◄
Supermarket bleaches.

The active reagent in household bleaches is sodium chlorate(I), NaClO. To increase the cleaning power of these bleaches, manufacturers usually add detergents, and to improve their smell they add perfumes. Sodium chlorate(I) is a strong oxidising agent which bleaches by oxidising coloured materials to colourless or white substances.

The half-equation when sodium chlorate(I) acts as an oxidising agent is:

$$ClO^-(aq) + 2H^+(aq) + 2e^- \rightarrow Cl^-(aq) + H_2O$$

A student was asked to determine the concentration of sodium chlorate(I) in a supermarket bleach.

Using a measuring cylinder, 100 cm³ of the bleach was added to a graduated flask and made up to a volume of 1000 cm³. 10.0 cm³ of the diluted solution was then pipetted into a conical flask, followed by the addition of excess potassium iodide.

The iodine produced was finally titrated with 0.10 mol dm⁻³ sodium thiosulfate solution giving an average accurate titration of 26.60 cm³.

1 Write a half-equation for the oxidation of iodide ions to iodine.

2 Write a balanced equation for the reaction of chlorate(I) ions with iodide ions in acid solution to form iodine, chloride ions and water.

3 Write a balanced equation for the reaction of iodine with thiosulfate ions during the titration.

4 Using your answers to questions 2 and 3, calculate the number of moles of thiosulfate that react with the iodine produced by 1 mole of chlorate(I) ions.

5 Calculate the number of moles of thiosulfate in the average accurate titration, and hence the number of moles of sodium chlorate(I) in 10 cm³ of the diluted bleach.

6 Calculate the mass of sodium chlorate(I) in 100 cm³ of undiluted bleach. (Na = 23.0, Cl = 35.5, O = 16.0)

7 What precautions should the student take to ensure that the result is accurate?

8 What could the student do to improve the reliability of the result?

9 What must the student do to ensure the result is valid?

10 Use the practical guidance entitled 'Errors and uncertainty' on the Dynamic Learning Student website to answer the following questions.

www
Practical guidance

    a) Calculate the uncertainty and percentage uncertainty in:

        i)   the volume of undiluted bleach taken

        ii) the volume of diluted bleach pipetted

        iii) the volume of thiosulfate titrated

        iv) the concentration of the thiosulfate solution.

    b) Calculate the total percentage uncertainty in the mass of sodium chlorate(I) in 100 cm³ of undiluted bleach.

11 Express your result for the mass of sodium chlorate(I) in undiluted bleach in the form $x \pm y$ g per 100 cm³.

Test yourself

30 Write half-equations for the reactions between acidified potassium manganate(VII) and:
  a) iron(II) sulfate solution
  b) hydrogen peroxide solution.

31 Use your answers to question **30** to calculate the volume of 0.02 mol dm⁻³ potassium manganate(VII) solution required to oxidise 20 cm³ of:
  a) 0.10 mol dm⁻³ iron(II) sulfate solution
  b) 0.200 mol dm⁻³ hydrogen peroxide solution.

32 All the iron in 1.34 g of some iron ore was dissolved in acid and reduced to iron(II) ions. The solution was then titrated with 0.020 mol dm⁻³ potassium manganate(VII) solution. The titre was 26.75 cm³. Calculate the percentage by mass of iron in the ore. (Fe = 55.8)

33 0.275 g of an alloy containing copper was dissolved in nitric acid, and then diluted with water producing a solution of copper(II) nitrate. An excess of potassium iodide was then added. The copper(II) ions reacted with the iodide ions to form a precipitate of copper(I) iodide and iodine. In a titration, the iodine reacted with 22.50 cm³ of 0.140 mol dm⁻³ sodium thiosulfate solution. (Cu = 63.5)
  a) Write equations for:
     i)   the reaction of copper(II) ions with iodide ions to form copper(I) iodide and iodine
     ii) the reaction of iodine with sodium thiosulfate during the titration.
  b) Calculate the percentage by mass of copper in the alloy.

REVIEW QUESTIONS

1 Chemical reactions can be identified by two types of catalysis – homogeneous and heterogeneous.

a) Explain the term 'homogeneous catalysis' and state the most important feature of transition metal ions which allows them to act as homogeneous catalysts. **(2)**

b) In aqueous solution, I^- ions slowly reduce $S_2O_8^{2-}$ ions to SO_4^{2-} ions.

i) Write an equation (or two half-equations) for the reaction. **(2)**

ii) Suggest why the activation energy of the reaction is high, resulting in a slow reaction in the absence of a catalyst. **(1)**

iii) Write two equations (or two pairs of half-equations) to show the role of iron salts in catalysing the reaction. **(2)**

c) In Periods 5 and 6 of the periodic table, the catalytic efficiency of transition metals as heterogeneous catalysts tends to be poor at the ends of the transition series, but high in the middle.

i) Suggest two reasons why the efficiency of transition metals as heterogeneous catalysts is poor at the ends of the transition series. **(2)**

ii) Suggest why their efficiency as heterogeneous catalysts is high in the middle of the transition series. **(2)**

d) In catalytic converters used to 'clean' the exhaust gases from petrol engines, a catalyst reduces nitrogen oxides using another pollutant gas as the reducing agent. State a suitable catalyst for catalytic converters, identify the reducing agent and write an equation for a possible reaction that occurs. **(3)**

2 a) Write the electronic structure of:

i) a scandium atom **(1)**

ii) a copper atom **(1)**

iii) a Cu^{2+} ion. **(1)**

b) Both scandium and copper are *d-block elements*, but only copper is a *transition element*. Explain the meaning of these terms. **(3)**

c) Aqueous Cu^{2+} ions react with excess ammonia solution to form $[Cu(NH_3)_4(H_2O)_2]^{2+}$ ions.

i) Write the name of the $[Cu(NH_3)_4(H_2O)_2]^{2+}$ ion. **(1)**

ii) What is the overall shape of the $[Cu(NH_3)_4(H_2O)_2]^{2+}$ ion? **(1)**

d) Explain why the complexes of copper(II) ions are usually coloured. **(4)**

3 Chromium shows its highest oxidation state in the oxoanion, CrO_4^{2-}.

a) Calculate the oxidation number of chromium in CrO_4^{2-}. **(1)**

b) The mixture changes colour when dilute acid is added to a solution containing CrO_4^{2-} ions.

State the changes in colour and write an equation for the reaction that occurs. **(3)**

c) When sulfur dioxide is bubbled into a solution of CrO_4^{2-} ions, the colour changes and chromium is reduced to a simple ion. State the new colour and the formula of the new simple ion. **(2)**

d) A sample of an oxochloride of vanadium, $VOCl_x$, containing 0.012 moles, required $20.0\,cm^3$ of $0.100\,mol\,dm^{-3}$ potassium dichromate(VI) solution for oxidation of the vanadium to its +5 oxidation state.

i) Copy and balance the half-equation below for the action of dichromate(VI) as an oxidising agent:

$$Cr_2O_7^{2-}(aq) + \ldots H^+(aq) + \ldots e^-$$
$$\to \ldots Cr^{3+}(aq) + \ldots H_2O(l) \quad \textbf{(2)}$$

ii) How many moles of dichromate(VI) reacted with the oxochloride of vanadium? **(1)**

iii) How many moles of electrons were taken by the $Cr_2O_7^{2-}$ ions? **(1)**

iv) Calculate the change in oxidation state of the vanadium during the reaction. **(1)**

v) Write the formula of the oxochloride of vanadium showing the correct value of x. **(1)**

4 This question concerns the chemistry of transition metals.

a) Define and explain the terms:

i) transition metal **(3)**

ii) oxidation number **(3)**

iii) complex ion. **(3)**

b) Discuss with examples, equations and observations the typical reactions of the ions of transition metals. **(9)**

5 Describe, using suitable examples and diagrams, the different shapes and different types of stereoisomerism shown by the complex ions of transition metals. In your diagrams, show clearly the shape and/or type of stereoisomerism involved. **(12)**

6 The reaction scheme below involves various compounds of copper.

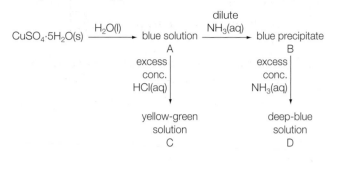

a) Write the formulae of the species responsible for the colour in each of the products A to D. **(4)**

b) Describe and explain, with an equation, what you would see when solution C is diluted with excess water. **(6)**

c) When aqueous sodium hydroxide is added to copper(II) sulfate solution, a blue precipitate is formed. However, if excess edta solution is first added to the copper(II) sulfate solution, before the aqueous sodium hydroxide, no precipitate forms.

Write an equation for the formation of the blue precipitate with aqueous sodium hydroxide and explain why no precipitate forms if excess edta is added to the copper(II) sulfate solution before the sodium hydroxide. **(5)**

The periodic table of elements

Key

| relative atomic mass |
| **atomic symbol** |
| name |
| atomic (proton) number |

| 1.0 **H** hydrogen 1 |

(1)	(2)											(13)	(14)	(15)	(16)	(17)	0(8) (18)
																	4.0 **He** helium 2
6.9 **Li** lithium 3	9.0 **Be** beryllium 4											10.8 **B** boron 5	12.0 **C** carbon 6	14.0 **N** nitrogen 7	16.0 **O** oxygen 8	19.0 **F** fluorine 9	20.2 **Ne** neon 10
23.0 **Na** sodium 11	24.3 **Mg** magnesium 12	(3)	(4)	(5)	(6)	(7)	(8)	(9)	(10)	(11)	(12)	27.0 **Al** aluminium 13	28.1 **Si** silicon 14	31.0 **P** phosphorus 15	32.1 **S** sulfur 16	35.5 **Cl** chlorine 17	39.9 **Ar** argon 18
39.1 **K** potassium 19	40.1 **Ca** calcium 20	45.0 **Sc** scandium 21	47.9 **Ti** titanium 22	50.9 **V** vanadium 23	52.0 **Cr** chromium 24	54.9 **Mn** manganese 25	55.8 **Fe** iron 26	58.9 **Co** cobalt 27	58.7 **Ni** nickel 28	63.5 **Cu** copper 29	65.4 **Zn** zinc 30	69.7 **Ga** gallium 31	72.6 **Ge** germanium 32	74.9 **As** arsenic 33	79.0 **Se** selenium 34	79.9 **Br** bromine 35	83.8 **Kr** krypton 36
85.5 **Rb** rubidium 37	87.6 **Sr** strontium 38	88.9 **Y** yttrium 39	91.2 **Zr** zirconium 40	92.9 **Nb** niobium 41	95.9 **Mo** molybdenum 42	[98] **Tc** technetium 43	101.1 **Ru** ruthenium 44	102.9 **Rh** rhodium 45	106.4 **Pd** palladium 46	107.9 **Ag** silver 47	112.4 **Cd** cadmium 48	114.8 **In** indium 49	118.7 **Sn** tin 50	121.8 **Sb** antimony 51	127.6 **Te** tellurium 52	126.9 **I** iodine 53	131.3 **Xe** xenon 54
132.9 **Cs** caesium 55	137.3 **Ba** barium 56	138.9 **La*** lanthanum 57	178.5 **Hf** hafnium 72	180.9 **Ta** tantalum 73	183.8 **W** tungsten 74	186.2 **Re** rhenium 75	190.2 **Os** osmium 76	192.2 **Ir** iridium 77	195.1 **Pt** platinum 78	197.0 **Au** gold 79	200.6 **Hg** mercury 80	204.4 **Tl** thallium 81	207.2 **Pb** lead 82	209.0 **Bi** bismuth 83	[209] **Po** polonium 84	[210] **At** astatine 85	[222] **Rn** radon 86
[223] **Fr** francium 87	[226] **Ra** radium 88	[227] **Ac*** actinium 89	[261] **Rf** rutherfordium 104	[262] **Db** dubnium 105	[266] **Sg** seaborgium 106	[264] **Bh** bohrium 107	[277] **Hs** hassium 108	[268] **Mt** meitnerium 109	[271] **Ds** darmstadtium 110	[272] **Rg** roentgenium 111							

Elements with atomic numbers 112–116 have been reported but not fully authenticated

*Lanthanide series

140 **Ce** cerium 58	141 **Pr** praseodymium 59	144 **Nd** neodymium 60	[147] **Pm** promethium 61	150 **Sm** samarium 62	152 **Eu** europium 63	157 **Gd** gadolinium 64	159 **Tb** terbium 65	163 **Dy** dysprosium 66	165 **Ho** holmium 67	167 **Er** erbium 68	169 **Tm** thulium 69	173 **Yb** ytterbium 70	175 **Lu** lutetium 71

*Actinide series

232 **Th** thorium 90	[231] **Pa** protactinium 91	238 **U** uranium 92	[237] **Np** neptunium 93	[242] **Pu** plutonium 94	[243] **Am** americium 95	[247] **Cm** curium 96	[245] **Bk** berkelium 97	[251] **Cf** californium 98	[254] **Es** einsteinium 99	[253] **Fm** fermium 100	[256] **Md** mendelevium 101	[254] **No** nobelium 102	[257] **Lr** lawrencium 103

Index

Page numbers in **bold** refer to illustrations.

Index